DEDICATED TO THE MEMORY OF

ALEXANDER AGASSIZ

AND

JOHN ELLIOTT PILLSBURY

THE FOUNDERS OF THE OCEANOGRAPHY

OF THE CARIBBEAN SEA

DATE DUE

Stratification and Circulation in the Antillean-Caribbean Basins

PART ONE

VEMA RESEARCH SERIES

NUMBER II

Stratification and Circulation
in the Antillean-Caribbean Basins

PART ONE

SPREADING AND MIXING OF THE WATER TYPES

WITH AN OCEANOGRAPHIC ATLAS

by GEORG WÜST

WITH THE ASSISTANCE OF ARNOLD GORDON

COLUMBIA UNIVERSITY PRESS

NEW YORK AND LONDON 1964

THE PUBLICATION OF THIS VOLUME WAS MADE POSSIBLE BY
A GIFT FROM THE G. UNGER VETLESEN FOUNDATION

GEORG WÜST is Visiting Professor of Geology
(Oceanography) in Columbia University's Lamont
Geological Observatory in Palisades, New York, and
Professor Emeritus in Christian Albrechts University of
Kiel, Germany.

FOREWORD

This volume (with atlas) and the volume that will follow are the first comprehensive description of the water masses of the Antillean-Caribbean basins, their interaction with the atmosphere and circulation in their depths. This systematic and extensive study of the partly enclosed basins follows the pattern set in Professor Wüst's former studies of the Atlantic Ocean and the Mediterranean Sea.

His core method for indicating the thermal-haline and oxygen constitution of oceanic basins in relation to permanent circulation is also thoroughly described in this atlas. We hope that ultimately all the earth's water masses may be known and understood through this successful method.

Geologists as well as oceanographers will be glad that it is the Caribbean which he has chosen to examine so carefully, for there remain many unanswered problems about the formation and history of this basin.

Professor Wüst is Professor Emeritus and past Director of the Institut für Meereskunde at Kiel University and is Visiting Professor of Geology (Oceanography) at Columbia University for the period 1960–1964. A grant from the Ford Foundation made possible his tenure at Columbia, where this book was written in the years 1961, 1962, and 1963. This study has been supported by the United States Atomic Energy Commission under contract AT(30-1)2663. A grant from the Vetlesen Foundation made the publishing possible.

New York
December, 1963

MAURICE EWING
Higgins Professor of Geology in Columbia University
Director, Lamont Geological Observatory

CONTENTS

Foreword, *by Maurice Ewing*   vii

I. INTRODUCTION: HISTORICAL REMARKS   3

II. PRINCIPLES OF THE CORE METHOD   5

III. DISTRIBUTION OF SURFACE TEMPERATURE
AND HEAT BUDGET   11

IV. DISTRIBUTION OF SURFACE SALINITY
AND WATER BUDGET (PLATES I–VI)   17

V. ANNUAL VARIATIONS OF SURFACE CURRENTS
(PLATES VII–X)   26

VI. GEOGRAPHIC NOMENCLATURE OF BASINS AND
RIDGES: DISTRIBUTION OF HYDROGRAPHIC
STATIONS (PLATES XI–XII)   29

VII. WARM WATER CIRCULATION (PLATES XIII–XV)   31

VIII. COLD WATER CIRCULATION IN INTERMEDIATE
LAYERS (PLATES XVI–XXXI)   34

IX. NORTH ATLANTIC DEEP WATER CIRCULATION
(PLATES XXXII–XLII)   40

X. RENEWAL OF DEEP WATERS IN OXYGEN SECTIONS
THROUGH MAIN PASSAGES (PLATES XLIII–XLV)   46

XI. ANTARCTIC AND CARIBBEAN BOTTOM WATERS
(PLATES XLVI–XLVIII)   47

XII. THE SILL DEPTHS OF MAIN PASSAGES IN
LONGITUDINAL SECTIONS OF POTENTIAL
TEMPERATURE (PLATES XLIX–LI)   48

XIII. CONCLUDING REMARKS   50

REFERENCES   52

OCEANOGRAPHIC ATLAS, PLATES I–LI   55

APPENDIX: DATA USED IN THE CONSTRUCTION OF
CORE CHARTS AND SECTIONS   131

FIGURES

1. Vertical distribution of salinity at four stations   7
2. Vertical distribution of oxygen at four stations   8
3. Normal curve of the t_p/s-correlation (100–4000 meters)   9
4. Average sea surface temperature for the warmest month   12
5. Average sea surface temperature for the coldest month   13
6. Difference in surface temperature between the warmest and coldest months   14
7. Annual variations of surface water temperatures   16
8. Stations and boundary used in the evaluation of water budget   15
9. Annual variations of water temperature at the indicated levels   16
10. Distribution of two-degree square averages of surface salinity   19
11. Relation between the semiannual rates of surface salinity and (E-P)   24
12. Location of segments of the current system   27
13. Annual variations in current speed   28
14. Vertical temperature, salinity and density curves for the warm water sphere   31
15. Schematic block diagrams of the spreading of main water masses in the Atlantic   35
16. Schematic diagram of the longitudinal spreading of the cold water types in the West Atlantic   35
17. Spreading of the Subantarctic Intermediate Water in the Atlantic   36
18. T/S-correlation in core layer of Subantarctic Intermediate Water   37
19. Distribution of oxygen in a winter section south of Greenland   40
20. Oxygen content in the core of the Middle North Atlantic Deep Water   41
21. Correlation between salinity and oxygen in the Middle North Atlantic Deep Water   44
22. Mean vertical distribution of potential temperature in Virgin Islands basins   49

Map: Physiographic diagram of the Caribbean Sea   30

Stratification and Circulation
in the Antillean-Caribbean Basins

I. INTRODUCTION: HISTORICAL REMARKS

This book forms the first part of a two-part study on the stratification and circulation of the water masses in the basins of the Antillean-Caribbean region between 8° N. and 25° 30′ N. latitude and between 55° W. and 89° W. longitude. It includes the southwest sector of the North America basin.

In the history of oceanography the first major American oceanographic endeavor took place in the source region of the Gulf Stream system during the period, 1867–89. By the initiative of the U.S. Coast and Geodetic Survey, extensive physical observations were made during this time on U.S.S. *Blake*, particularly in the depths of the Caribbean Sea and its passages, by Commanders Bartlett, Sigsbee, and Pillsbury. In 1884–86 the research vessel *Albatross* contributed some stations mainly with near surface and bottom measurements. The first monograph on the Caribbean Sea and the adjacent areas based on the findings of the *Blake* cruises, 1877–80, was published in two volumes by A. Agassiz (1888). This monograph is still today a classical "Contribution to American Thalassography" not only with regard to the physical oceanography in the depths but also to the deep-sea deposits, to the pelagic fauna and flora and to the characteristic deep-sea types of organisms. The direct current measurements of Pillsbury during 1885–89 at thirty-nine anchor stations of long duration were the first made in depths of the Florida Straits and of the passages on the Antillean Arc and were published in the Appendices of five Reports of the U.S. Coast and Geodetic Survey (1886, 1887, 1889, 1890, 1891). The main results of these classical measurements, to which we return, have been used for special studies in four later publications. (Wüst, 1924; v. Schubert, 1932; Dietrich, 1937b; and Model, 1950.)

In this first period, all measurements of temperature in the depths were made by maximum-minimum thermometers (after Miller-Casella), which had an accuracy of approximately ±0.2° C. They cannot be used today for studies in depths of more than 2000 meters inside the Antillean Arc and in depths more than 5500 meters outside the Antillean Arc because of the temperature increase due to the adiabatic effects below these depths. Later on the first measurements with the Negretti-Zambra reversing thermometers brought only a very small improvement in the accuracy of the measurements because they were not supplied with auxiliary thermometers (Tanner, 1897; Wüst, 1936, p. 16). With regard to salinity, the older measurements made with hydrometers can only be used today as auxiliary values with some corrections. With regard to the entire problem of the applicability of the older measurements of temperature and salinity, that is, for the period, 1869–1905,

studies in full detail have been published by L. Möller (1926) and G. Wüst (1936, pp. 12–31 and pp. 224–33) to which we here only refer. Our critical remarks also concern the more recent bottom observations in temperature made by cable and survey ships. Most of them were probably measured with maximum–minimum thermometers. Therefore, we have used them as auxiliary values only outside the Antillean Arc in the North America Basin and in depths less than 5500 meters.

The second period of improved methods was in our region initiated by the *Bache*-sections through the Florida and Antillean Current where for the first time exact serial measurements of temperature (by modern reversing thermometers) and salinity (by chlortitration) have been made (Bigelow, 1917; Vaughan, 1918). A test of the modern accuracy of these measurements has been published by the author (Wüst, 1924). In the same publication, the high quality of Pillsbury's current measurements has been verified. His discovery of the steep slope of the lower boundary of the Florida current (layer of no motion) dipping from its western to its eastern side and its applicability for the construction of velocity profiles (isotachs-diagrams) was proved by the comparison with the geostrophic currents and volume transports perpendicular to these baroclinic fields in the cross sections. Therefore, "Pillsbury's observations of currents, carried out from a vessel anchored in deep water in a swift stream, are among the classical data in physical oceanography," as Sverdrup *et al.* (1942, pp. 673–74) have stated "not so much because they give complete information as to the average currents, but mainly because they made possible a convincing demonstration of the correctness of the later methods used for computing relative currents" (Wüst, 1924). Sverdrup *et al.* have further said: "This single example, therefore, has greatly contributed to increasing confidence in the correctness of computed relative currents in general" (Sverdrup *et al.* 1942, p. 675).

Between 1913 and 1928 the Danish expeditions with *Margrethe* and *Dana I* and *II* contributed exact serial measurements in the Antillean-Caribbean Basins. However, the second culmination of American oceanography in these regions was initiated by the increasing number of cruises and stations of Woods Hole research vessels since 1932. For the period, 1932–37, A. E. Parr (1935a and b, 1937a, b, and c, 1938) and G. Dietrich (1937a and b, 1939) used the observations made by *Dana*, *Mable Taylor*, and *Atlantis* for important studies of the oceanographical conditions in the entire Central American Sea.

Since this time, particularly since 1948, the American oceanographic activity in the Atlantic has taken more and more the pattern of a systematic oceanographic survey. This progress has encouraged me to begin this book as a new analysis of the partly enclosed Antillean-Caribbean basins. With the help of the greatly increased number of serial measurements and other observations, this book will continue and extend the mentioned studies of A. E. Parr (1935–38) and G. Dietrich (1937–39) in the same region.

Our work, which is accompanied by an atlas of fifty-one plates and extensive lists of the observations used, is based on all available data of thirty research vessels and additional bottom observations of survey ships, that is, on 1,725 hydrographic stations, from which more than 50 per cent are deeper than 1000 meters (Appendix, Table I). Also, the latest concepts of the bathymetry are considered in collaboration with B. Heezen and Marie Tharp. In addition, reference has been made to the contoured plotting sheets (B.C. Series) from the U.S. Hydrographic Office. As for serial measurements, the Woods Hole Oceanographic Institution has made the greatest contribution to the source material. Its observations of temperature and salinity are among the most precise. Between 1932 and 1961 the Woods Hole research vessels *Atlantis*, *Caryn*, *Crawford*, and *Albatross III* made 821 stations on about thirty oceanographic cruises through the Antillean-Caribbean Region.

Maurice Ewing has been of considerable help to this study by providing me with research and technical assistants. He enlarged the library of Lamont Geological Observatory by acquiring literature in physical oceanography, particularly the grand expeditionary reports, textbooks, publications of source material, oceanographic journals, and other periodicals. Since 1955, M. Ewing has organized seven, mainly geophysical, cruises of *Vema* through the Antillean-Caribbean Region.* In crucial regions, these have contributed 75 hydrographic stations in connection with geochemical measurements and a large number of new precision depth records and thermal gradient measurements in the near-bottom layers (R. Gerard, M. G. Langseth, and M. Ewing, 1962). Thirty-two other research vessels and survey ships have contributed about 900 stations and bottom observations as shown in the Appendix, Table I.

We have received valuable help from W. C. Jacobs, Director of the U.S. National Oceanographic Data Center in Washington, D.C., who has provided copies of serial and surface measurements. D. C. Carritt and Joe Barrett of Woods Hole Oceanographic Institution provided us with unpublished data of a recent cruise (1961) and information on some analytic difficulties in earlier oxygen determinations. In the collection and analysis of the mass of data since 1961, I enjoyed the continuous advice and support of research scientist R. Gerard of the oceanographic laboratory of Lamont Geological Observatory as well as the assistance of A. Gordon, S. Jacobs, and R. Sexton. I was given valuable technical help by B. Burcaw who made the final drawings of all maps, sections, and diagrams for this study. Finally, I wish to thank Mrs. Jeanne Stolz for her help in making the English manuscript more idiomatic and in preparing the tables for photo-offset print.

* The geophysical results of these *Vema* cruises are published in numerous papers of M. Ewing, J. Ewing, C. B. Officer, B. Heezen *et al.* (*See* References.)

II. PRINCIPLES OF THE CORE METHOD

Our study concerns two central problems of physical oceanography: the interaction between sea and atmosphere at the surface and, mainly, the circulation patterns at the surface, in the depths, and at the bottom. For both tasks, the construction of new charts was necessary. With regard to the depths, our atlas differs principally from the normal atlases of the oceans or parts thereof which present the horizontal distribution of temperature, salinity, density, and oxygen only in standard depths or the vertical distribution of these properties in more or less arbitrarily chosen sections or both. Such maps and sections are valuable for the geographical understanding of an oceanic region in its physical-chemical manifestations. In an endeavor to indicate the thermohaline and oxygen constitution of oceanic basins in relation to the permanent circulation of the water masses, our procedure is not to present the distribution of data in such horizontal and vertical sections but to present them in curved (or inclined) surfaces which correspond to the topography or contours of the so-called core layers (Kernschichten) of the different water types.

Until the *Meteor* Expedition, 1925–27, with its dense network of stations and measurement points, oceanographers were compelled to deduce the principal characteristics of the deep circulation from isolated sections of temperature, salinity, and oxygen. A three-dimensional representation and an understanding of the permanent circulation pattern in the whole expanse of an oceanic basin cannot be obtained in this manner. Similarly, the spatial spreading and mixing of the water types from their point sources cannot be deduced from the normal temperature, salinity, and oxygen charts plotted for horizontal levels, that is, for selected standard depths (25, 50, 100, 200, 300, 400, 500, 1000, 1500, 2000, 2500–5000 meters), because the core layers of the various water types rise and fall. Therefore, they are only fragmentarily manifested in such horizontal charts. For these reasons, other methods of deducing, in a systematic manner, the spatial circulation must be used: either the core method, as in former circulation studies of the Atlantic Ocean (Wüst–Defant, 1936) and of the Mediterranean Sea (Wüst, 1960 and 1961), or the method of isentropic analysis (Montgomery, 1938; Parr, 1938). For the latter method, the surfaces of constant density or constant entropy are of special importance. The isentropic method offers proper approximation of the circulation pattern in upper layers of the tropics and subtropics, that is, for density surfaces between $\sigma_t = 26.1$ and $\sigma_t = 27.0$ or between 0- and 600-meter depths, as it was shown by Montgomery (1938). Isentropic analysis is used by meteorologists to study the flow patterns in the atmosphere, where provided there is

no condensation, such a surface is also a surface of constant entropy. In the deep oceans, the entropy is a poorly defined function of the two factors: temperature and salinity. An isentropic surface does not coincide, particularly in greater depths, with the surface of constant potential density which does not remain invariable under adiabatic deformations. This is shown by the author in two longitudinal sections of potential density through the deep and bottom waters of the West Atlantic and East Atlantic trough (*Meteor* reports, 1936 Vol. VI, 1, Figs. 15 and 16). The difference between σ_t and σ_{t_p} is negligible in the warm water sphere. But in the cold water sphere the potential density is not more well defined. At the same time the vertical gradients become very small in greater depths. These considerations make it understandable that the circulation pattern in the upper Atlantic layers deduced by Montgomery with use of isentropic analysis was in fair agreement with Defant's results (1936) who has used for the subtropical undercurrents in the Atlantic warm water sphere mainly the "Kernschicht" method (after the author). In these near-surface layers the Kernschicht very approximately lies on a surface of constant density. Therefore, and because of the limits of applicability of the isentropic-analysis method and other points of view (for instance, the dependence of density on mixing of different water types and the small vertical gradients of density in greater depths) we have, for the deduction of the circulation pattern in the Antillean-Caribbean warm water and cold water spheres, principally used the "Kernschicht" method or "core" method. On the other hand, the isentropic-analysis method can only be used directly in the warm water sphere in such cases where the serial measurements have been made in very small vertical distances, that is, at least in the standard depths of 10, 25, 50, 75, 100, 125, 150, 175, 200, 250, 300, 400, 500, and 600 meters, as was mostly the case in Atlantic *Meteor* stations. However, not many expeditions have made observations in such small distances. Therefore, it is obvious that in the isentropic analysis, more or less subjective interpolations have to be made.

All our core charts are designed in the Mercator projection, which in the small latitudes between 8° and 25° N. sufficiently approach an equal-area projection. They correspond in their quadrangles and in the topography of the islands and continental areas with the generalized bathymetric map of the Hydrographic Office, HO No. 5487 entitled "Bathymetrical Contour Lines of the Caribbean Sea" in the natural scale 1 : 2872239 (16° N.) (1939, revised 1958). However, with regard to the bathymetry, because of the increase of soundings in many areas, our chart differs from the chart of the Hydrographic Office prepared by H. H. Hess, 1939, which gave the first modern morphological picture.

In spite of the fact that "the core method has proved very successful" (Sverdrup *et al.*, 1942, p. 146) as a technique for the deduction of the general features of circulation in the Atlantic Ocean only a small number of systematic studies have been made with its help in open oceans or enclosed ocean basins (Wüst, 1936; Defant, 1936; Wyrtki, 1961; Wüst, 1960–61). Therefore, it seems to be appropriate to describe this method in more detail. It consists of the following procedures, based on all available observation material:

1. Construction of *core charts of the various water types*, characterized by intermediate maxima or minima of temperature-*T*, salinity-*S*, and oxygen-O_2, using observed values only.

2. Construction of *charts of the potential bottom temperature-* T_p and *bottom salinity*, because the near bottom waters also form in the deep basins a core of spreading of this special water type depending on the bathymetrical conditions. Therefore, the adiabatic effect has to be eliminated from the observed temperature in situ and the potential bottom temperature-T_p has to be used.

3. Construction of *longitudinal vertical sections* of temperature, salinity, oxygen, and potential temperature *along the axis of the main spreading* of the various water types derived from the above-mentioned charts.

4. Construction of *diagrams of the T/S, O_2/S, and T_p/S-correlations* not only as originally introduced by Helland-Hansen (1916) for the vertical stations but mainly for the more or less undulating surfaces of the whole core layers and of the bottom layer. Such correlation diagrams are useful:

(a) for *testing the comparability of the available data* and for eliminating some doubtful values in salinity, temperature, and oxygen. By the O_2/S correlation, a decision can be made whether the oxygen determinations of various expeditions indicate systematic differences in O_2 because of using different analytic methods or because of unperiodical fluctuations. In such cases, for each expedition or each period, special core maps and sections of oxygen must be drawn.

(b) for deriving the *so-called "normal curves"* through the clouds of points. Such normal curves of *T/S* and T_p/S relation, consisting in pieces of straight lines can be used for defining the original water type in its source region at one end point and for calculating the mixing effects just to the other end point of the straight lines. In this way, it is possible to estimate from the normal curve the percentage amount of the original water type at any locality of the core chart just to the region where the last traces of this particular water type disappear.

By these four techniques, the mean steady state of spreading of the water types within an entire ocean basin and various core layers can be quantitatively traced, and the effects of turbulent diffusion can be studied by quantitative approaches. However, they are not appropriate for the deduction of current velocities

and volume transports. The latter have to be deduced from dynamic computations of cross sections perpendicular to the axis of the main spreading of the water types by using the geostrophic equation. Such computations give reasonable quantitative results under the supposition that in the depths quasi-stationary conditions predominate, or, in other words, that a balance between the pressure gradients of a baroclinic mode and the Coriolis force exists. In addition reasonable assumptions on the reference level (layer of no motion) must be made. So far as it is possible today, such computations must be controlled by direct current measurements in the depths over long periods of time. These quantitative studies which have to be extended to the vertical components of velocity and to the coefficients of turbulent diffusion are reserved for some chapters in Part Two of this study on the "Stratification and Circulation in the Antillean-Caribbean Basins."

In the application of the above-characterized core method, we are confronted by two problems:

1. the choice among the properties as to the best indication for the special core layer

2. the determination of the corresponding values of depth, *S*, O_2, *T* and T_p for the construction of the various core charts either by using the observed data or by interpolated values between them at the various stations.

The spreading and mixing processes can be best studied by:

1. The *core of the Surface Waters*, characterized by a temperature maximum depending on the heat budget and by a salinity distribution depending on evaporation minus precipitation, runoff, and the horizontal advection of currents.

2. *The core of the Subtropical Underwater*, characterized by an intermediate maximum of salinity in depths *between 50 and 200 meters*.

The boundary between the Antillean-Caribbean warm water and cold water spheres is, as in the Atlantic Ocean (Wüst, 1936, p. 207, and Defant, 1961, p. 593), best defined by the center or core of the intermediate oxygen minimum, which approximately corresponds to the 8°–10° surface and 34.90–35.00‰-surface. Because of the systematic differences between the oxygen determinations in various periods we must construct at least two charts, that is, where the oxygen minimum shows its highest and lowest absolute values. These two charts are based on:

3a.–3b. *The core of the intermediate oxygen minimum in 400–600 meter* depth in 1932–37 and 1954–58.

In the *Antillean-Caribbean cold water sphere*, we have for circulation studies three additional cores:

4. The core of the *Subantarctic Intermediate Water*, characterized by an intermediate salinity minimum in various depths *between 700 and 850 meters*.

5. The core of the *North Atlantic Deep Water*, characterized by the upper intermediate oxygen maximum in various depths *between 1800 and 2500 meters*.

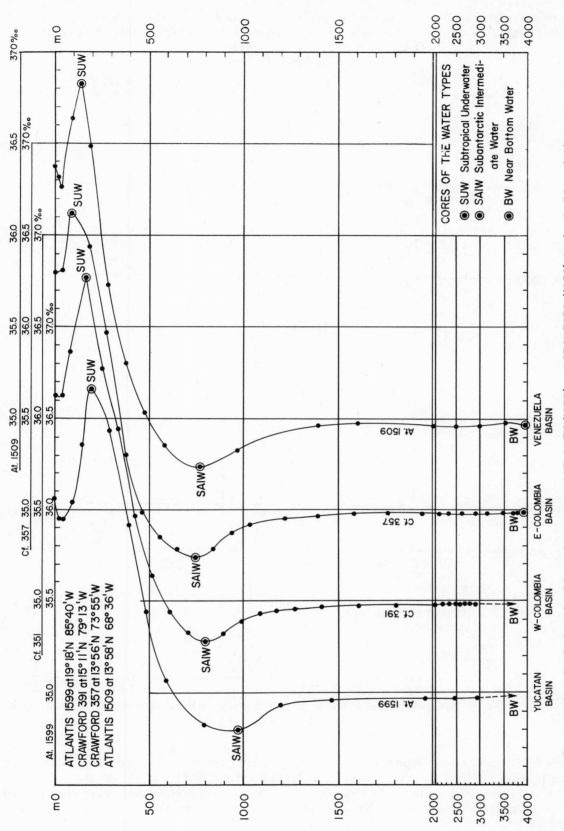

Fig. 1 Vertical distribution of salinity at four stations of ATLANTIS (1933) and CRAWFORD (1958) in the Caribbean basins

6. and 7. The cores of the *Caribbean Bottom Water* (inside the Antillean Arc) *and the Antarctic Bottom Water* (outside), characterized by the potential temperature and the salinity in the near-bottom layers of the basins.

plotted against each other, the points fall, in spite of the distances of the stations, on a well-defined curve, *the T_p/S normal curve*, which consists of several pieces of approximately straight lines. The inflection points of

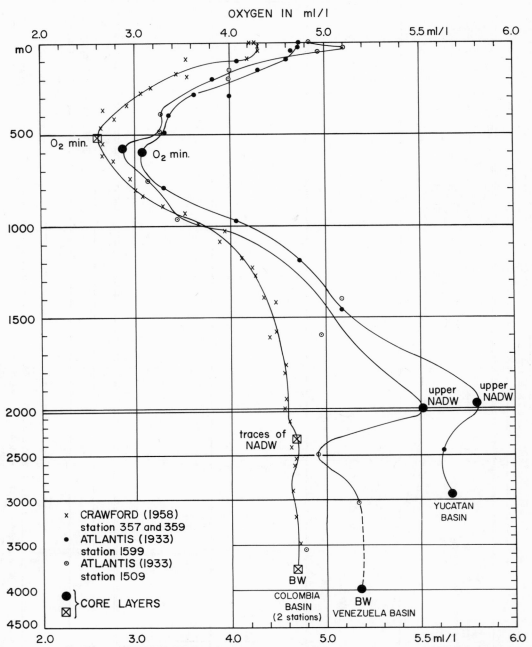

Fig. 2 Vertical distribution of oxygen at four stations in central regions of the Caribbean basins
(see explanations in Fig. 1)

The following vertical curves represent the vertical distribution of salinity (Fig. 1) at 4 deep stations (of 3 basins) in distances of ~5° longitude (along the axis of the main-spreading of the 4 water types). They demonstrate that the stratification follows the similar basic rule. The cores are defined by the intermediate and bottom maxima or minima or both. In the curves of the T_p/S-correlation (Fig. 3), where the potential temperatures and the salinities of the various depths and stations are

the latter represent the cores of the various water types, the straight lines the vertical mixing of these water types. Curves of equal density are superimposed on this diagram; the numbers at the points give the depths of the observations in hectometers. This T_p/S diagram (Fig. 3) shows clearly the basic rule of stratification and mixing in the Caribbean water masses. It is surprising how small the spread of the points is on both sides of the normal curve. The depth along the normal curve (given in hectometers at the measurement points) varies for each station. Superimposed on our diagram are the lines of equal density between $\sigma_t = 23.0$ and $\sigma_t = 29.0$, which permit us to estimate for each point of the normal curve, the corresponding density with an accuracy of about ± 0.05.

Contrary to the vertical distribution of salinity, temperature, and density, as shown by Figs. 1 and 2,

Venezuela basins (after *Atlantis* observations, 1933). It would be understandable that in the more enclosed Colombia Basin the ventilation and renewal of the deep water masses and, therefore, the amounts of oxygen in these depths would be smaller and less variable from year to year. However, the fact that such systematic differences are determined in all levels suggests the idea that they are primarily caused by differences in the

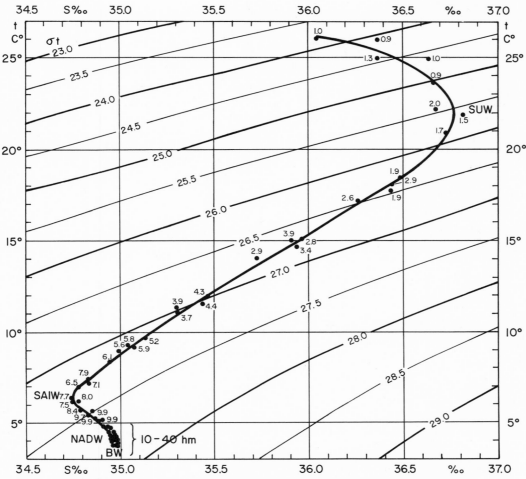

Fig. 3 Normal curve of tp/s – correlation (100 – 4000 m) in central regions of three Caribbean basins (with regard to the abbreviations of water types and positions of the stations see Fig. 1. The numbers at the observation points in Fig. 3 are hectometers)

the vertical curves of oxygen do not present such regular shapes, but show larger differences between the four representative stations for the three main basins of the Caribbean Sea (Fig. 2). The oxygen minima are well defined between 500 and 600 meters and indicate similar amounts between 2.6 and 3.1 ml/l. But in the main oxygen maxima, representing the core of the North Atlantic Deep Water in 1900–2300 meters, there are larger differences observed between the three basins and not very well defined secondary cores in 3000–4000-meter depth. Most surprising is the fact, that, in the whole water column between 0 and 4000 meters, the consistent oxygen values of the two *Crawford* stations (1958) in the Colombia Basin are as much as 10–15 per cent lower than in the adjacent basins, the Yucatan and

analytic methods used during the expeditions of the International Geophysical Year (1954–58) and earlier Woods Hole expeditions (1933–37), a question to which we later return.

The accuracy in the values of the core layers depends primarily on the distance between measurement points in the station verticals and secondarily on the limits of error in the determination of the various properties. In the *Meteor* stations and also in the stations of several other Atlantic expeditions, the observations of T, S, and O_2 are normally made at standard depths. These standard depths are between 25 and 200 meters in distances of 25 meters, between 200 and 300 meters in distances of 50 meters, between 300 and 1000 meters in distances of 100 meters, between 1000 and 2000 meters in distances of 200 meters, between 2000 and 3000 meters in distances of 250 meters, and finally, between 3000 and 5000 meters mostly in distances of 500 meters. In the warm water sphere of the Antillean-Caribbean basins many expeditions have chosen greater distances than the above mentioned, that is, that the observed data do not always permit a sufficiently exact determination of the depth and the characteristic values of the cores. But it is an error to believe that by graphical interpolation the data for the core can in such cases be improved because, in the neighborhood of the point-like corners of the intermediate maxima and minima, the construction of vertical curves is more or less subjective and arbitrary. Any two different authors will probably put the turning points of the vertical curves at different places of the diagram. On the other hand, it must be taken into consideration that vertical curves of temperature and salinity of a special station cannot be constructed independently from each other because these two parameters are related by the density. Each constructed bulge in the salinity curve has to be necessarily connected with a special shape of the temperature curve, which can only be obtained by repeated attempts. In other words an objective improvement of the basic data cannot be obtained in such cases by graphical

interpolation. Therefore, in this comparative study, as in our former studies on the Atlantic and Mediterranean circulation, we have preferred to use the observed data nearest to the core and to omit such stations where the vertical distances of the observations are too large or the limits of error of the measurements exceed the tolerable limits. A test with help of the T/S, T_p/S, or O_2/S-correlation can facilitate such final decisions. However, by such a procedure an exact topography (in meters) of the core surface cannot be derived. But, on the other hand, reasonable approaches are obtained in the core charts of salinity, oxygen, and potential temperature.

From these considerations it follows that our core charts only represent the presently possible approaches with regard to the permanent features of deep circulation. In the future, when it will become possible to make continuous exact records of the parameters T, Cl, S, σ_t, and O_2 by electronic methods, better results will be obtained in such core studies. For a test of our results, all observed data used in the construction of the various core maps and core stations are reproduced according to geographical latitude and longitude in the "Lists of Data" (Appendix). These tables form the source material for our study.

III. DISTRIBUTION OF SURFACE TEMPERATURE AND HEAT BUDGET

For an understanding of the stratification and circulation patterns in the depths of the Antillean-Caribbean basins, it is necessary to first study the interaction between sea and atmosphere at the surface, that is, the distribution of the winter and summer surface temperatures depending on the heat budget and the distribution of the winter and summer salinities depending on the water budget.

Our knowledge of the oceanic climatological conditions is mainly based on weather observations made on moving merchant and naval ships, on stationary lightships and weather ships and on coastal meteorological stations. For the North Atlantic, including the Central American Seas, the "Climatological and Oceanographic Atlas," Vol. I, edited by the U.S. Hydrographic Office and the U.S. Weather Bureau (Washington, D.C., 1959) and the atlas of the "Monatskarten für den Atlantischen Ozean" (Hamburg, 1956) give, by numerous charts, valuable climatological information. F. A. Fuglister (1947) supplemented the one-degree square averages of sea surface temperature available in the Hydrographic Office with bathythermograph records in the file of the Woods Hole Oceanographic Institution and with observations made from lightships recorded by Rathbun (1887) and summarized by Parr (1933). In his charts of the average monthly sea surface temperatures of the western North Atlantic Ocean (Fuglister, 1947), improved detail has been achieved. In Figs. 4–6 only the Caribbean portion from three Fuglister charts (after conversion from Fahrenheit to Celsius degrees) are reproduced: (a) chart of the average sea surface temperatures for the warmest month (September respectively August); (b) chart of the average sea surface temperature for the coldest month (February); and (c) chart of the difference in surface temperature between the warmest and coldest months. From these three charts, it is obvious that in the Antillean-Caribbean region the monthly averages are between 25° C. and 29° C. during the whole year and that in the interior of the Caribbean Sea the difference between the warmest and coldest month is only in the range of 2° to 3° C. It is important to note in Fig. 4 that in August-September the thermal equator (dashed line), which in the open Atlantic lies in the equatorial zones between 0° and 12° N., crosses diagonally from southeast to northwest the northern areas of the Caribbean basins between 12° and 22° N. In other words our region represents, particularly in summer, a tropical ocean.

Colón (1960 and 1963) determined the following annual variations of surface water temperatures at the east and west sides of the Caribbean current (Fig. 7),

which are converted by the author from Fahrenheit to Celsius. From these two curves it becomes obvious that in the interior of our basins there are only two seasons: the winter season, from December to May, with temperatures approximately between 25.5° and 27.0° and the summer season, from June to November, with temperatures approximately between 27° and 28.5°.

In his important papers (1960, 1963), Colón studied the heat budget of the Caribbean Sea, that is, the heat flux from the sea surface to the atmosphere over the Caribbean Sea as a residual in a computation of the monthly heat balance of the oceanic body using a ring of 14 radiozonde-radiowind stations and other climatological and oceanographical information. In her monograph on "Large-Scale Interaction of Properties Between Sea and Air" (which forms an extensive chapter of Section 2), in the new textbook entitled *The Sea* (edited by Hill), Joanne Malkus (1962) has published an excellent summary of the "Joint air-sea energy budget study of the Caribbean region." This chapter is mainly based on the papers of Riehl *et al.* (1945–59), Colón (1960, 1963), and her own papers (1949–58). Here we make principal use of these studies only with regard to semiannual results. We agree with the following concepts of J. Malkus: In the Caribbean Sea, "there were enough oceanographic data to undertake a joint air-ocean budget . . . . It will be of considerable value to all marine scientists to understand the approaches, difficulties and questions raised by such an inquiry as well as to learn of its physical results in a region which mothers both the Gulf Stream and much of North American (and probably hemispheric) weather conditions" (Malkus, 1962, p. 148). The framework of Colón's studies (1960, 1963) is given by Fig. 8, in which the location of the aerological stations and the elliptic boundary (dashed curve) are given for his evaluation of energy flux and which we also use for the calculation of semiannual values of the heat and water budgets. After Colón's heat budget the following semiannual values of total radiation absorbed by the entire Caribbean Sea within the elliptic frame (area of 2.19×10^{16} cm²) represent the best approaches:

Winter (December–May) 6.21×10^{18} *cal day^{-1}*

Summer (June–November) 6.31×10^{18} *cal day^{-1}*

The difference between the two averages is relatively small. Therefore, it is understandable (provided that the average horizontal advection of heat by currents is in both seasons in the same order of magnitude) that the

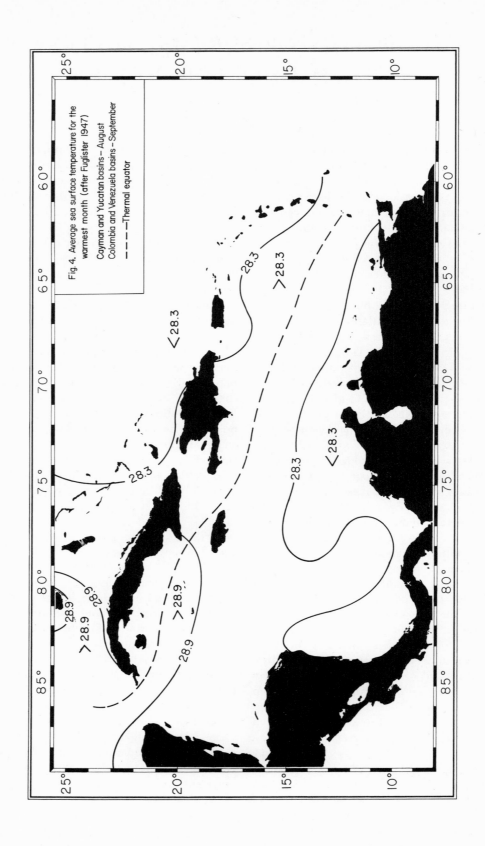

Fig. 4. Average sea surface temperature for the
warmest month (after Fuglister 1947)

Cayman and Yucatan basins – August
Colombia and Venezuela basins – September
– – – –Thermal equator

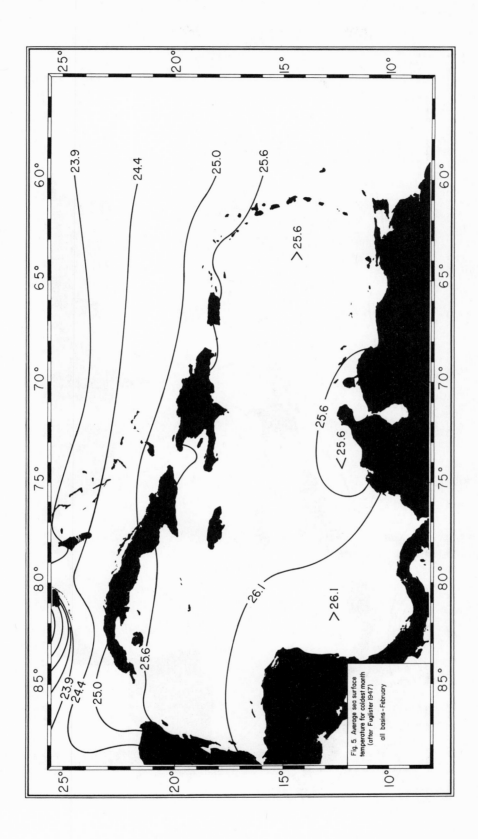

Fig. 5. Average sea surface temperature for coldest month (after Fuglister 1947) all basins – February

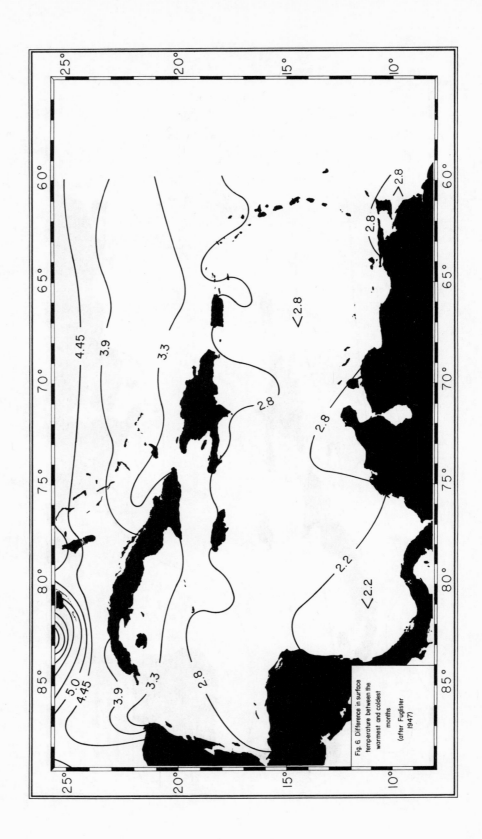

Fig. 6 Difference in surface temperature between the warmest and coldest months (after Fuglister 1947)

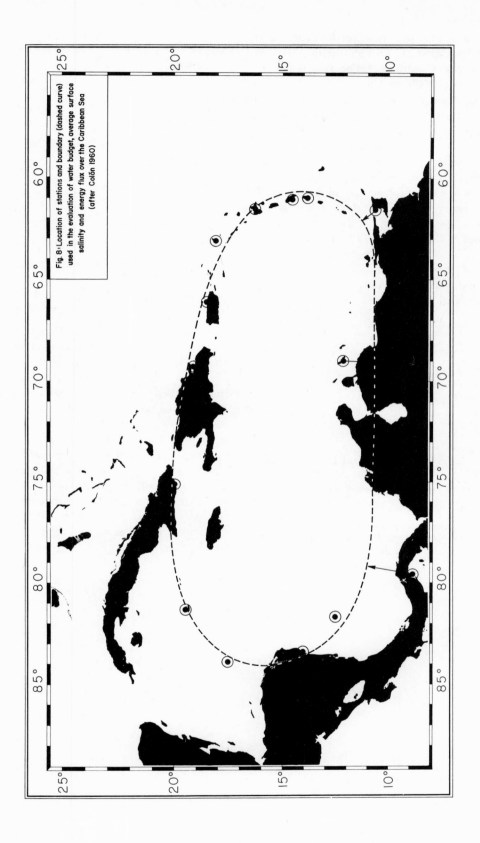

Fig. 8: Location of stations and boundary (dashed curve) used in the evaluation of water budget, average surface salinity and energy flux over the Caribbean Sea (after Colón 1960)

winter and summer averages of surface temperatures
only differ in the range of 2° to 3° C.

The evaluation of seasonal changes in heat content
was carried out by Colón (1960, 1963) within the near-
surface layers of the Caribbean. For this purpose, a
tabulation of about 8000 monthly *BT* temperature
soundings averaged for one-degree quadrangles (in an
uneven distribution over the months) was compiled on
the initiative of J. Malkus at the Woods Hole Oceanographic Institution. "In constructing the ellipse of
averaged temperature depth distribution for each month
[shown in Fig. 9] a small, but important, adjustment was
made presumably to correct for slightly unrepresentative
sampling in summer when the data coverage was
sparsest" (Malkus, 1962, p. 153). The annual amplitude
was reduced from 3.3° (after the *BT*'s) to 2.6° C. (after
Fuglister, 1947), and the amplitudes at depth were
proportionally adjusted. The annual range, 2.6° C. at
the surface, remains approximately the same between
0 and 15 meters and is reduced to 87 per cent at 30

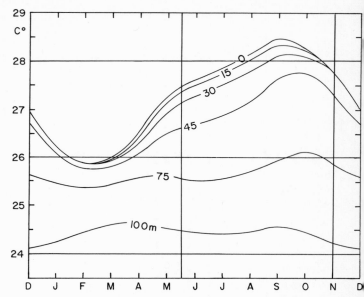

Fig. 9   Annual variation of water temperature at the indicated levels (meters)
averaged over the Caribbean sea (after Colón 1960 and Malkus 1963)

meters, 76 per cent at 45 meters and 26 per cent at 75
meters. At 100 meters the seasonal cycle has practically
vanished. This is, at the same time, the average depth
of the very sharp pycnocline, that is, of the strongest vertical gradient in density because here the thermocline
coincides with an additional steep salinity increase in an
inversion of the gradient of salinity. From this diagram
it may be concluded that *in the depths greater than 100
meters no seasonal variations of temperature or of salinity take
place, that is, that practically stationary conditions prevail*.
They are only superimposed by small unperiodic
fluctuations which, in the present state of oceanography,
can be ignored in such studies on the permanent
circulation patterns in the depth, assuming the mean
steady state.

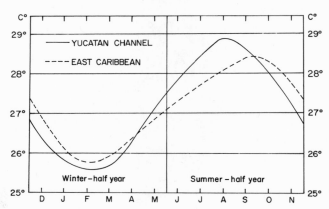

Fig. 7   Annual variation of surface water temperatures at the east and
west sides of the Caribbean current (after Colón 1960)

IV. DISTRIBUTION OF SURFACE SALINITY AND WATER BUDGET

The first attempt to construct monthly and quarterly maps of the surface salinity in the Caribbean Sea was undertaken by G. Böhnecke (1936) in the atlas to *Meteor*-Reports, Vol. V. This atlas consists of 74 mostly colored charts (T, $S‰$, and σ_t) for the entire Atlantic Ocean. Böhnecke's construction of isohalines in our region was mainly based on salinity observations (chlorinity titrations) of merchant vessels along a restricted number of tracks. These tracks, for the period 1902–30, were published in the *Bulletin Hydrographique* (Copenhagen) and, for the period 1914–29, in the *Archiv der Seewarte*, Bd. 49, 2 (Hamburg, 1930). At this time only a small number of observations by scientific expeditions could be used by G. Böhnecke, such as *Challenger* (1873–76) and *Albatross* (1883–88) (both revised hydrometer readings); *Margrethe*, 1913; *Bache*, 1914; *Dana*, 1920–22 (these three by chlorinity titrations) and *Carnegie*, 1928 (Wenner's salinity bridge). It is a well-known fact that in such observations—except the chlorinity titrations of scientific expeditions—there is often a tendency to a little too high values.

In Böhnecke's monthly charts for the Antillean-Caribbean region, the isohalines were frequently drawn by dashed lines indicating hypothetical constructions. In the northwest portions of the Central American Sea (Yucatan Sea, Gulf of Mexico, and Florida Straits) the isohalines were entirely omitted.

Also, in three of Böhnecke's quarterly charts, similar uncertainties are perceptible, but to a smaller extent. Such difficulties might have been the reason that W. Krauss (1962) in his later analysis of the surface salinity distribution in the Atlantic Ocean has used quarterly averages of two-degree quadrangles instead of one-degree squares as Böhnecke did. Parr (1937, 1938) has drawn three small special salinity charts of the years, 1933, 1934, and 1937, in some smaller areas of our region by using observations of three *Atlantis* cruises.

In his remarkable, partly theoretical, studies on the average hydrographic conditions at the surface of the Atlantic Ocean, Krauss (1958, 1962) with regard to salinity came to the conclusion "that in the central areas . . . precipitation and evaporation fix the salinity at the surface, that however the strong runoff of fresh water from the continents considerably reduce the salinity in the border regions." (Krauss, 1962, p. 502 in free translation.) Impressive examples for such a reduction are, in the *Meteor*-Atlas Vol. V, given in all seasons by the amazing far-reaching influences of the Amazon River discharge within Guiana Current between 0° and 12° N. along the northeast coast of South America. These low salinity waters are reinforced in June to November by the equatorial low salinity belt of the doldrums in their most northern position between 5° and 15° N. Probably because of the lack of observations and of their uneven distribution, the *Meteor* atlas does not indicate additional influences of the Orinoco and Magdalena rivers on the Caribbean surface salinity during the rainy season (June–November). Van Andel and Postma (1954) and Richards (1960) were the first to mention that the "Orinoco water may be of major importance in the Caribbean" for creating low salinity waters along the northern Venezuelan coast "around both sides of the island of Trinidad." (Richards, 1960, p. 617.) No indications of a similar influence of the Magdalena River have been found in all mentioned studies.

DISTRIBUTION OF SALINITY IN WINTER AND SUMMER (PLATES I–IV)

By the systematic Caribbean cruises of the modern expeditions, the number of exact surface salinity values has increased since 1931 and a better distribution of data has been obtained. However, the author is convinced that because of some still-existing gaps, particularly in summer, the construction of monthly and quarterly salinity charts would not give representative pictures. Therefore, we have resolved to construct only semiannual charts for which approximately 2000 stations are today available; namely, about 1400 for the winter season (including spring) and about 600 for the summer season (including autumn). During the latter period, our construction of isohalines presents particularly in the Yucatan Sea and above the Beata Rise still larger questionable gaps.

The sources of data for our semiannual surface salinity charts which concern mainly the period 1931–61 and continue the former studies of Böhnecke (and Krauss) are the following:

(a) About 1450 hydrographic stations shown on our Caribbean Sea station map (Plate XII) and listed in our card files of serial measurements from depths greater than 200 meters (Table 1). The salinity values of this period are determined by precise chlorinity titrations or salinometer readings.

(b) About 500 surface salinities (chlorinity titrations) partly from survey and merchant vessels listed in the "Bulletin Hydrographique pour les années 1931–1955" (Copenhagen).

(c) Fifteen additional data from the card files of the U.S. Oceanographic Data Center.

As auxiliary values we have used the precise surface salinities of about 50 *Dana II* stations, 1921–28, and five additional former data in order to fill some gaps in our basic material.

In restricting our construction mainly to these systematic and precise observations during the last three decades as reported by reliable scientific institutions, we may assume that the distribution of the Caribbean data is more even that in the *Meteor* atlas and that the frequency of suspicious values is minimized. We placed only sixteen observations in parenthesis to characterize them as doubtful.

The source material was entered and averaged for the two years in one-degree quadrangles, as shown in the following:

1° Long.

1° Lat. | 5.78 | Average semiannual surface salinity: 35.78‰
        | (4) | Number of observations averaged

Plates I and II show the statistical results of this data processing. In the winter seasons the one-degree quadrangle averages cover rather evenly the Antillean-Caribbean basins; however, in the summer seasons there are still some larger regions without data, particularly in the Cayman-, Yucatan-, and northwest Colombia-basins. With the exception of these areas where we had to put some question marks and dotted isohalines, it has proved possible to construct representative isohalines for every 0.25‰ in both half-years.

In both quadrangle charts the broken dashed line approximately corresponds with the elliptic boundary line of the area for which Colón (1960, 1963) has computed the heat balance between the atmosphere and the water body of the Caribbean Sea. In both studies the shallow waters (less than 200 meters in depth) have been excluded in order to minimize the confusing problems of some minor coastal complications.

In the winter–spring chart of surface salinity (Plate I), that is, during December to May, we have in most parts of the Antillean-Caribbean Region relatively high salinities of 35.75–36.75‰. South of Hispaniola, Jamaica, and Cuba we find a tongue-like belt of lower salinities (<35.75‰). This belt extends from a source region in the southeast corner of our map (<30.0‰) with a small interruption south of Puerto Rico to the west northwest through the whole Caribbean Sea just to the northwestern border region of the deep Yucatan Basin. This far-reaching influence by the combined effects of the Amazon River discharge and of the salinity minimum in the equatorial doldrum belt (between 0° and 7° N.) is not so well defined in Böhnecke's two corresponding quarterly maps (December–February and March–May) no doubt because of the lack of data as well as its uneven distribution. The belt of low salinity water masses transported by the Guiana and Caribbean currents shows on our chart three patches (<35.5‰), apparently rudiments of the stronger low salinity belt

in the summer half-year. The absolute maxima (of more than 36.5 respectively 37.0‰) are situated in the north and northeast outside the Antillean Arc and in two smaller areas north of the Venezuela and Colombia coasts.

Quite different conditions, that is, relatively low salinities, exist in the summer–autumn chart (Plate IV). Instead of one point source of low salinity water, there are now four such point sources:

(a) low salinity water (<33.5) by Amazon River discharge

(b) low salinity water (<33.5) by Orinoco River discharge

(c) low salinity water (<34.5) at the eastern margin of our chart in the doldrums region which shifts in summer with the sun's altitude and the thermal-haline equator in the Western Atlantic from 10°–15° N. to 15°–20° N.

(d) low salinity water (<34.5‰) by Magdalena River discharge

The main tongue-like belt of low salinity water (lower than 35.25‰) crossing our region from east southeast to west northwest is the combined effect of these four point sources. Because of the lack of data and the uneven distribution, the two quarterly summer maps in the *Meteor* atlas do not show the two interior point sources of low salinity water and corresponding evidence of an extended low salinity belt. In summer absolute salinity maxima of more than 36.5‰ exist only in the most northern areas of our region outside the Antillean Arc.

The total of one-degree quadrangles is 160 within the Caribbean Sea (elliptic area). In the winter half-year there are 42 one-degree quadrangles without observations, that is, 25 per cent; in the summer half-year, 85 (53 per cent). From the two charts of salinity distribution (Plate III and Plate IV) interpolations in average salinity are made for the 42 and 85 one-degree quadrangles without observations. In summation of the observed and interpolated one-degree square averages and dividing by 160, the averages of salinity, in Table 1, are found for the Caribbean Sea.

Table 1

AVERAGES OF SURFACE SALINITY OF THE CARIBBEAN SEA (ELLIPTIC AREA)

	Winter half-year	Summer half-year	Entire year
S ‰	35.90_0 ‰	35.17_6 ‰	35.53_8 ‰

The difference of the two seasonal averages is 0.724 ‰

COMPARISON WITH FORMER RESULTS

For a better comparison we have prepared the following Table 2, containing the two-degree quadrangle averages of surface salinity in the elliptic area of the Caribbean Sea according to the *Meteor* atlas (1936) and to the present study (1963). In 1962 W. Krauss published an extensive table of the quarterly and annual salinity averages for each two-degree quadrangle of the entire

Atlantic Ocean between 70° N. and 62° S. North of 10° N. these averages are based on Böhnecke's quarterly charts and south of 10° N. on four new improved quarterly charts constructed by Krauss with the help of additional source material of the period 1927–51. In the Antillean-Caribbean Region the two-degree quadrangle quarterly averages of Krauss (1962) are exclusively related to Böhnecke's construction of iso-halines in Beilage XXVII to XXXI of the *Meteor* atlas (1936). From Krauss's values we have derived the two-degree quadrangle averages for the winter half-year (December–May) and the summer half-year (June–

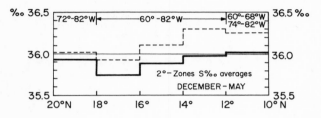

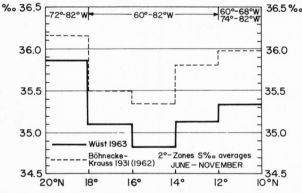

Fig. 10 Distribution of 2° square averages of surface salinity in the Caribbean sea (without Yucatan basin)

November). In Table 2 we have confronted these values of the period 1901–30 with our new values of the period, 1931–61, the last of which are derived from the 718 observed and from 127 interpolated one-degree square averages in our charts. This was done by summation and division within each of the 160 two-degree quadrangles of the concerned Caribbean area.

Table 2 and Fig. 10 disclose amazing systematic differences between the two periods. The total numbers of observations used by the author are 501 in December–May and 217 in June–November (1931–61) whereas in Böhnecke's charts (1901–30) the corresponding numbers are 355 and 180 respectively. Our total averages are for the winter half-year 35.90‰ and for the summer half-year 35.17‰ in salinity, that is, 0.22‰ and 0.52‰ respectively lower than calculated by Krauss from Böhnecke's charts. Fig. 10 shows that such a systematic difference also exists in the zonal distribution of the two computations. The question arises as to whether these differences would mainly be genuine fluctuations or of methodical origin. It is the opinion of the author that the latter is the case, that is, that the higher values derived from the *Meteor* atlas (1936) by Krauss (1962) are mainly the consequence of the smaller number of

exact observations and of their uneven distribution. Perhaps different methods in computing the two-degree quadrangle averages used in Krauss's paper (1962) and in the present paper have contributed additionally to this result. However, a clear decision in which amount smaller genuine fluctuations have secondarily contributed to the systematic differences at present cannot be made. The spreading of the salinity averages in the one-degree quadrangles indicates that such unperiodic variations are more pronounced in the salinity averages than in the temperature averages, the last of which are based on 10–100 times as many observations.

EVAPORATION
(According to Colón and former authors)

For a quantitative understanding of the salinity differences between winter and summer, it is necessary to discuss the corresponding differences of evaporation, precipitation, and runoff in the elliptic area of the Caribbean Sea. Colón's important study (1960)—upon which Joanne Malkus (1962) has given her remarkable summary (*The Sea*, edited by Hill, Chapter 4, paragraph 5A, 1962, p. 148)—is based on three equations:

$$LP - Q_{va} + Q_s + R_a = 0$$
$$Q_s + Q_e = R - S - Q_{vo}$$
$$L(E - P) = Q_e - LP = Q_{vw},$$

where L is the heat of vaporization, P precipitation in grams (or cm) per cm^2 per sec., Q_{va} is the heat flux divergence of horizontal ocean-heat and potential energy transport in the atmosphere in cal per cm^2 per sec., Q_s is the sensible heat flow in cal/cm^2/day, Q_e is the latent heat flux, R_a the radiation balance, R is the earth's surface radiation balance, S the storage of heat in the 90 meter-deep layer, Q_{vo} the oceanic heat flux divergence, Q_{vw} the water-vapor flux divergence in the atmosphere, and E is the evaporation in cm/day.

In his meteorological oceanographic study, Colón has integrated the components over the volume bounded laterally by the elliptic ring of stations using climatological and oceanographic data for each month of the year. "The Caribbean Sea is particularly suited for this purpose. A small, nearly enclosed water body, it contains one well-defined sea current with entrance in the Lesser Antilles and exit in the Yucatan Channel," as Joanne Malkus has stated (1962, p. 151). It is not the task of our book to go into all the details of such a heat budget. Here we refer to the mentioned studies of Colón and Malkus and only take from Colón's Table 4 the seasonal variations of evaporation in cm/day, from which values we derive the following quarterly and semiannual rates (see Table 3). From this table we learn that the highest evaporation (46 cm/quarter) takes place in winter, the lowest (33 cm/quarter) in summer. In his charts of evaporation Jacobs (1951) came to a similar result for the Caribbean Sea but with lower absolute values: 36 cm/quarter in the winter season (December–February) and 29 cm/quarter in the summer

Table 2

TWO-DEGREE QUADRANGLE AVERAGES OF SURFACE SALINITY IN THE CARIBBEAN SEA (WITHOUT YUCATAN BASIN)*

DECEMBER – MAY

N	After:	W82°	80°	78°	76°	74°	72°	70°	68°	66°	64°	62°	Average of 2°-zones	Total number of observations	Total average S‰
20°	Böhnecke 1936	5.86	5.95	5.90	6.19	6.21							B 36.02		
	Wüst 1963	5.98	6.04	6.05	5.98	5.66							W 35.94		
	B–W	-0.12	-0.09	-0.15	0.21	0.55									
18°	Böhnecke 1936	6.05	5.80	5.86	6.25	5.96	5.95	5.92	5.97	6.00	5.87	5.56	B 35.93		
	Wüst 1963	5.92	5.85	5.51	5.75	5.80	5.54	5.53	5.69	5.94	5.95	5.78	W 35.75		
	B–W	0.13	-0.05	0.35	0.50	0.16	0.41	0.39	0.28	0.06	-0.08	-0.22		B 355	B = 36.12
16°	Böhnecke 1936	6.50	5.74	5.96	6.37	6.15	6.08	6.27	6.31	6.18	5.87	5.82	B 36.11	W 501	W = 35.90
	Wüst 1963	5.97	5.84	5.60	5.93	5.91	5.96	5.57	5.79	5.83	5.64	5.75	W 35.89		
	B–W	0.53	-0.10	0.36	0.44	0.24	0.12	0.70	0.52	0.35	0.23	0.07			
14°	Böhnecke 1936	5.91	5.77	6.12	6.51	6.66	6.51	6.66	6.58	6.40	6.30	5.89	B 36.30		
	Wüst 1963	5.93	5.96	6.11	6.42	6.24	6.02	5.98	5.98	5.97	5.58	5.55	W 35.98		
	B–W	-0.02	-0.19	0.01	0.09	0.42	0.42	0.68	0.60	0.43	0.72	0.34			
12°	Böhnecke 1936	6.41	6.21	6.48	6.98				6.90	6.82	6.10	(4.11)	B 36.25		
	Wüst 1963	5.77	5.82	5.75	6.10				6.67	6.57	5.80	5.64	W 36.02		
	B–W	0.64	0.39	0.73	0.88				0.23	0.25	0.30	-1.53			
10°		W82°	80°	78°	76°	74°	72°	70°	68°	66°	64°	62°	60°		

JUNE – NOVEMBER

N	After:	W82°	80°	78°	76°	74°	72°	70°	68°	66°	64°	62°	Average of 2°-zones	Total number of observations	Total average S‰
20°	Böhnecke 1936	6.20	6.25	6.41	6.00	5.95							B 36.16		
	Wüst 1963	5.75	5.86	5.87	5.95	5.90							W 35.87		
	B–W	0.45	0.36	0.54	0.05	0.45									
18°	Böhnecke 1936	6.12	5.09	6.03	5.93	6.30	5.50	5.23	4.90	4.93	5.59	4.91	B 35.50		
	Wüst 1963	5.56	5.39	5.39	5.51	5.27	5.24	4.79	5.10	4.76	4.56	4.65	W 35.11		
	B–W	0.56	-0.30	0.64	0.42	1.03	0.26	0.44	0.20	0.17	1.03	0.26		B 180	B = 35.69
16°	Böhnecke 1936	(5.90)	6.01	5.98	5.82	5.70	5.23	5.05	4.81	4.57	4.71	4.97	B 35.34	W 217	W = 35.17
	Wüst 1963	5.57	5.17	5.08	5.59	5.17	4.85	4.47	4.43	4.44	4.03	4.34	W 34.83		
	B–W	(0.33)	0.84	0.90	0.33	0.53	0.38	0.58	0.38	0.13	0.68	0.63			
14°	Böhnecke 1936	6.00	5.96	5.73	6.25	6.42	6.24	6.01	5.97	5.95	4.78	4.57	B 35.81		
	Wüst 1963	5.72	5.34	4.66	4.92	5.00	5.98	5.69	5.05	5.04	4.94	4.11	W 35.13		
	B–W	0.28	0.62	1.07	1.33	1.42	0.26	0.32	0.92	0.91	-0.16	0.46			
12°	Böhnecke 1936	(5.80)	5.93	6.14	6.18				6.70	6.63	5.50	4.95	B 35.98		
	Wüst 1963	5.56	5.52	5.08	(5.27)				6.03	6.10	4.40	(4.75)	W 35.34		
	B–W	(0.24)	0.41	1.06	(0.91)				0.67	0.53	1.10	(0.20)			
10°		W82°	80°	78°	76°	74°	72°	70°	68°	66°	64°	62°	60°		

* The two-degree quadrangle averages from Böhnecke's charts (1936) are computed by Krauss (1962).

Table 3

SEASONAL AND SEMIANNUAL AVERAGES OF EVAPORATION RATES *E**

Season	Winter (Dec.–Feb.)	Spring (March–May)	Summer (June-Aug.)	Autumn (Sept.–Nov.)	Annual average of E cm/year
E cm/quarter	46[a]	38	33[b]	44	161
E cm/half-year	84[a]		77[b]		161

[a] Represents maxima

[b] Represents minima

* Derived from Colón's monthly heat budget of heat transfer from Caribbean Sea to atmosphere (Colón, 1963).

season (June–August), that is, between 11 per cent and 22 per cent lower than Colón. It is interesting to compare the present results for mean annual evaporation with those of former authors, see Table 4, as was done by Joanne Malkus (1962, Table XII).

Table 4

COMPARISON OF ANNUAL EVAPORATION COMPUTATIONS FOR THE CARIBBEAN REGION BY VARIOUS AUTHORS*

	Method	Evaporation cm/year
Colón (1960)	Energy budget	161
Colón (1960)	Formulas—Marine Atlas (U.S. Navy)	146
Budyko (1956)	Formulas—Atlas of the Heat Balance (USSR)	138
Jacobs (1951a)	Formulas—U.S. Weather Bureau Climatic Charts	124
Wüst (1936)	Budget (Lat 10°–20° N. Atlantic)	146

* From J. Malkus (1962, Table XII).

In 1957 the author increased the reduction factor 0.53 for the averages of the pan measurements to 0.55, that is, by 6 per cent for the entire world ocean. Using this higher coefficient the evaporation of Lat. 10°–20° N. in the Atlantic Ocean would be 152 cm/year, that is, only 4 per cent smaller than Colón's value derived from his energy budget (1963). Anyone who has tried to apply reasonable physical approaches in such heat and water budgets knows that according to Colón, "it is rather difficult to evaluate the accuracy of computations of this type. Too many factors enter into it that are inadequately known." However, it seems to the author that for the present Colón's approach is the most reasonable. Only by an improvement in atmospheric radiation determinations, in precipitation measurements and in precise measurements of the vertical gradients of temperature and water vapor above the sea surface will better approaches be possible in this fundamental problem of joint air-sea budgets. Here, as in all natural sciences, the statement made by Viktor Hensen, founder of quantitative planktology is valid: "Genuine science progresses by putting smaller errors at the place of bigger ones."

PRECIPITATION (PLATES V–VI)

In some publications (Wüst, 1936, 1950, 1954a, and 1954b) the author has emphasized that the charts of precipitation over the oceans—such as the charts of Meinardus (1934) and the former charts of Schott (1926, 1935)—cannot be directly used in quantitative computations of oceanic water budgets. These charts were based on gauge measurements at coastal stations of islands and continents and on qualitative ships' observations of rain-frequency. Because of a more or less steep horizontal gradient of precipitation from the coast to the open sea, the author feels it is necessary to reduce the zonal averages (derived from the mentioned charts) by an average coefficient of about 0.80, that is, by 20 per cent. In the above-mentioned publications, this problem of reduction for "land effect" was discussed in more detail. In this respect, his estimation of a reduction coefficient has been increasingly substantiated by the contributions of Mosby (1936), Kuhlbrodt (1938), Schott (in his later revised precipitation map of the Atlantic Ocean, 1942), Albrecht (1940, 1949, 1951), Bergeron (1950), Möller (1951), W. C. Jacobs (1951), Prager (1952), Brogmus (1952), Reichel (1952), Skarr (1955), Wyrtki (1956), and Dietrich (1957).* Contrary to these conceptions Drozdov (1953), Budyko (1954), Carter (1956), Riehl and Malkus (1958), and Malkus (1962) deny the necessity of a perceptible reduction of coastal rain measurements and are more in favor of the most recent Russian global pictures of oceanic rainfall patterns (Drozdov, 1953). "They were," according to Malkus (1962), "obtained by direct extrapolation between (coastal) stations without any arbitrary reductions to correct for land effect and are in better agreement with still earlier determinations of Meinardus (1934)." Riehl and Malkus (1958) and Malkus (1962, pp. 129–31) suggest that "the higher Russian values are the better ones, as does our increased knowledge of rainfall dynamics. Since it is now known that, even in the tropics, all significant rainfall occurs in major synoptic-scale storms, it is likely that coast effect on precipitation has been considerably overrated in the past."

The promising experiments made with rain gauges

* With regard to the references of the mentioned publications, see Wüst (1950b and 1954a).

on research vessels like *Meteor*, 1925–27 (Kuhlbrodt, 1938), on lightships (Prager, 1952), and on weather ships (Skarr, 1955) enable us to make a decision whether a reduction for coast effects (on the average of 20 per cent) is preferable. Kuhlbrodt, Prager, Skarr, and Roll have given valuable advice for the best mounting of rain gauges on or above the lifeboat deck. After their experiences in direct precipitation measurements on sea they are in favor of a considerable reduction of coastal measurements.

In Table 5, we show the zonal ten-degree square averages of precipitation over the Atlantic Ocean between 30° N. and 30° S. according to the results of Kuhlbrodt's direct rain measurements on board *Meteor*, 1925–27, and the annual precipitation chart revised by Schott in 1942 as well as quarterly precipitation charts (for the entire earth) of Möller (1951). Naturally it is reasonable to assume that because of disturbing wind effects aboard a driving ship like *Meteor* the direct rainfall measurements (by recording rain gauge, normal rain gauges mounted in gimbals after Hellmann, or marine rain gauges) would sometimes have the tendency to give too low values. However, Kuhlbrodt (1938) has tried to eliminate such disturbances in the processing of data. On the other hand, the total amounts of precipitation in the cross sections of the various 10° zones are related from 23 to 62 days in sea or one to two months of a particular year. Extrapolations for semiannual averages can only be regarded as rough approaches. However, in the subtropics and tropics (except the doldrums) the annual range of precipitation is mostly relatively small. In the last two columns of Table 5, the author presents the results of his former computations (1950, 1954) of the annual zonal averages in the Atlantic from the precipitation charts of Schott (1942) and Möller (1951). In these two charts the "land effects" are, in a reasonable manner, eliminated under the assumption that there is in most regions a horizontal gradient of precipitation from the coasts to the open sea.

On the other hand, Skaar has stated that in the older charts (using also the frequency data) "the amount of precipitation falling on sea may be overrated on account of the relatively high numbers of occurrences." Schott in his revised chart (1942, p. 426 and in his Plate XIV) as well as Möller (1951, S. 1–4) came to the conclusion that on the oceans the precipitation chart by Meinardus (1934) must be reduced in the absolute amounts, namely, in the tropics a little more than in the higher latitudes and on the whole by 20 per cent. With regard to details, we refer to the contributions to this reduction problem of "land effects" by the author (1950, 1954b) Schott (1942), and Möller (1951). The comparison between the three end columns in Table 5 clearly demonstrates in the magnitude fair agreement between the various approaches, which we regard as the physically most reasonable ones at this time. These results may encourage the marine meteorologists to reform slightly the system of regular meteorological observations on board merchant and naval ships, light and weather ships by introducing daily measurements of precipitation with rain gauges at appropriate places. At the same time more exact measurements of air and water temperature and water vapor are desirable by using ventilated psychrometers and recording water thermographs. Only in this way, could better approaches in heat and water budgets be obtained in the future.

At present Möller's "Vierteljahrskarten des Niederschlags für die ganze Erde" (quarterly precipitation charts for the entire earth) represent the best approaches for the Caribbean Sea. By superposition of two quarterly maps by Möller (1951) the isohyets are determined for our semiannual charts of precipitation in December–May and June–November (Plates V and VI). By the hatching of the intervals 200–400, 400–600, 600–1000, and >1000 mm., the distribution of semiannual precipitation in winter and summer is clearly demonstrated. The winter half-year is the dry season with semiannual precipitation of less than 200 mm.; only in the Mosquito

Table 5

AVERAGE PRECIPITATION IN THE ATLANTIC OCEAN BETWEEN 30° N. AND 30° S.

| | | Rain measurements on board Meteor* | | | | Averages from charts | |
| | | | No. of days in sea (n) | Measured rainfall cm/n | Extrapolated rainfall cm/quart. | Schott† 1942 cm/yr. | Möller‡ 1951 cm/yr. |
Latitude	Cross-section no.	Months in 1925–27					
30°–20° N.	—	—	—	—	—	40	52
20°–10° N.	XIII, XIV	March–May	49	5.5	11	50	58
10°–0° N.	IX, X, XI	Oct.–Feb.	58	24.7	39[a]	140[a]	154[a]
0°–10° S.	VIII, XI	Aug.–Jan.	52	4.1	7	40	28
10°–20° S.	VI	May	23	0.3	1.2[b]	23[b]	20[b]
20°–30° S.	II, VII	July–Sept.	62	10.1	15	40	42

[a] Represents maxima
[b] Represents minima
* According to E. Kuhlbrodt in *Meteor* Reports, Vol. XIV (1938).
† According to G. Schott, Geographie des Atlantischen Ozeans, Third Edition (1942). Zonal averages computed by Wüst (1950).
‡ According to F. Möller, Vierteljahrskarten des Niederschlags für ganze Erde (1951). Zonal averages computed by Wüst (1954).

Gulf is high rainfall of more than 1000 mm. during the six months of winter and spring. Rather different conditions exist in the summer seasons (June–November) where the semiannual values of the elliptic area are between 300 and 800 mm. and the absolute values of the Mosquito Gulf increase to more than 2000 mm./half year. The semiannual averages of precipitation in the central Caribbean Sea (elliptic area of Colón) are determined by the research assistant, S. S. Jacobs (1963), with the help of polar-planimeter and indicate the following values in Table 6. In Schott's precipitation

Table 6
AVERAGE PRECIPITATION IN THE CENTRAL CARIBBEAN SEA (ELLIPTIC AREA)

Winter (December–May)	205 mm/half-year
Summer (June–November)	505 mm/half-year
Total for entire year	710 mm/year

map (annual average of the Atlantic Ocean in Schott, 1942, Plate XIV) a small number of isohyets are drawn in the Caribbean area for 500 and 1000 mm/year. A rough estimation there gives an average of about 650 mm/year. In Drozdov's chart (1953, Morskoi Atlas II, Chart 48), two isohyets of 1000 meters cross the western half of the elliptic area, mainly from north to south, and only in the southeastern area is precipitation of ∼500 mm. assumed. In other words according to Drozdov, the

average rainfall in the Caribbean Sea would be in the size of 880 mm, that is, 24 per cent higher than our value in Table 6. Comparison with the measured *Meteor* values between 10° and 20° N. is not possible because in the open Atlantic the rainfall strongly decreases from west to east, where the annual rainfall has its minimum with less than 100 mm.

DISCHARGE OF MAIN RIVERS

Besides the two main factors of the water budget, evaporation and precipitation, there is a smaller one—the influence of the river discharge into the Caribbean Sea. Contrary to the well-organized hydrological surveillance in the United States and most of the European countries where extensive runoff data are published, only a relatively small number of data are available for the river discharges in South and Central America. The following Table 7 is compiled from published and private information* about the runoff figures for the three main South American rivers—the Magdalena, Orinoco, and Amazon rivers. The last, though not flowing directly into the Caribbean Sea, can be traced in salinity with the Guiana current to the east side of the Antillean Arc and combined with the North Equatorial Current into the Caribbean Sea (see pp. 17–18).

* The author wishes to thank Bruce Heezen for private information and Charles B. Hitchcock for the same as well as for the literature available on this subject in the library of the American Geographical Society, New York.

Table 7
RIVER DISCHARGES COMPILED FROM VARIOUS SOURCES
(where different units have been used the values are recalculated in $m^3 \cdot sec^{-1}$)

	Discharge	Source[a]
Magdalena River	$7.5 \cdot 10^3$ (Mean)	1
	$11.5 \cdot 10^3$ (Max.: Oct.–Dec.)	1
	$\overline{3.5* \cdot 10^3}$ (Min: Jan.–March)	1
	$7.5 \cdot 10^3$ (Mean)	2
	$9.4 \cdot 10^3$ (1. Max: Nov.–Dec.)	3
	$\overline{7.4 \cdot 10^3}$ (2. Max: August)	3
	$2.4* \cdot 10^3$ (Min: Feb.–March)	3
Orinoco River	$14 \cdot 10^3$ (Mean)	1
	$17 \cdot 10^3$ (Mean)	2
	$34 \cdot 10^3$ (Mean)	4
	$85 \cdot 10^3$ (Max: August)	4
	$\overline{8.5* \cdot 10^3}$ (Min)	4
Amazon River	$106–124 \cdot 10^3$ (Mean)	5
	$146 \cdot 10^3$ (Max: Jan.–Feb.)	1
	$85* \cdot 10^3–113 \cdot 10^3$	2

Maxima indicated by underscoring; minima indicated by asterisk*

[a] The sources represented by numbers 1–5 are as follows: (1) I. V. Samojlov, Die Flussmündungen (Gotha, 1956), pp. 542–52; (2) L. B. Leopold, Rivers. American Scientist, L (1962), 514–15, Table 2, Great Rivers of the World (discharge over 35,000 cubic feet per second at the mouth); (3) Bruce Heezen, Private Communication of Measurements in 1945–49 (1963); (4) Charles B. Hitchcock (American Geographical Society), Private Communication of Measurements at Palna 1951 and of Estimations of Averages at Palna (1963); and (5) R. Keller, Gewässer und Wasser haushalt des Festlandes (Berlin, 1961, Table 12).

Because of the lack of more detailed data, it is impossible to show the continuous seasonal fluctuations or to calculate the average runoff figures for both seasons during the period 1931–61. In spite of this, it seems appropriate to assume that the values of river discharge follow, with short delay, the variations of precipitation. According to the sparse information, we can assume that in the Caribbean region the river discharges of the Orinoco and Magdalena rivers have their peak flows in August to December, approximately when (Möller, 1951) the precipitation has its maximum (September–November) and evaporation and surface salinity are in their minimum. The total runoff to the Caribbean Sea is unknown. Therefore, we cannot estimate its effect in cm height of water on the water budget. Furthermore, the many passages along the boundary of this area make such calculation impossible.

WATER BUDGET AND SURFACE SALINITY IN SEMIANNUAL AVERAGES

Because of the lack of more detailed data, the entire study on the surface salinity and the water budget of the Caribbean Sea has to be confined to semiannual averages. This procedure is an appropriate approach because, generally speaking, there are only two main seasons in the Caribbean area: the sunny season and the rainy season. The first is characterized by a semi-arid (more subtropical) climate with sunshine, higher evaporation, small precipitation, small runoff, and high surface salinity; the second, by a semihumid (more tropical) climate with more cloudiness, smaller evaporation, high precipitation, high runoff, and low surface salinity. These conditions are shown in Table 8. The climatologically important value of $E - P$ is, in the winter season, nearly two and one-half times as large as in the summer season. This mainly accounts for the fact that the surface salinity maximum occurs in the winter season and is on the average $0.72_4\,\%_0$ higher than in the summer season. This annual variation is rather large when we consider that in the open North Atlantic Ocean the annual range of surface salinity is—except for the Newfoundland region—less than $0.20\%_0$. Our annual average, $E - P = 89$, is in fair agreement with

the value interpolated from Dietrich's chart (1937, Fig. 73) of the distribution $E - P$ which is based on the Atlantic Ocean studies of W. C. Jacobs (1951). From Dietrich's chart for the Caribbean area we read off $E - P = 80$ cm/year. The two very similar numbers are obtained by two different methods.

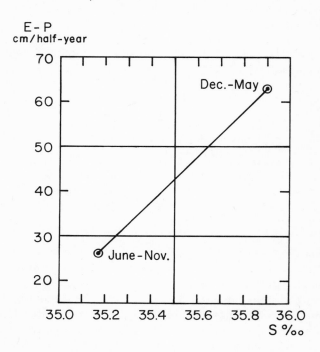

Fig. 11   Relation between the semiannual rates of surface salinity S and E - P in the Caribbean Sea

As we have already mentioned, the mean annual runoff-R is unknown, and we cannot express it in cm water height as in the water budget of the Mediterranean and Baltic seas. But we may suggest that its contribution to the water budget lies within the limits of error of E and P, and that corresponding to P the amount of R would be higher in summer than in winter. As shown, the diagram (Fig. 11) indicates the relation between the semiannual rates of the surface salinity and the difference $E - P$ in the elliptic area of the Caribbean Sea corresponding to Table 8.

✓ Table 8

WATER BUDGET AND SURFACE SALINITY OF THE CARIBBEAN SEA (ELLIPTIC AREA)

(in semiannual and annual averages)

	Evaporation cm	Precipitation cm	E − P cm	Runoff R cm	E − (P + R) cm	Surface salinity
December–May (cm/half-year)	84	21	63	very low	high	$35.90_0\,\%_0$
June–November (cm/half-year)	77	51	26	low	lower	$35.17_6\,\%_0$
Total for entire year (cm/year)	161	72	89	—	—	$35.53_8\,\%_0$

For more or less enclosed seas like the Baltic Sea and the European Mediterranean Sea, the following equation of a water budget (in m³/sec) is valid:

$$E - (P + R) = \text{inflow-}I, \text{ minus outflow-}O$$

When the difference $I - O$ for the main passages would be in our area accurately known, the order of magnitude of $E - (P + R)$ could be computed. Here the words of warning of H. Stommel (1958, p. 143) must be quoted: "Although we do know something about seasonal changes in the shallow wind drift currents in the upper 100 m of the ocean, and although we do have fairly adequate data, from tide gauges and the submarine cable for a study of the Florida Current, we know virtually nothing about changes in the transport of the Gulf Stream itself." The last statement is valid also for the source region of the Gulf Stream system, the Caribbean Sea, where cross sections (for dynamic computations of the geostrophic volume transports) as well as direct current measurements in the eastern passages (Pillsbury, 1888) are made only during the winter half-year.

Therefore, at present it is not possible to compute the half-year averages of $E - (P + R)$ in our area from the mean differences (calculated or observed) of the volume transports $I - O$, but it is possible in the Mediterranean and Baltic seas. After the estimations of Sverdrup *et al.* (1942, Fig. 187) both (inflow, outflow) are in the Caribbean Sea about 26×10^6 m³/sec. We may assume that the differences of $I - O$ and of $E - (P + R)$ are only some per mill of this amount.

COMPARISON WITH MEDITERRANEAN WATER BUDGET

In spite of some similarities in their intercontinental situation, their depths and basin-ridge structure, the so-called "American Mediterranean Sea" and the "European Mediterranean Sea" present remarkable differences in their water budgets and the renewal of their water masses. These differences are mainly caused by the dissimilar degree of isolation, that is, by the sill depths and the dimensions of their oceanic passages as well as by differences in their climate and water budgets. The water exchange with the ocean through the passages of the Central American Sea is about fifteen times as great as in the Mediterranean Sea. The Central American basins are to a maximum depth of 1750 meters integral parts of the open Atlantic Ocean because of its numerous passages through the Antillean Arc, whereas the European Mediterranean Sea is a strongly enclosed sea with only one very narrow passage of a breadth of eight sea miles and with a sill depth of approximately 320 meters. Therefore, the Central American Sea is a passage sea within which—contrary to the very high positive salinity anomaly of the Mediterranean Sea (according to Dietrich, 1937, between 3–4‰) —its annual average of salinity shows only a small anomaly from the average for 10°–20° N. of the Atlantic (Böhnecke's atlas, Plate XLIV). All these factors including the climatic differences produce quite a different water budget in the Mediterranean Sea, as shown by Table 9. These are the latest physically reasonable estimations (Wüst, 1959 and 1960, p. 116, footnote 6).

Table 9

AVERAGE ANNUAL WATER BUDGET
OF THE MEDITERRANEAN SEA
(EXCLUDING THE BLACK SEA)[a]

Evaporation[b], E cm/year	145
Precipitation[c], P cm/year	40
$E - P$ cm/year	105
Runoff[d], R cm/year	15
$E - (P + R)$ cm/year	90
Surface salinity ‰	about 38.5

[a] After Wüst (1959, 1960).
[b] According to Sverdrup (1942) and Wüst (1952 and 1959).
[c] Averages computed by Wüst (1959) from Carter (1956).
[d] Averages computed by Wüst (1959) from Carter (1956).

Because of the differences in the water budgets of the two concerned seas, the author prefers to replace the name, "American Mediterranean Sea," introduced by Krümmel (1907) and used by Dietrich (1937, 1957) and Sverdrup *et al.* (1942) with the more appropriate one, "Central American Sea," which consists of the "Caribbean Sea" and the more or less independent "Gulf of Mexico."

Later we will also see that the origin of the various deep water masses, their stratification and circulation, are principally different in the Central American and in the Mediterranean Seas.

V. ANNUAL VARIATIONS OF SURFACE CURRENTS (PLATES VII–X)

In the discussion on the semiannual range of the surface salinity and the water budget we have not yet considered the semiannual range of advection by the Guiana, North Equatorial, and Caribbean currents from the southeast and east. The Northeast Trade Winds which come from the east northeast and east in the Caribbean Sea are the driving forces of the surface currents. They produce in part a boundary gradient current, the Guiana Current (along the northeastern South American coast) and in part the wind-driven Equatorial Current and its continuation in the mainly wind-driven Caribbean Current. This system of gradient currents, superimposed by the pure wind-driven currents, is subject to manifold modifications in velocity and direction by the orography of the Central American Sea and its passages, particularly by the lateral eddies and countercurrents along the coasts. But generally speaking, the classical description by Pillsbury is valid: The stress to the west prevails. "Not a stream, but a sea is in motion." Since the Northeast Trades fluctuate in position and velocity with the seasons, we must expect that the velocities of the above-mentioned currents also vary with them. The following remarks on the observation of surface current by merchant vessels are appropriate. We quote the clear description given in "Meteorology for Mariners" (London, Meteorological Office, 1956, pp. 171–72):

For constructing current charts, as many observations as possible are required during many years. The only way of obtaining enough observations is by the co-operation of merchant shipping. The method used in making the observations is to calculate the difference between the "dead reckoning" position of the vessel, after making due allowance for leeway, and the position by astronomical or land fix. The result is the set and drift experienced by the vessel during the interval since the previous astronomical or land fix. The current found by this method is that for a mean depth of about half the ship's draught. It will be correct only if the ship's true course and speed through the water are known. Knowledge of the true course involves a precise knowledge of the error of the compass, sound judgement of the leeway made and the leeway allowed for when setting the course, and good steering. An accurate estimate of leeway can only be made by experience, bearing in mind that the greatest effect will be with the wind direction abeam when the ship is light. For the speed through the water a compromise between log distance and distance by engine revolutions, after making due allowance for slip, gives perhaps the best results. Much will depend on local circumstances, e.g., in rough weather with the propeller often clear of the water, it will not be possible to assess the slip with any degree of accuracy; the same is true to a limited extent when the ship is "flying light" or when she has been a long time out of dock. It should be possible from time to time to test the accuracy and compute the percentage error of one or more logs by comparison with each other and with runs over a known distance in still water. Judgement is necessary as to the appropriate length of log-line to use at varying draughts. In other words, the dead-reckoning position to use is that which the navigator might expect the ship to be in if all considerations except current were taken into account.

A precise knowledge of the ship's position is essential. The noon position which is so often used depends for its value on the run between observations, and can thus only be considered accurate to a limited extent. When taking a sun sight it is very often possible to obtain a cross with either the moon or the planet Venus. Occasionally Jupiter is visible, whilst a single bearing of a point of land may be used in conjunction with the foregoing and a full land fix should be used if available. Stellar observations at morning and evening twilight undoubtedly give the best positions at sea. In the space of 24 hours a ship may experience two or more distinct currents; observations at short intervals are therefore to be preferred. It is recognized that individual current observations are frequently only approximately accurate, and that in some cases the accuracy may be less than in others. In compiling the current charts, however, such casual errors tend to cancel out in the long run providing that the number of observations in each part of an ocean is large enough. There is another reason why many current observations are required; the day-to-day currents in the oceans are very variable and the general current trend in any small region cannot be determined until there are enough observations to be representative of all the variations, both in direction and rate which can occur in that region.

It is advisable to remember this careful description of the observation method and of its sources of errors, when using the mean ocean current charts for the different months. On the other hand, these current charts published by the Hydrographic Offices and Meteorological Offices are at present the best and only information on climatological averages. They also give a consistent picture of annual variations in the current speeds within certain segments of our current system. From the data published in the form of an Atlas by the U.S. Navy Hydrographic Office (1946), Fuglister (1951) has calculated the annual variations for the one-degree squares and the averages of the following segments in the Antillean-Caribbean Region (Fig. 12). Iselin and Fuglister (1948) have shown that the "Median Position" method, on which all such current calculations are based (by integrating over the main current and all possible countercurrents and eddies) gives *much lower values of speed* "than would be the case if they applied only to the main current." The chosen three segments are located in areas, "where the largest number of observations are available and where the arrows on the charts pointed in approximately the same direction throughout the year." (Quoted from Fuglister 1951, p. 120.) After an analysis of the averages of resultant

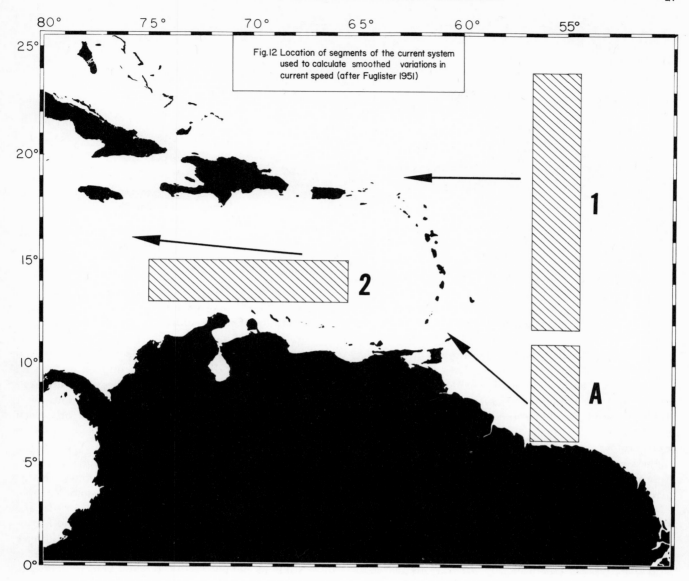

Fig.12 Location of segments of the current system used to calculate smoothed variations in current speed (after Fuglister 1951)

drifts for all quadrangles in each of the three segments, the curves of the annual variations in the current speeds are, according to Fuglister, constructed and recalculated in sm/hour (Fig. 13). These curves indicate that the time of maxima and minima varies from segment to segment. The Guiana Current is as a boundary gradient current the strongest of the three averaging 0.93 sm/hour. Its annual range has also the greatest amplitude (0.67 sm/hour). The maximum occurs in April–May, the minimum in September, as a consequence of the shifting of the doldrum area with the sun's altitude to 10° N. The velocity (0.32) and the amplitude (0.06) are the smallest in the North Equatorial Current. The maximum occurs in July and the minimum in November. The Caribbean Current in speed (0.7) and in amplitude (0.30) takes a middle between the two others. This fact demonstrates their superpositions. The semiannual averages of speed are given in Table 10.

The differences are relatively small particularly in segments 1 and 2 indicating that on the average over the half-years, the factor of the differences in advection plays a secondary role in the water budget. Finally,

Fuglister (1951) has shown that in the North Equatorial segment (1) and in the Caribbean segment (2) the curves of the annual variations in the current speed and in the wind speed have the same shape, indicating that the northeast-east trade winds are the main driving forces for these currents.

For the construction of the current charts of the Antillean-Caribbean region for January, April, July and October (Plates VII–X), the "Climatological and Oceanographic Atlas for Mariners," Vol. 1, Atlantic

Table 10

SEMIANNUAL AVERAGES OF
CURRENT SPEED

	Winter half-year (sm/h)	Summer half-year (sm/h)	Winter-summer difference (sm/h)
A Guiana Current	1.08	0.77	0.31
2 Caribbean Current	0.72	0.68	0.04
1 North Equatorial Current	0.31	0.32	−0.01

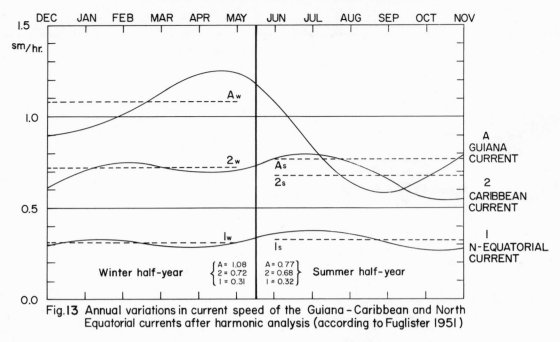

Fig.13 Annual variations in current speed of the Guiana - Caribbean and North
Equatorial currents after harmonic analysis (according to Fuglister 1951)

Ocean (edited by the U.S. Weather Bureau and the U.S. Hydrographic Office, Washington, D.C., August, 1959) was used but with some small changes and additions made. Instead of equal arrows and printed numbers of average speed we have used arrows with different numbers of wings for the different intervals of velocity. Furthermore, we have added by encircled numbers the highest ever-observed drifts which have been reported approximately in the direction of the adjacent current arrows. These extreme values are taken from the "Monatskarten für den Nordatlantischen Ozean" (edited by the German Hydrographic Institution, Hamburg, 1956) and recalculated from sm/24 h to sm/h. The American current charts are compiled principally from ship drift reports forwarded by the various merchant marine ships to the U.S. Navy Hydrographic Office. From these drift observations, the sets and average speeds of the *prevailing* current are calculated for each one-degree quadrangle. By a prevailing current in one direction is understood a current of a predominating direction, that is, where the constancy of current is 25 per cent or more of all observations. The charts also give the average rate of the currents actually experienced in the predominant direction. As mentioned previously, such averages tend to give too small values due to different reasons. Therefore, we have added in encircled numbers the reported extreme drifts which approach or exceed 2 sm/h near the main axis of the Caribbean Currents after the entrance through the Antillean Arc. In the passages we find this axis between 10° and 13° N., in the Colombia Basin and across the Jamaica Ridge between 13° and 16° N., in the Cayman and Yucatan Basins between 16° and 20° N. In other words, the main axis of the Caribbean Current crosses the Caribbean Sea in a more or less diagonal direction from east southeast to west northwest and northwest. It is interesting to note that the average velocity between Tobago and Barbados directly measured by Pillsbury from anchored stations at the surface was 1.5_5 sm/h, that is, in the same order of magnitude as the adjacent observed maxima drifts (between 1.3 and 1.6 sm/h). The study and the comparison of the four current charts (Plates VII–X) give all the information we want. It is unnecessary to describe these features here in detail.

VI. GEOGRAPHIC NOMENCLATURE OF BASINS AND RIDGES: DISTRIBUTION OF HYDROGRAPHIC STATIONS (PLATES XI AND XII)

The generalized bathymetric chart (Plate XI) is based on the available bathymetric source material and in some crucial regions on the distribution of the potential bottom temperature. Contour lines are only drawn for 1000 meters, 2000 meters, 3000 meters, 4000 meters, 6000 meters, and 8000 meters. Only in the southern entrance to the Yucatan Basin and in the northern Venezuela Basin is the 5000-meter contour line given in order to indicate the free connection between the Yucatan and Cayman basins and the Dominica Trench south of Puerto Rico. North of the Puerto Rico Trench, the existence of the Outer-Ridge and its gaps is indicated by the 5500-meter contour line. The symbols concern the position of the near bottom temperature and salinity data used as auxiliary values for the construction of the isobaths in some deep-sea regions. (For explanation of symbols, see Appendix Table I). By the hatching of depths shallower than 2000 meters, our generalized chart gives a clear picture of the basin-ridge structure. The names used are inscribed in the basins and trenches as well as on the ridges and rises. Outside the Antillean Arc, we have the southeastern segment of the North America Basin with the Puerto Rico Trench, the Outer Ridge, its central gap, and the Vema Gap connecting the northern abyssal plains. Within the system of the Antillean Arc, there are four smaller basins, that is, from north to south: Hispaniola Basin (>4000 meters), Virgin Islands Basin (>4000 meters), Tobago Basin (>3000 meters), and Barbados Basin (>2000 meters). Inside the Antillean Arc, the Caribbean Sea is divided into five basins (1–5) by four ridges (a–d). Their names (Table 11) are from northwest to southeast.

The major morphological features of the Caribbean and Antillean area are shown in the map (at p. 30), which is a portion of the physiographic diagram of the South Atlantic Ocean by B. C. Heezen and M. Tharp (1961).

The textures of the relief are sketched at a vertical exaggeration of 25:1; thus the areas of little or no relief such as the continental shelf and the abyssal plains are left blank. Representative depths are in corrected meters.

In the ridge and rises, our chart (Plate XI) and the later longitudinal and cross-sections (Plates XVIII–XXXI) show some new ideas about the gaps and sill depths in the Outer Ridge, the Cayman Ridge, the Beata Rise, and the Aves Ridge as well as in the main passages of the Antillean Arc: Windward Passage, Anegada-Virgin Islands Passage, and Dominica Passage. These sill depths, which will be discussed later, have a decisive influence on the water renewal in the interior basins. As previously argued we do not regard the Caribbean Sea as a part of an "American Mediterranean Sea." We prefer the name "Central American Sea." We omit in our study the more or less independent "Gulf of Mexico" but include, however, the Antillean sector of the North America Basin, without it the stratification and circulation of the Caribbean Sea cannot be understood. The whole quadrangle of the North Atlantic between 8° and 25½° N. and between 55° and 89° W. is referred to in this study as the "Antillean-Caribbean Region."

By the increasing activity of scientific expeditions since 1932, the entire area is now covered with a network of hydrographic stations (Plate XII) in which we have also included the station work of previous oceanographic expeditions and vessels between 1873 and 1928 as shown in the "List of Vessels Contributing Oceanographic Data from depths >200 m in the Antillean-Caribbean Region" (Appendix, Table I). A large gap still exists in the area of the Beata Rise where only some older stations of *Albatross I* (1884–86) are available as auxiliary values for the upper and bottom layers. Naturally the quality of the data from various times

Table 11

NORTHWEST TO SOUTHEAST DIVISION OF THE CARIBBEAN SEA

1 Basin	a Ridge	2 Basin	b Ridge	3 Basin	c Rise	4 Basin	d Ridge	5 Basin
Yucatan (>5000 m)	Cayman R.	Cayman (With Cayman Trench >6000 m)	Jamaica R.	Colombia (>4000 m)	Beata R.	Venezuela (With Dominica Trench >5000 m)	Aves R.	Grenada (>3000 m)

and vessels is different. Therefore, it is necessary to test the data, so far as possible, by T/S and S/O_2-correlation diagrams using the less precise serial measurements as auxiliary values and eliminating the doubtful values. The data which we have used in the construction of the contour lines in our core charts are published in the Appendix (Tables II–VI). In the Antillean-Caribbean region there is a remarkable dependence of oceanographic activity on the seasons. Approximately 90 per cent of all data has been gathered during the winter half-year. This has unfortunately prevented the author from studying the interesting summer conditions of the warm water sphere. Because of the thermal equator shifting in mid and late summer to the Caribbean seas, we find at this time the highest tropical temperature (29° C.) at the surface and much rain (505 mm. during June to November)—in general not as pleasant as during the normal tourist season preferred hitherto by American oceanographers. *It would be a promising task to fill this gap by future systematic cruises.*

VII. WARM WATER CIRCULATION

Important extensive studies on the circulation in the Atlantic warm water sphere were published by A. Defant (1936) and R. B. Montgomery (1938). They used all data available at the time, although by different methods, as is pointed out earlier (p. 5). Defant showed that the core of the subtropical intermediate salinity maximum is most significant for the deduction of the circulation in the lower stratum of the warm water sphere—in depths of 100 to 140 meters. Montgomery preferred to use the isentropic analysis along surfaces of constant density. According to him the $\sigma_t = 26$ surface demonstrated best the outstanding features of the flow pattern near the salinity maximum (Montgomery, Fig. 10). From the salinity distribution within its core Defant derived a chart of the currents in the lower warm water sphere (Defant 1936, Beilage XLV) in which only the tropical convergence zones are without any subtropical salinity maximum. From these charts we learn that the subtropical salinity waters are formed at the surface of the Atlantic central waters in 20°–25° N. and in 10°–15° S. where the difference $E - P$ is a maximum (Wüst, 1936). From such central regions they are transported by the subtropical undercurrent in the western half of the ocean to the entrance of the Caribbean Sea. This region was omitted in both mentioned studies. It is remarkable that by the deep-reaching gradient forces of the Guiana Current, subtropical high salinity water masses are also transported from the southern hemisphere to our concerned area.

The continuation of these branches of the subtropical undercurrent into the Caribbean Sea was for the first time shown in charts of maximum salinities by Parr (1937, 1938). By compiling Defant's and Parr's results, Dietrich in 1939 constructed a new complete core chart of the distribution of the salinity maximum. He found the main tongue of this high salinity subtropical undercurrent ($>37.0‰$) north of Hispaniola and a remarkable uniformity of lower salinities (36.0–36.7‰) in the entire Caribbean Sea, which according to Parr is a consequence of intensive lateral mixing.

SUBTROPICAL UNDERWATER (PLATE XIII)

By the largely increased number of hydrographic stations, a new improved chart of the spreading of the subtropical underwater within its core (intermediate salinity maximum) can be presented in Plate XIII by isohalines for 0.1‰ intervals and by the inscribed numbers of the core depths. Parr (1937, Fig. 36) showed that the maximum salinity core layer ($>36.6‰$) has a thickness in general of only 25–125 meters and in the central

regions of the Caribbean Sea of only 50–75 meters. A typical example of the thickness of the core and its relation to the thermocline is given by the vertical curve of S‰ and T° C. at *Atlantis* station 1509 (Venezuela Basin in 13° 58′ N. and 68° 36′ W.) in the following Fig. 14. In this case the vertical distance of observations between a 50- and 200-meter depth was 50 meters and only two observations were made within the core layer (36.6‰), namely in 100 and 150 meters. After these observations the depth of the center of the core would be

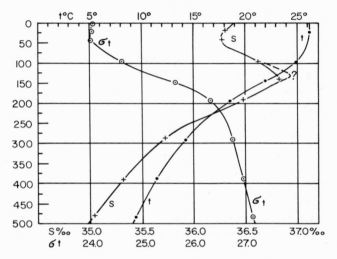

Fig. 14 Vertical temperature, salinity and density curves for the warm water sphere at Atlantis station 1509 (13°58'N– 68°36'W)

$>$? Subjective interpolation

150 meters, the corresponding salinity 36.82‰-values, which we have accepted as possible approaches. Naturally by graphical interpolation other possibilities in the evaluation of the core values would be open, one of which we have indicated by an interrupted curve, as a subjective attempt. Therefore, for a more precise determination of the core center, it would be necessary to decrease the distance between measurement points to 25 meters only, as was done in the tropics and subtropics by the *Meteor* expedition. However, not many Caribbean expeditions have made observations at vertical distances of 25 or 50 meters. For instance, *Crawford* station observations (1958) were normally made in 0, 50, 100, 200 and 300 meters, that is, in depths >100 meters only in a distance of 100 meters. Therefore many *Crawford* stations could not be used for the present purpose. Only when at least two observations in the core layer are available can the salinity and the depth of the core center be determined with some accuracy. A test of the comparability of the core data with the help of T/S-

correlation diagrams is not possible here because the core is a part of the thermocline (and of the pyncoline) where the temperature has its steepest vertical gradient (Fig. 14). As a result of the spreading of the T/S points, a normal curve cannot be constructed for this core as a test. Therefore, we have preferred to use the observed data nearest to the core and to omit such stations where the vertical distances of the measurement points are too large or the limits of the observation errors exceed the tolerable decimals. By a comparative study of adjacent stations, their quality, and vertical distance of measurement points, it was possible to select a sufficient number of stations which permitted a physically reasonable construction of isohalines. In the Appendix, Table II, these observations in the core of the subtropical underwater are listed.

The chart (Plate XIII) discloses (supported by hatching of three salinity intervals) some interesting new features of the flow pattern and of the mixing processes. In two main tongues the subtropical underwater spreads to the west from its point source ($>37.2‰$) at $21°–23°$ N. and $55°$ W. The long arrows indicate the axis of this main spreading. The two main tongues of spreading are the following:

1. North of $19°$ N. the spreading of high salinity waters of more than $37.1‰$ to the west which north of Puerto Rico and Hispaniola is divided into four branches of decreasing salinity as a consequence of lateral mixing.

(a) to the northwest in the axis of the Antillean Current as far as $75°$ W.

(b) to the west through the Hispaniola Basin and then partly through the Old Bahama Channel, partly through the Windward Passage and the northern border regions of the Cayman and Yucatan basins with salinities of $>36.8‰$ as far as $81°$ W.

(c) to the southwest and west through the northern passages of the Antillean Arc but only as far as $69°$ W.

(d) to the southwest and west to the southern passages of the Antillean Arc on both sides of St. Lucia Islands.

2. In $13°–14°$ N. the last mentioned branch enters and continues inside the Antillean Arc in the axis of the farthest spreading to the west and northwest. This main axis coincides with the high speed axis of the Caribbean surface current.

At first this subtropical undercurrent crossed in a small tongue of $>36.8‰$ later of $>36.7‰$, in a diagonal direction the southern and central region of the Venezuela, Colombia, Cayman, and Yucatan basins. It is the outstanding feature of the flow pattern in the Caribbean lower warm water sphere. Because of the frequently too large vertical distance between measurement points and their uneven vertical distribution, it is not possible to construct a chart of the topography of the center of this core layer as Defant could do by lines of equal core depth with the help of the *Meteor* stations in the tropics and subtropics of the open Atlantic. In our chart we have characterized the core depths only by

inscribed numbers of the small intervals, within which the intermediate maxima in the various areas were observed. From the study of these numbers (in parenthesis) we learn that the core depth increases from 50–100 meters at the left side of the main axis to 100–200 meters at the right side. The same slope and the increasing thickness of the subtropical high salinity core can better be studied in the cross-sections perpendicular to the main axis (Plates XX–XXXI). The longitudinal section along the axis, to which we return later, clearly shows the small ribbon-like structure of the subtropical underwater core layer (Plate XIX). The Caribbean surface current and the Caribbean Subtropical Undercurrent represent the main sources of the Gulf Stream System. Furthermore, our chart indicates by small arrows some lateral branches, some overflows over the passages and a number of countercurrents (particularly in the Mosquito Bay). The conditions above the Beata Rise are still unknown.

INTERMEDIATE OXYGEN MINIMUM (PLATES XIV AND XV)

Seiwell (1938, Fig. 13) was the first to construct a core chart of oxygen distribution at depth of the minimum oxygen concentration in the Caribbean Sea region. He mainly used the oxygen determinations of the two *Atlantis* cruises 1933 and 1934. In spite of the fact that Seiwell (1938, p. 54) was skeptical about applying oxygen (as a nonconservative property) in overflow studies, he has drawn contour lines of oxygen for each 0.1 mm/l. in the mentioned chart. In this respect Dietrich followed his example and also used contour lines for 0.1 mm/l. intervals in his similar chart of the oxygen distribution within the core of the main oxygen minimum (Dietrich, 1939, Fig. 35). Normally the oxygen values are published to 0.01 ml/l. Wattenberg (1933) estimated that the total error of good titrations due to the method is between ±0.05 and ±0.10 ml/l., or 2 to 3 per cent at an average of 3 ml/l. Water samples taken from uncoated water bottles give values which are too low by additional percentage, a question to which we later return. Richards in 1957 called the Winkler method "still adequate, sensitive, accurate and of rugged reliability." However, Carritt *et al.* recently became aware of occasional larger systematic errors on some former expeditions (particularly during the IGY period of 1954–58) caused by different procedures used in standardizing the titersolution. In a letter Carritt informed the author about some results of his study on the Winkler method indicating that "one well-published procedure gave results which were on the average ten per cent too low." In any case, the construction of contour lines at intervals of only 0.1 ml/l. does not appear to be justified at present. Therefore, the author prefers to use contour lines at intervals of 0.25 ml/l. in his oxygen core charts. Because of the difference between the oxygen determinations for the period 1932–37 and those for the period 1954–58 (the Atlantic IGY Program), the author has constructed two charts of the oxygen distribution in the core of the main oxygen minimum, one for each period: 1932–37 (Plate XIV) and 1954–58 (Plate XV).

Qualitatively, the two charts disclose like features: high oxygen values in the North America Basin northwest of the great Antillean Islands from which overflow branches start to the southwest through the Windward, Mona, and Anegada-Virgin Islands Passages; low oxygen values within the Caribbean basins with a minimum belt between 10° and 15° N. The absolute values of oxygen differ, however, between the two periods by 8–10 per cent. The IGY values are the lower ones. In both charts the core depths are pratically the same: 300–500 meters in 10°–18° N., 600–800 meters in ∼20°–23° N. and 800–1000 meters outside the Antillean Arc in 23°–25.5° N. These core depths approximately coincide with the surfaces of 8°–9° temperature and 34.9–35.0‰ salinity, as is later shown by the longitudinal section of T, S and O_2 along the axis of the Subantarctic Intermediate Water (Plate XIX). In other words the boundary between the warm water and the cold water spheres can also be characterized (as in the open Atlantic) by the core of the intermediate oxygen minimum. However, this boundary cannot be explained by a lack of sufficient renewal of the water masses, that is, by dynamical reasons and cannot be regarded as a layer of very slow advection. Here the gradient forces of the Caribbean current reach deeper than the oxygen minimum layer in the adjoining parts of the open Atlantic, whence it is transported with them to the Antillean-Caribbean basins. On the other hand, besides the horizontal advection we must take into account the biochemical processes, such as the loss of oxygen by respiratory, chemical and enzymatic oxidation, or decomposition of organic matter. Therefore, the values of the oxygen minimum are only part of an indication of the rate in the renewal of the water masses.

VIII. COLD WATER CIRCULATION IN INTERMEDIATE LAYERS

In the European Mediterranean Sea the deep circulation takes place in a deep warm water sphere of more than 13° C. with very high salinities of 38‰ all the way down to the bottom which is more than 4000 meters. *The Mediterranean deep and bottom waters are formed inside its basins* (Wüst, 1961). Contrary to these conditions, the warm water circulation in the Caribbean basins takes place only between 0 and 600 meters. Its deep circulation, however, takes place in a very deep-reaching cold water sphere of 3° to 7° C. with salinities of less than 35‰. These differences are another reason to replace the frequently used name "American Mediterranean Sea" with the more appropriate one "Central American Sea," which consists of the "Caribbean Sea" and its more or less independent annex the "Gulf of Mexico" (as pointed out earlier on p. 29).

The intermediate deep and bottom waters of the Caribbean Sea are formed far outside the Antillean Arc, that is, at the surface of the subpolar regions in the open Atlantic Ocean. The block diagram of the entire Atlantic subdivided into four layers (Fig. 15) gives a clear schematic picture about the sources of origin of the four main water types in the Atlantic cold water sphere, about the topography of its cores and their spreading. Thick arrows indicate the axis of the main spreading; interrupted arrows, the lateral branches. In the four layers we find an intensification of the circulation on the western side, but partly in opposite directions. Later dynamic computations of the geostrophic velocities and volume transports (Defant, 1941; Wüst, 1955 and 1957) have quantitatively verified our earlier results of the qualitative core method (Wüst, 1936). The block diagram is understandable without further comment and presents the general picture of the spreading and mixing processes in the entire space of the "Atlantic Valley" better than any detailed description.*

The next figure (Fig. 16) gives a schematic picture of the meridional spreading in the cores of the main Atlantic water types, which was designed by the author (1936) for a longitudinal section along the west side of the ocean. In the cold water sphere an interhemispherical exchange of the various water types crosses the Equator in different layers and in opposite directions. This unsymmetrical exchange extends from the high latitudes of one hemisphere to the middle and high latitudes of the other one.

In the cold water sphere of the Antillean-Caribbean basins, there are the following four core layers in which the spreading and mixing processes of the intermediate, deep, and bottom water masses can be best studied:

1. The core of the Subantarctic Intermediate Water characterized by the intermediate salinity minimum in various depths between 700 and 850 meters

2. The core of the middle North Atlantic Deep Water characterized by the upper intermediate oxygen maximum in various depths between 1500 and 2500 meters

3 and 4. The cores of the Caribbean Bottom Water (inside the Antillean Arc) and of the Antarctic Bottom Water (outside) both characterized by the potential temperature and salinity in the near-bottom layers

The core of the Mediterranean Water in the Upper North Atlantic Deep Water, which is characterized north of the Equator by an intermediate maximum of salinity between 1250 and 1500 meters, is disregarded in this study. In the western third of the North America Basin only very small traces of this lateral injection and diffusion of Mediterranean waters are indicated by a small salinity maximum. On the other hand, it is doubtful whether this small inversion is caused only by the last very small traces of the Mediterranean Water or by occasional small injections of the last traces of the Subantarctic Intermediate Water. In any case neither a well-defined intermediate salinity maximum in 1250 meters nor a well-defined intermediate salinity minimum in 900 meters can be identified outside the Caribbean Sea north of 20° N. and west of 55° W.—in this portion of the Antillean sector of the North America Basin.

SUBANTARCTIC INTERMEDIATE WATER (PLATES XVI AND XVII)

In 1936 the author demonstrated in core charts (of depth and salinity) the core topography and the spreading of the Subantarctic Intermediate Water along the center of the salinity minimum in the open Atlantic between 48° S. and 20° N. (Wüst, 1936). Although the details of the processes in the source region are not quite understood, the fact is generally accepted that near the Polar Front

---

* With regard to the graphical method of block diagrams developed by W. M. Davis at the beginning of this century, it is appropriate to quote the words of a founder of physical geography, W. Berghaus: "Haftet doch kein Eindruck dauernder als derjenige, welcher unmittelbar auf unsere Sinne wirkt; so auch graphische Darstellungen, die uns die Phänomene der physikalischen Geographie übersichtlich vor Augen legen. Sie bringen das erst gleichsam ins Leben, zur lebendigen Anschauung, was in der schriftlichen Darstellung oft als toter Buchstabe verborgen bleibt" (Berghaus, 1837, Vorwort).

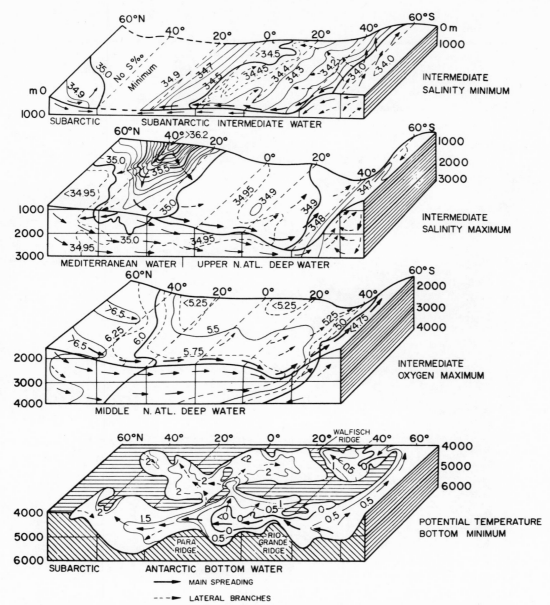

Fig. 15 SCHEMATIC BLOCK DIAGRAMS OF THE SPREADING OF MAIN WATER MASSES IN THE ATLANTIC COLD WATER SPHERE IN 4 CORE LAYERS (after WUST 1950ᵃ WITH SOME CORRECTIONS)

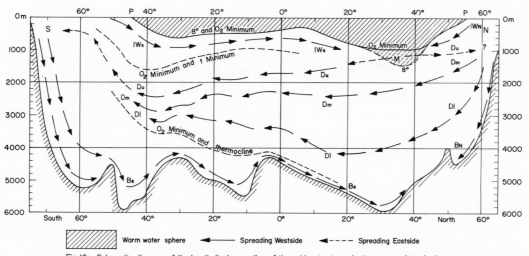

Fig. 16 Schematic diagram of the longitudinal spreading of the cold water types in the western Atlantic Ocean

IWₛ = Subantarctic intermediate water
Dᵤ = Upper N. Atlantic deep water
Dₘ = Middle N. Atlantic deep water
Dl = Lower N. Atlantic deep water
P = Polarfront

IWₙ = Arctic intermediate water
M = Mediterranean water
Bₛ = Antarctic bottom water
Bₙ = Arctic bottom water

(after METEOR report Vol. VI, I, p. 246 1936)

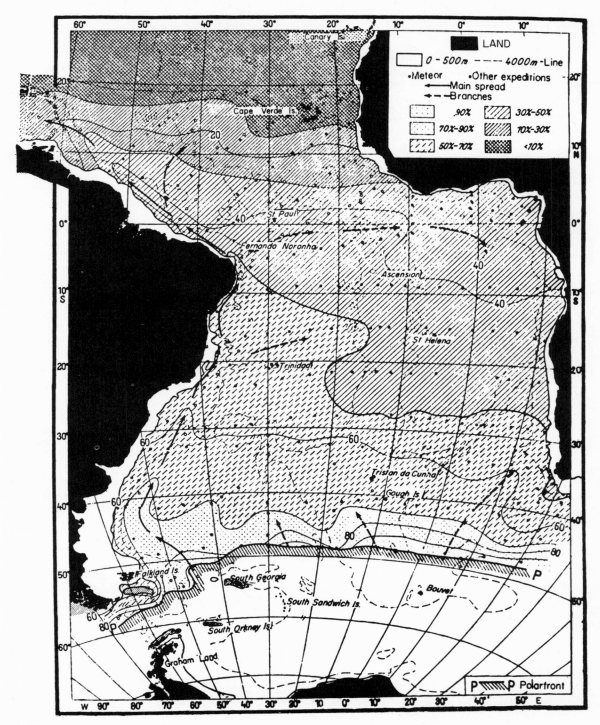

Fig. 17 Spreading of the subantarctic intermediate water represented by lines of equal percentage content of this water type (METEOR rep. VI, 1). The full arrows indicate the main course of the water spreading and the dashed arrows indicate the side branches of it

(in 48°–52° S.) the Subantarctic Intermediate Water descends to deeper layers and spreads north. The core of this water type north of 40° S. extends over the whole breadth of the ocean at depths between 700 and 900 meters. North of 30° S. we find more and more an intensification of the northward spreading on the western side, obviously as an effect of the Coriolis force. Therefore, close to the South American continental slope, we can speak of a Subantarctic Intermediate Current. This is proved by Defant's dynamic calculations which, on the west side of the ocean (south of 5° N.) indicate velocities between 6 and 12 cm/sec. (Defant, 1941). In the central and eastern parts of the South Atlantic, there are evidently no measurable permanent currents. But turbulent and lateral diffusion processes maintain the intermediate salinity minimum. It is surprising that north of the equator the axis of the main spreading persists on the western side and does not shift toward the east to correspond to the opposite sign there of the Coriolis force. In these regions the deeply penetrating gradient forces of the mainly wind-driven Guiana-Antillean and Caribbean Current systems evidently extend their influences upon the further spreading of the Subantarctic Intermediate Water in

be 30 to 35 per cent. For the Antillean-Caribbean basins, where in 1936 only eight marginal stations could be used, there are now about 540 stations at our disposal. Plate XVI shows for these basins the new picture of the spreading within the Subantarctic core layer in 700 to 850 meters. The main inflow of this water type with

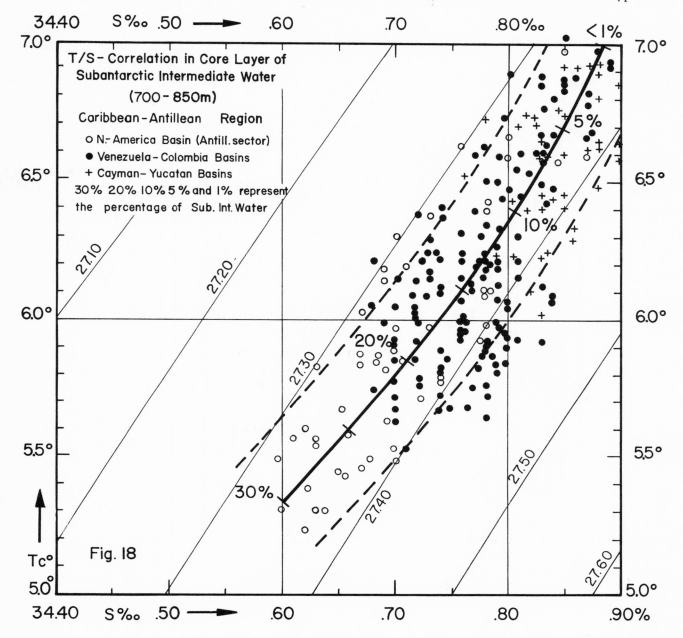

Fig. 18

700- to 850-meter depths to the northwest and west. Its final well-defined admixtures are found at the Yucatan Straits in 22° N. as is shown later. With the help of the T/S correlation, a standard curve was constructed by the writer (1936) for the entire area of the Atlantic where this water type is found. From this curve the percentage of the Subantarctic component for all stations south of 19° N. was derived. In this way, the spreading of the Subantarctic Intermediate Water was represented by contour lines of equal percentage for this water type (Fig. 17). In 8° to 12° N. outside the Antillean Arc we found the subantarctic component to

salinities of less than 34.70‰ takes place through the two passages on both sides of St. Lucia Island. These two tongues later combine and cross the central regions of the Venezuela, Colombia, Cayman, and Yucatan basins along an axis which coincides with the axis of the strongest surface currents of 1 to 2.5 miles per hour (or 50 to 130 cm/sec.). The contour line of 34.85‰ characterizes the last well-defined admixtures of the Subantarctic Water. Outside of this isohaline, only isolated traces of this water type are to be found with values between 34.86 to 34.89‰, as in the Gulf of Mexico, Straits of Florida, and north of the great

Antillean islands. This is shown by the T/S correlation (Fig. 18) which presents some corrections of our former diagram. The new observations disclose a modest spreading of the points. About 88 per cent of them show deviations of less than $\pm 0.05\%_0$ (in salinity) from the standard curve. The point $S = 34.85\%_0$ on the curve represents 5 per cent for the Subantarctic component. Therefore, it is reasonable to use this salinity as the limit for the contour lines in the core map. The standard curve shows relatively small deviations from the density of $27.36\,\sigma_t$. This corresponds to a slow isentropic advection in this area. Here the spreading of the Subantarctic Intermediate Water in its axis has lower velocities than along the South American continental slope south of $10°$ N., probably in the order of a few cm/sec.

We use the normal curve of the T/S-diagram (Fig. 18) by projecting the salinities on it in order to estimate for each station the percentage content of the Subantarctic Intermediate Water. The corresponding values of $S\%_0$ and per cent SIW are tabulated in Table 12. In Plate

Table 12

TABLE FOR ESTIMATION OF PERCENTAGE CONTENT OF THE SUBANTARCTIC COMPONENT IN THE CORE OF THE SUBANTARCTIC INTERMEDIATE WATER WITH HELP OF THE STANDARD-CORRELATION CURVE

$S\%_0$	% SIW	$S\%_0$	% SIW
34.60	30	34.76	15
.62	28	.78	13
.64	26.5	34.80	11
.66	25	.82	8.5
.68	23	.84	6
34.70	21	.86	4
.72	19	.88	2
.74	17		

XVII the result of this interpretation of the data is presented by contour lines of the subantarctic component (in per cent) for each 5 per cent. By dotted contour lines, the generalized topography of the center of the core layer is represented for each 50 meters. On the left side of the axis of the main spreading, the depth of the core lies in 650–700 meters; on the right side in 850 meters. The lines of equal percentage amount clearly show—supported by the hatching of the intervals—the spreading and mixing effects and the location of the main axis of the Subantarctic Intermediate Current. This current starts in the southeast corner of the chart in $8°$ N. with more than 30 per cent and crosses the Antillean Arc through the St. Lucia Passage and the Venezuela and Colombia basins from east to west. At the Jamaica Rise it has lost by mixing 10 per cent of the Subantarctic component. In the Cayman and Yucatan basins, only traces of less than 5 per cent of the original water type are to be found in depths between 700 and 850 meters.

LONGITUDINAL SECTION ALONG AXIS OF SUBANTARCTIC INTERMEDIATE CURRENT (PLATES XVIII AND XIX)

The vertical structure of the Subantarctic Intermediate Water and its dependency on increased mixing effects are clearly demonstrated by the longitudinal section. It shows the stratification in salinity, temperature, and oxygen between 0 and 2000 meters along the axis of the spreading of the Subantarctic Intermediate Water. The location of the section and the position of the stations used is shown in Plate XVIII. This characteristic chief longitudinal section begins outside the Antillean Arc 200 miles southeast of the Barbados and follows the main axis of the Subantarctic Intermediate Current for a distance of 2250 miles (4200 km). This axis also approximately coincides with the axis of the Subtropical Undercurrent in 75- to 150-meter depths, where with Pillsbury's direct current measurements in the passages in 1885–89 we may assume mean velocities between 40 and 60 cm/sec. (Model, 1950). Our section crosses the Antillean Arc through the south St. Lucia Passage and then cuts the south Venezuela and the central Colombia basins from east to west. Thence it turns northwest crossing the western Jamaica Passage and the west Cayman and Yucatan basins. Ninety per cent of the serial measurements used in our section were made by Woods Hole ships during winter months in the following periods (from left to right): 1933–35; 1954–58; 1937–38; and 1952 (Plate XIX).

The salinity section shows clearly by the hatching the tongue-like spreading of the Subantarctic Water between 500 and 1000 meters, its increasing salinity, and its decreasing vertical extent from east to west and northwest. This pattern is mainly a consequence of the turbulent vertical exchange coefficients, which Defant (1936) computed as 5–10 g/cm sec^{-1}. Quite different conditions exist in the Subtropical Undercurrent which in depths between 75 and 200 meters is characterized by an intermediate salinity maximum of more than $36.5\%_0$ (the small hatched ribbon in our section). Contrary to the Subantarctic Intermediate Current, there is no continuous change in salinity and thickness of the core layer in the Subtropical Undercurrent, over the stretch of 4200 km. Why? In 1936 and 1939 the answers were given by Defant and Montgomery for similar conditions of this Undercurrent in the open Atlantic. In both cases the average thickness of the core is only 50 to 75 meters, as was pointed out earlier. The comparison of the salinity section with the temperature section shows that the salinity maximum coincides all the way with the very steep thermocline and because of the corresponding salinity inversion also with the strongest vertical gradient in density, that is, a very steep pycnocline. The spreading of this subtropical intermediate water type is also caused by advection and vertical turbulent diffusion. But because of the high stability of the stratification within the pycnocline, the effect of the latter process is strongly restricted so that the horizontal spreading in our section seems to have the character of a nearly laminar flow. This has been confirmed by Montgomery who found the coefficient of vertical eddy diffusivity as only 0.4 g/cm sec^{-1}. By including the effects of lateral mixing Defant (1962) has estimated that the turbulent diffusion coefficient cannot be far from the molecular diffusion coefficient for salt in water (0.011).

Although in the longitudinal sections of salinity and temperature, the serial measurements of the various cruises are well matched, but this is not the case in the oxygen section as was shown earlier by the core charts of the oxygen minimum. The oxygen determinations for the various periods of years are obviously not comparable. By hatching the intermediate oxygen minimum (<3 ml/l.) and the intermediate oxygen maximum (>5.5 or 6.0 ml/l.) the inhomogeneity of the observations is demonstrated. The oxygen values for the whole water column determined on Woods Hole ships between 1954 and 1958 (and also by *Vema*) are on the average 10 per cent lower than the values of *Dana* in 1922 and of *Atlantis* in 1933–35, 1937-38, and partly of *Atlantis* in 1952. The question is thus raised the second time whether in the period 1954–58 mainly systematic errors in the titrations have contributed to these anomalies, as Carritt has recently assumed, a question to which we return later. In any case, we must divide our longitudinal section in five parts, each valid only for the special period of years.

The five parts agree fairly well in the depth of the core within the oxygen minimum. This core coincides with the isotherms for 8° and 9° and with the isohalines for 34.9 and 35.0‰ (as is shown by the line of black crosses). In other words, the boundary between the warm water and the cold water spheres is here (as in the open Atlantic) also characterized by the core of the intermediate oxygen minimum as we have pointed out earlier. This boundary also coincides with the upper boundary layer of the Subantarctic Intermediate Water. We repeat here that it cannot be explained by a lack of sufficient renewal of the water masses, that is, by dynamic reasons and cannot be regarded as a layer of very slow advection. Here the gradient forces of the Caribbean current reach deeper than the oxygen minimum in the adjoining parts of the open Atlantic whence it is transported with them to the Antillean-Caribbean basins. The dynamic boundary layer, that is, the reference layer (layer of no motion) for dynamic computations, inside the Antillean Arc is in depths below the Subantarctic Intermediate Water—probably in an inclined surface between 900 and 1200 meters—when we transfer Defant's oceanographical (dynamic) triangulation method (1941) from the open Atlantic to the Caribbean basins. However, the discussion of the problem of the reference level in the Caribbean Sea is reserved for Part Two of this study, in which the results of the dynamic computations will be presented.

CROSS-SECTIONS
(PLATES XX–XXXI)

Perpendicular to the axis of the Subantarctic Intermediate Current in the Caribbean Sea, we have constructed four meridional sections of salinity and temperature across the Venezuela and Colombia basins, a fifth across the Yucatan Strait, a sixth across the Puerto Rico Trench and through the gap of the Outer Ridge. The location of these six cross sections (Plates XX–XXI) and the position of the stations belonging to them are shown in Plate XVIII.

In the Venezuela and Colombia basins the layer of the intermediate salinity minimum (hatched area <34.8‰) is most developed in the south along the Venezuelan and Colombian continental slope. It is missing in the north along the slopes of Jamaica, Hispaniola, and Cuba. At the same time the core of this intermediate salinity minimum lies in the south 150 meters higher than in the north. Even in depths of 700–850 meters, both differences still indicate a small influence of the Coriolis force. In the salinity profiles across the Yucatan Strait and across the Antillean current, we do not find a clear intermediate salinity minimum (<34.8‰). However, in 700- to 900-meter depths the last weak traces of this water type with values between 34.87–34.90‰ are not well defined.

Indications of transverse components to the south are disclosed in depths of more than 2000 meters by the precise salinity determinations of the Woods Hole research vessels. In the profiles II through VI we find small salinity inversions with maxima (of more than 34.98‰)— sometimes in two different core layers, that is, in ∼2500- and in ∼4000- meter depths. These meridional components indicated by small arrows are probably caused by overflow processes of high salinity North Atlantic Deep Water over the main northern passages (sill depths between 1600 and 1750 meters) to which we return later.

Inside the Antillean Arc the intermediate temperature minimum (<4.1° C.) occurs between 1600- and 2700-meter depths. From these depths the adiabatic temperature increase starts toward the bottom. At the bottom the temperatures attain values a little higher than 4.2° C. In the relatively shallower Yucatan Strait, the temperature minimum (<4.1° C.) is at the bottom. Here no adiabatic temperature increase takes place.

Outside the Antillean Arc in the Puerto Rico trench, the intermediate temperature minimum (<2.0° C.) occurs in ∼6000-meter depths, below which we observe an adiabatic increase. The overflow of Antarctic Bottom Water through the gap (sill depth 5000 meters) of the Outer Ridge is indicated by small arrows to the north in the salinity section as well as in the temperature section. This small-scale overflow connects in these great depths the near bottom waters of the Puerto Rico Trench with those of the northern abyssal plain.

The sections II–VII will be used in Part Two of this study for the dynamic calculation of the geostrophic currents and of the volume transports perpendicular to them, a task which is already started.

IX. NORTH ATLANTIC DEEP WATER CIRCULATION

At the end of the preceding chapter, we referred to the problem of the overflow of the Middle North Atlantic Deep Water into the Caribbean basins. Rather than using sections of salinity and temperature, this problem can best be studied by core charts and sections of oxygen in the deep layers and potential temperature in the near deep-sea bottom layers. The North Atlantic Deep Water is best characterized by the core of the upper oxygen maximum. This water type is formed above the submarine slopes of South Greenland. It is well known that here during February–March small-scale, vertical convection and larger scale inclined advection of heavy and high oxygen water masses take place. This was clearly shown for the first time by Wattenberg's (1938) oxygen winter section (Fig. 19). These processes give rise to the North Atlantic Deep Current between 2000 and 2500 meters, which is characterized by the upper intermediate oxygen maximum (greater than 6.0 ml/l.). This southward flow is a permanent feature of the deep circulation and due to the Coriolis force is most developed as a boundary current along the western continental slope

of the North Atlantic (Fig. 20). The core chart (Wüst, 1936, Table XVIII) was mainly based on the oxygen determinations of 187 *Meteor** and 63 *Atlantis* stations, which match sufficiently well. Forty-seven stations of four other research vessels (*Dana*, *Armauer Hansen*, *Discovery*, and *Margrethe*) were also used. The titrations of the *Discovery II* Expedition 1931, between 50° S. and 15° N., have, on the average, systematically given 4 per cent lower values than the other observations. Corresponding to the dynamic computations of Defant (1941) and of the writer (Wüst, 1955 and 1957) and to the recent direct current measurements of Swallow and Worthington (1961) farther north on the Blake Plateau, the velocities of this deep current (which in the North Atlantic can be called a countercurrent below the Gulf

* The Nansen water bottles of the *Meteor* expedition (1925–27) consisted in brass cylinders and were coated outside and inside with tin. They were manufactured by the Mechanical Workshops of Marx and Berndt (Berlin) and were larger and more stable than the original Bergen model (Bergen Nautik). Corrosion effects on the oxygen content were not observed (Wüst, 1932).

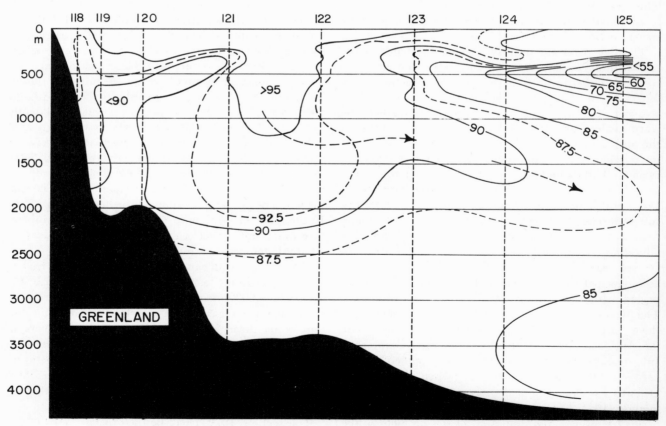

Fig.19 Distribution of oxygen (in percentage) in a section from the southern tip of Greenland to a region southeast of the Great Banks of Newfoundland (according to Wattenberg, METEOR report IX, 1, Abb. 18, 1938)

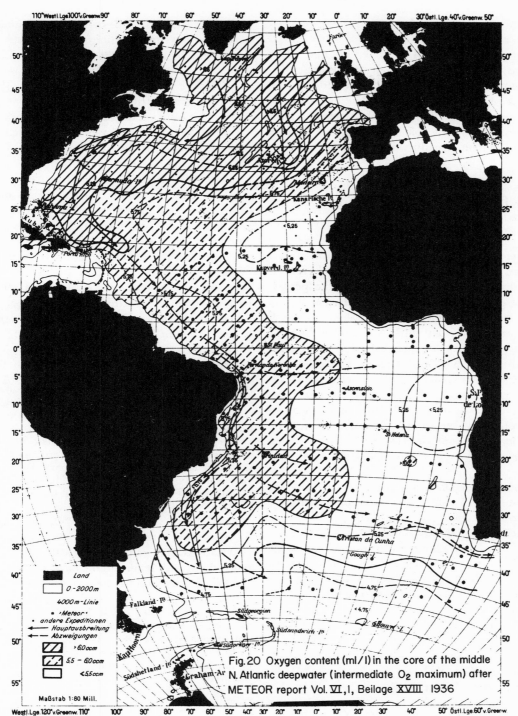

Fig. 20 Oxygen content (ml/l) in the core of the middle N. Atlantic deepwater (intermediate O₂ maximum) after METEOR report Vol. VI,1, Beilage XVIII 1936

Stream system and also below the Antillean-Guiana Current system) are in the range of 6 to 18 cm/sec.* In other words, the renewal of the North Atlantic Deep Water is much faster than was assumed before 1955 when the author published his first paper on the amazing high velocity boundary currents on the west side of the Atlantic (Wüst, 1955).

We examined the origin and the spreading of the deep water in the Mediterranean Sea, which is also characterized by an intermediate oxygen maximum in 1500 to 2500 meters but with lower values (between 3.8 and

* In a later paper, Swallow (1962) has given a cautious summary on our present knowledge of the deep currents, based on indirect methods as well as direct measurements.

4.6 ml/l.) as in the Atlantic. The schematic block diagram for the Mediterranean deep circulation (Wüst, 1961) clearly demonstrates that the deep and bottom waters here are formed during the winter inside the basins at the surface of the most northern border regions of the Balearic Basin and in the Adriatic Sea. These relatively cool, heavy and highly oxygenated water masses sink in shallower depths at first vertically by small-scale convection. Then they slide by inclined advection (in the case of the Otranto sill by occasional overflow) along the continental slope to depths of more than 2000 meters where they spread southward and eastward by slow advective flow. This flow was clearly shown by the oxygen distribution in the core layer in

1500 to 3000 meters where the 120 available oxygen values from nine expeditions (*Thor* 1908–10, *Najade* 1910–14, *Dana* 1928 and 1930, *Atlantis* 1948 and 1958) could be used as if observed synoptically (Wüst, 1961, Fig. 5). But it must be considered that the Mediterranean oxygen values generally are relatively low and that the possible different sources of error in the determinations do not play an important role when contour lines of equal oxygen content are drawn only in intervals of 0.2 ml/l.

DIFFERENCES BETWEEN OXYGEN DETERMINATIONS OF VARIOUS EXPEDITION PERIODS

Quite different and highly variable conditions exist in the oxygen distribution of the Antillean-Caribbean basins according to the oxygen values for the period, 1921–61. Here we could use for the circulation studies the oxygen determinations taken by eight research vessels at approximately 350 stations in twelve different years. In this period the oxygen values of the several expeditions fluctuate outside and partly also inside the Antillean Arc to an amazing extent, namely, by magnitudes of 0.5 to 0.9 ml/l., that is, 9 to 17 per cent. Therefore in contrast to the Mediterranean Sea six special core charts of the oxygen distribution must be constructed for each year or each couple of years in which the particular oxygen determinations have been made.

These variations for which the high oxygen values of the deep waters (>5 ml/l.) are particularly sensitive can be due to four causes:

1. Periodic and unperiodic changes in the climatic conditions of the source region and consequently in the oxygen distribution and the derived circulation pattern in the core of the North Atlantic Deep Water

2. Biochemical processes such as decomposition of organic matter

3. In the Caribbean basins the possibly varying influence of the narrow main passages with their sill depths between 1600 and 1750 meters, that is, 250–900 meters shallower than the core depth of the Middle North Atlantic Deep Water outside the Antillean Arc (2000–2500 meters). A slight rise in this great layer of North Atlantic Deep Water (setting south) outside the Windward and Virgin Islands-Anegada Passages would more or less immediately cause an inclined advection of highly saturated water masses along the inner slope of the thresholds

4. Systematic differences between the deep-water oxygen determinations of various expeditions using different methods (water bottles and titer solutions)

Ad 1. In his fundamental paper on the "Oxygen Distribution in the Atlantic Ocean" Wattenberg (1938) discussed in a special chapter the question of the seasonal variations of the oxygen content in the North Atlantic Deep Water. From all the "pros and cons" Wattenberg came to a negative result when he said that, "At present,

it is very unlikely, to correlate unambiguously the horizontal oxygen variations with seasonal processes in the source region" (p. 98 in free translation by the writer).

Ad 2. We refer to our earlier remarks (p. 32) based on Richards's contributions.

Ad 3. Opposed to this idea is our result that the variations between 1922 and 1961 outside the Antillean Arc are parallel to the variations in the Cayman and Yucatan basins as we will later see.

Ad 4. We refer to our earlier remarks (p. 32) and add the following contributions to the question about the comparability of oxygen determinations by various expeditions, which only recently became available to the author.

(a) In the introduction to the report on the "Oceanographical data from the R. S. *Discovery II*, International Geophysical Year Cruise 3, 1958" (WHOI Reference 59–54) Worthington (November, 1959) published the following remarks on the oxygen determinations of the "Atlantic IGY Program" 1954–58:

The Winkler titration was used to determine oxygen. A discrepancy of about 3% occurred between the American oxygen results (using a potassium dichromate standard) and the British results (using a binidiodate standard). Recent comparisons by Carritt (1959) have suggested that the American technique of standardization was in error and accordingly the English results [of the cruise 3 in 42°–60° N. added by the author] have been tabulated here. The oxygen data for the first two *Discovery* IGY cruises (Worthington, 1958) were tabulated using the American system. They can be made approximately comparable to the data presented here by multiplying all the results by 1.03 but they should, in any case, be regarded with some suspicion.

(b) In the report on the "Oceanographical Data from *Crawford*, International Geophysical Year Cruise 17" (WHOI Reference 59–9) Metcalf (April, 1959) has pointed out with regard to the oxygen determinations by the Winkler method the following:

Dissolved oxygen determinations were carried out by the Winkler method. Recently suspicions have arisen concerning the reliability of the oxygen data. The sampling bottles used were untreated brass Nansen bottles, and it is evident that the oxygen content of the original sample undergoes modification in the bottle, possibly through the chemical reaction with the brass. Temperature, time, amount dissolved oxygen and the condition of the bottles are probably among the factors involved.

(c) The SCOR-UNESCO Chemical Intercalibration Tests (Results of 2d series, R. S. *Vityaz* August 2–9, 1962) published by D. J. Rochford (1963) for the International Indian Ocean Expedition have brought the following important main results:

The Winkler technique despite the minor modifications introduced by the participating countries [U.S.A., Japan, U.K., Australia, U.S.S.R.] gave results within a standard deviation of 1.2% of the mean and all oxygen profiles agreed to within these limits [all samples taken from the U.S.S.R. 200 l. sampler]. There was a large difference in oxygen values of samples from the U.S.S.R. Nansen bottle and those from all other types used.

From Rochford's Tables 12 and 13 we have derived the following condensed table (Table 13).

Table 13

VARIATIONS IN OXYGEN VALUES OF SAMPLES FROM DIFFERENT
NANSEN BOTTLES*

Mean thermometer depth (m)	I U.S.S.R.	II Average U.S.A., Australia, U.K.	Difference, I–II (in ml/l.)	(in per cent of II)
2420	3.54	3.78	−0.24	−6
2640	3.75	3.89	−0.14	−4
3275	4.10	4.26	−0.16	−4
3774	4.16	4.43	−0.27	−6
4300	4.15	4.50	−0.35	−8

* According to Rochford, 1963.

From these intercalibration tests it follows that the untreated (and new) U.S.S.R. brass Nansen bottles gave between 4 and 8 per cent too low oxygen values in depths deeper than 2420 meters. The highest differences of 8 per cent were found in the greatest depths at oxygen values of 4.5 ml/l. "It was not possible to decide whether the metallic U.S.S.R. bottles would eventually age to a satisfactory condition or whether the differences between the oxygen values from the U.S.S.R. and Australian bottles could be a permanent feature of the types of metal used in these bottles." (Rochford, 1963, pp. 19–20.) In any case, the report recommends that only plastic-lined Nansen bottles be used in the future.

We return to the earlier oxygen determinations in the Antillean-Caribbean region. It is probable that by the combination of the two sources of systematic error (American technique of titer-standardization, new brass Nansen bottles) all oxygen determinations of the Atlantic IGY program (cruises of *Altantis, Caryn, Crawford, Discovery II,* and *Vema* in 1954–58) were remarkably too low according to Carritt's personal information "on the average ten per cent being too low." It means that in some cases this systematic error could be in the magnitude of 15 per cent (too low). However, these values of the various research vessels taking part in this Atlantic IGY program correlate quite well and can be used for the construction of a relative core chart representing the *relative distribution of the oxygen* in the core of the upper oxygen maximum *during* 1954–58.

OXYGEN-SALINITY CORRELATION FOR THE VARIOUS EXPEDITION PERIODS 1921–1961 (PLATES XXXII–XXXIII)

In 1936 it was possible to incorporate the available Atlantic oxygen and salinity values (observed in the core layer of the Middle North Atlantic Deep Water west of the Atlantic Ridge by *Atlantis, Meteor, and Dana II*) in one S/O_2 correlation diagram (Fig. 21). Some *Dana II* observations gave too low values. In spite of some spreading of the correlation points, which is normal in such correlation diagrams of $S = f(O_2)$ a normal curve could be constructed. Between 35° N. (where the influence of Mediterranean water was still observed) and 50° S. the following corresponding values of O_2, $S‰$ and $T°$ C. could be computed:

Table 14

CORRESPONDING NORMAL VALUES OF O_2, $S‰$, AND T IN THE CORE OF THE MIDDLE DEEP WATER WEST OF THE ATLANTIC RIDGE BETWEEN 35° N. AND 50° S.*

Oxygen ml/l	Salinity S‰	Temperature ° C.
6.0[a]	34.99[a]	3.62
5.8	34.97	3.28
5.6	34.93	3.02
5.4	34.89	2.73
5.2	34.85	2.48
5.0	34.81	2.22
4.8	34.77$_5$	1.98
4.6	34.73[b]	1.60[b]

* According to Wüst, 1936.
[a] Represents maxima   [b] Represents minima

In the Antillean-Caribbean region the amazing variability of the oxygen determinations made by various expeditions since 1921–22 makes the construction of such normal curves impossible. However, the comparability of the oxygen data observed by the various research vessels during the *same* year (or the same couple of years as in the Atlantic IGY program) can be tested with the help of special oxygen-salinity correlation diagrams. This is done by the 24 correlation diagrams (Plates XXXII and XXXIII) for the various basins and periods of observation. They show clearly that the correlation between the two properties changes from year to year and from basin to basin, not only in the absolute values of oxygen but also in the slope of the normal curve. However, after elimination of some doubtful values, these diagrams manifest a sufficient comparability of the oxygen-data for each of the periods and basins.

OXYGEN DISTRIBUTION WITHIN THE CORE OF UPPER OXYGEN MAXIMUM IN SIX VARIOUS PERIODS BETWEEN 1921 AND 1961 ACCORDING TO THE DETERMINATIONS OF THE VARIOUS EXPEDITIONS (PLATES XXXIV–XLII)

The six charts demonstrate for each distinct period (1921–22; 1932–37; 1939; 1952; 1954–58, 1960–61) the oxygen content in the Antillean-Caribbean basins or parts of them as observed by the various expeditions

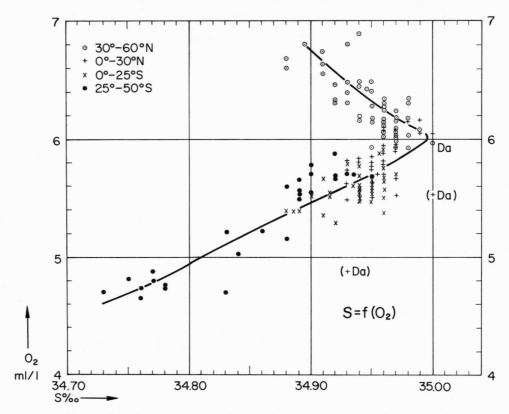

Fig. 21 Correlation between salinity and oxygen in the core of the Middle North Atlantic Deep Water in the West Atlantic (west of the central ridge) after METEOR report VI, I, p.161. 1936.

within the curved core between 1800 and 2400 meters (Plates XXXIV–XXXIX). Generally they disclose a very similar pattern of circulation and overflow, but only qualitatively. By hatching the areas greater than 6.0 ml/l. and by means of arrows, a clear impression is given of the main axis of spreading and of the quite different values for the renewal of the North Atlantic Deep Water in the Caribbean basins during these periods. For a better comparison and better understanding of the amazing differences, the mean values for each observation period and each basin were calculated (Plate XLI) whereby the suspicious low data for the period 1954–58 were included. The purpose of this diagram of 1962 was only to demonstrate the amazing variability in the determinations of the various expeditions (1921–61). Three maxima (1933–37, 1952, and 1961) and three minima (1921, 1939, and 1954–58) in the oxygen content are observed by the various expeditions in the seven basins. They are most pronounced in the best-ventilated basins outside and also partly inside the Antillean Arc in the following sequence:

1. Main tongue of North Atlantic Deep Current outside
2. Virgin Islands Basin
3. Cayman Basin
4. Yucatan Basin

Within the other more enclosed interior basins, the oxygen values are remarkably low and more uniform:

5. Venezuela Basin
6. Colombia Basin
7. Grenada Basin

This sequence permits some qualitative conclusions about the greater age of their water masses. However from these results, it appears that any hope to use such variations as a quantitative time scale of the renewal of the Caribbean deep waters (Worthington, 1955) must be abandoned.

By this analysis, the writer came to the following summary in his 1962 abstract (Wüst, 1963):

The variations in the oxygen determinations of the various Antillean-Caribbean expeditions since 1921 are here very probably a consequence of the analytic difficulties and of the state of the Nansen bottles and only in the second place, genuine unperiodic fluctuations.

In the meantime, all mentioned new information (pp. 42–43) has encouraged the author to compute the representative averages of the oxygen content in the concerned core layer by elimination of all suspicious basin averages and of all calculated averages which are based on less than nine observations for a single basin. The procedure is reasonable because the comparability of the averages also depends on the number and the even or uneven distribution of data. The result of such an elimination is given by the representative averages in the Table 15, which, for the sake of comparison, are reproduced a second time on Plate XLI. In this plate, only *Atlantis* stations of the periods 1932–37, 1952, and 1961 are used for six basins for which more than 9 observations (that is, between 9 and 34) were available. The mean depth of the core varies between 1800 and

Table 15

REPRESENTATIVE AVERAGES OF OXYGEN
CONTENT IN THE CORE LAYER OF NADW
WITH FIVE BASINS INSIDE THE
ANTILLEAN ARC, 1932–37

Basin	No. of observations	Oxygen average* ml/l.	Remarks
1. Cayman	16	5.87 ± 0.17	High
2. Yucatan	19	5.64 ± 0.33	oxygen
3. Venezuela	34	5.10 ± 0.13	Medium
4. Colombia	47	5.06 ± 0.21	oxygen
5. Grenada	9	4.79 ± 0.06	Low oxygen

* The standard deviations (in the average 0.20 ml/l. or 4 per cent) including the regional differences are relatively small. Therefore, the oxygen average of the various basins are representative for the period 1932–37.

2100 meters. From the inscribed oxygen values we learn that inside the Antillean Arc we have two high-, two medium-, and one low-oxygenated basins, as shown in Table 15. The genuine variations of the averages can be at present determined only for the axis of the North Atlantic Deep Current outside the Antillean Arc, where it is in the range of 2 per cent, or ±1 per cent from the total average (6.08 ml/l.). This deviation is in the order of magnitude of the standard deviation of the Winkler method, that is, 1.2 per cent of the mean, computed from the chemical intercalibration tests on board *Vityaz* and published by Rochford (1963). Our result, however, can only be regarded as a preliminary one. *The important question of the genuine unperiodic fluctuations in our concerned area is still unanswered and can only be discussed in more detail when the report of the International Oxygen Commission by Carritt on the limits of error in former oxygen determinations becomes available.* There is no doubt that such smaller scale genuine unperiodic fluctuations must exist in the Caribbean basins particularly because of variations of the overflow over the sills.

X. RENEWAL OF DEEP WATERS IN OXYGEN SECTIONS THROUGH MAIN PASSAGES (PLATES XLIII–XLV)

In the preceding chapter, it has been shown that the S/O_2 diagrams manifest a sufficient comparability of the oxygen data but within each period or each expedition program. Values of the various periods cannot be combined because of the systematic differences in oxygen between them. With this restriction, the following oxygen sections through the main passages must be considered in our study of the renewal of deep waters. The location of the oxygen sections and of the stations used are shown in Plate XL.

The oxygen section through the Windward Passage and the Cayman-Yucatan basins shows the vertical distribution of oxygen between 1000 and 8000 meters along the axis of the North Atlantic Deep Current (Plate XLIII). This section is only valid for the period 1933–34 where high values were determined by *Atlantis* in the North Atlantic Deep Water and its overflow. In this case, there are two intermediate core layers of more than 6.0 ml/l. in the Cayman Basin: one in an extensive spreading between 2200 and 3000 meters, the second and less important one in about 5000 meters as an occasional limited overflow over the sill by water masses of higher density. A slight rise in the great layer of North Atlantic Deep Water (setting south) outside the Windward Passage must as already pointed out cause a more or less immediate inclined advection of highly saturated water masses along the inner slope of the threshold down to the depths of 5000 meters where they meet their original density. A similar but smaller scale counterpart is given for 1933 (*Atlantis*) in the section through the Jamaica Passage and the central regions of the Colombia Basin (Plate XLIV). The southward overflow produces in the latter two weak advective processes in water masses of 5.25 to 5.50 ml/l.: one as an extensive horizontal advection between 1400 and 1800 meters, and a second but limited one in approximately 2500 meters. It is important to notice that this overflow comes over the Jamaica Passage from the north as was already pointed out by Dietrich (1937). The last oxygen section (Plate XLV) shows according to *Atlantis* determinations in 1932–37 the overflow over the Aves ridge and the Tobago sill. The 1850-meter deep Tobago sill does not prevent the overflow of highly oxygenated water (> 6.0 ml/l.) from the North America basin.

XI. ANTARCTIC AND CARIBBEAN BOTTOM WATERS
(PLATES XLVI—XLVIII)

The circulation of the bottom waters is best characterized by the potential temperature, salinity, and potential density of the layer next to the bottom. In the Mediterranean Sea, the author (1960–61) found slow advective processes. In the Antillean-Caribbean basins the circulation of the bottom waters is more complicated and in some of them more intense. In the Cayman and Yucatan basins it has a current-like pattern. For this study about 400 stations taken aboard 25 research vessels in the period 1921–61 were used. They were first tested on a T/S diagram (Plate XLVI). Two normal curves were constructed. One is valid for bottom depths between 4000 and 8000 meters which represents the conditions in the Antarctic Bottom Water in the southwest North America Basin. The other corresponds to the conditions at the bottom between 1800 and 4000 meters outside the Antillean Arc, from where the overflow of the North Atlantic Deep Water starts towards the interior basins. The spread in the two series of points is remarkably small. Most observations show deviations in temperature and salinity of between ± 0.01 and ± 0.02. All bottom observations within the inner basins fall within the two triangles on the left side of the upper normal curve.

The next chart (Plate XLVII) represents the distribution of the potential bottom temperature in basins deeper than 2000 meters. This depends very closely on the bathymetric conditions. Outside the Antillean Arc, two branches of the relatively swift Antarctic Bottom Current, with velocities of approximately 10 cm/sec (Wüst, 1955 and 1957) and with temperatures of less than 1.60°, flow to the northwest and west, separated by the Outer Ridge. The latter shows a gap and overflow north of Puerto Rico. Inside the Antillean Arc a similar swift bottom current exists in the deep channel-like Cayman Basin and Trench as a continuation of the strong overflow through the Windward Passage. The overflow through the Virgin Islands Passage does not produce such a stream-like pattern at the bottom of the expanding Venezuela Basin. Here, as well as in the Colombia Basin, sluggish advective processes are dominant in the bottom layer. It is remarkable that in the distribution of the potential bottom temperature of the southern Venezuela Basin, indications of a bottom countercurrent exist in the direction of the threshold of the Aves Ridge. This bottom current to the west transports the Venezuela Bottom Waters to the Grenada Basin. The chart of the bottom salinity (Plate XLVIII) confirms the results derived from the potential bottom temperature for the whole area. In both charts the conditions near the deep-sea bottom of the Colombia Basin are uniform: $T_p = 3.82°$–$3.83°$ C, $S = 34.96$–$34.97‰$. These differences are within the limits of error.

XII. THE SILL DEPTHS OF MAIN PASSAGES IN LONGITUDINAL SECTIONS OF POTENTIAL TEMPERATURE (PLATES XLIX–LI)

A fundamental question is still incompletely answered: What are the critical sill depths in the main passages between the basins of the Antillean-Caribbean region? This question can best be solved by vertical sections of potential temperature if there are not closely spaced bathograms available, as is still the case in most passages. The first successful estimates by this method were made by Dietrich (1937a, 1939), based on a relatively small number of stations. The following new sections of potential temperatures, based on five to ten times as many observations, permitted us to go into greater detail. The first (A) follows the axis of the Antarctic Bottom Current outside the Antillean Arc to the northwest, turns over the Silver Bank Ridge and the Windward Passage to the west along the axis of the bottom current in the Cayman Basin and ends after still another turn to the northeast in the Yucatan Basin (Plate XLII). This main longitudinal section shows the rapid and extensive overflow of water masses of 3.75° to 3.80° through the Windward Passage, which fill all depths of the Cayman trench between 4000 and 8000 meters and can be traced to the center of the Yucatan Basin. The sill depth of the Windward Passage found by this method agrees with Dietrich's result (1937) of 1600 to 1625 meters (Plate XLIX). The other section (C) goes through the Anegada Passage and Virgin Islands Passage to the northwest Venezuela Basin (Plate L). This second section gives two sill depths of 1950 and 2300 meters in

the Anegada Passage and a sill depth of approximately 1750 meters in the Virgin Islands Passage. In Fig. 22 the mean vertical distribution of potential temperature in the Virgin Islands Basin is compared with the vertical distributions of *Atlantis* station 5288 north of the Anegada Passage and of *Atlantis* station 5261 south of the Virgin Islands Passage. By projecting the bottom temperature of the Virgin Islands Basin on the vertical curve of AT 5288 and the bottom temperature of AT 5261 on the middle curve, we find the same decisive sill depths of 1950 meters in the Anegada Passage and 1750 meters in the Virgin Islands Passage. In spite of the fact that the sill depth of the Virgin Islands Passage represents the deepest connection between the Atlantic Ocean and the Central American basins, its overflow is of minor importance for the renewal of the Antillean-Caribbean Bottom Water masses as compared with that of the shallower, but wider, Windward Passage. The Anegada-Virgin Islands Passage overflow produces only a relatively thin bottom layer of less than 3.80° in the Venezuela Basin. Finally the potential temperature section through the South Aves (~2200 meters) and Dominica (1400 meters) Passages demonstrates the importance of the Venezuela Bottom Water for the renewal of the bottom waters in the Grenada Basin (Plate LI). Table 16 gives a summary of the recent determinations of the width and the deepest depth of the main passages. The most probable numbers of the sill depths are underlined.

Table 16

SILL DEPTHS BETWEEN THE BASINS OF THE ANTILLEAN-CARIBBEAN REGION*

	Width at 1500 m	Sill depths in true m by bathogram	Sill depths in true m by T_p and O_2 sections[c]
Windward Passage	12 miles	1650[a]	1600–1625
Virgin Islands Passage	8 miles	1960[b]	1725–1775
Anegada Passage	8 miles	2208[b]	North 1950
			South 2300
Dominica Passage	—	1372[b]	1400
Jamaica Passage	20 miles	1500[a]	1450–1500
	(at 1000 m)		
South Aves Passage	—	—	2200

* The most probable values are underscored.
[a] Heezen-Johnson-Allen, 1961.
[b] Frassetto-Northrop, 1957.
[c] Wüst-Gordon, 1962.

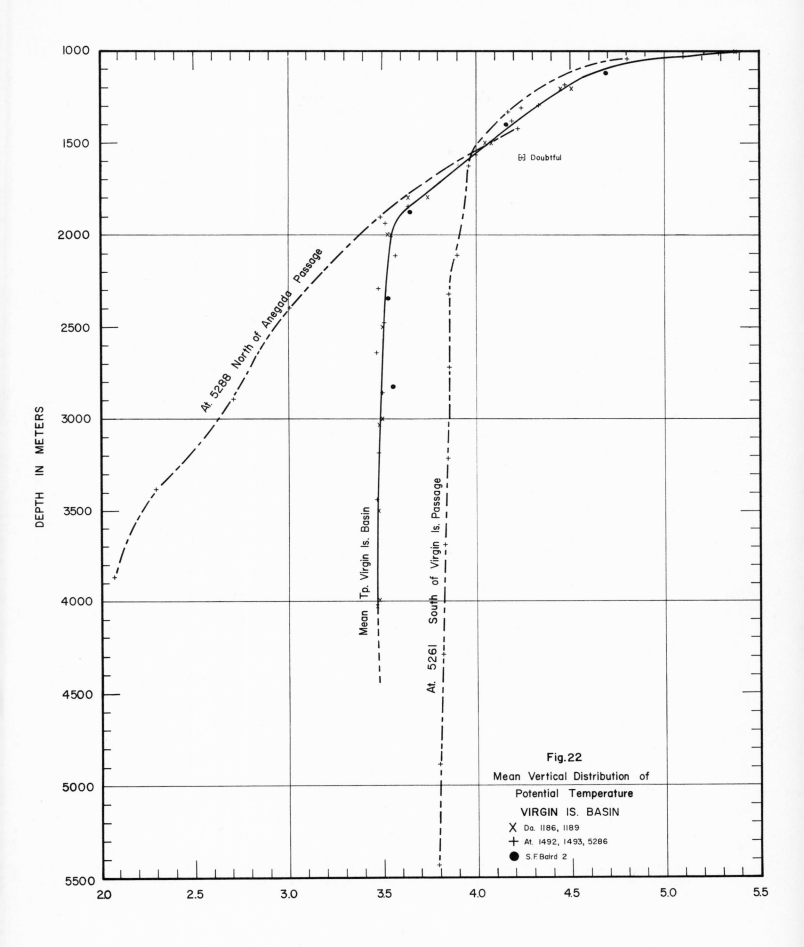

⊞ Doubtful

Fig. 22

Mean Vertical Distribution of

Potential Temperature

VIRGIN IS. BASIN

✕ Da. 1186, 1189

+ At. 1492, 1493, 5286

● S.F. Baird 2

At. 5288 North of Anegada Passage

Mean Tp. Virgin Is. Basin

At. 5261 South of Virgin Is. Passage

DEPTH IN METERS

XIII. CONCLUDING REMARKS

This study concerns two central problems of the physical oceanography of the Caribbean Sea: the interaction between sea and atmosphere at the surface and the stratification and circulation pattern in the depths of the warm water and cold water spheres, both based on all available data. For the latter task we have used a refined technique to trace quantitatively the large-scale spreading and mixing effects of the various Altantic water types within the Antillean-Caribbean basins. We have called this technique the "core method," one which we have already used in studies of the Atlantic and Mediterranean circulation problems (1936, 1960, and 1961). With the help of an increasing amount of data for the period 1932–61, we have constructed new surface and core charts, as well as vertical sections along and perpendicular to the main axis of the spreading which are all brought together in the atlas. This interpretation is the *first step in a physical and dynamical description of the general features of circulation* and is, in some respects, still incomplete. There are large gaps in the distribution of oceanographic stations generally during the summer half-year and also in winter in the Yucatan Basin and in the area on either side of the Beata rise. Because of the large systematic differences between the oxygen determinations among the various expeditions which used different methods, we do not have proof of marked genuine unperiodic fluctuations of the oxygen content in the Caribbean basins. Further pending comments by Carritt must be taken into consideration. Also, new chemical intercalibration tests such as used in the preparation of the International Indian Ocean Expedition (Rochford, 1963) are necessary to future international cooperation. The recently developed method by amperometric recording of the vertical distribution of oxygen and hydrogen sulfide in sea water also will probably improve the comparability of the chemical determinations by various expeditions (Grasshoff, 1962). Besides the electronic salinometer, new methods for continuous electronic recording of temperature, salinity, and pressure will in the near future bring a remarkable progress in the determination of core values. But all this only concerns the first step in the physical and dynamical description of the general features of circulation.

The second step is the dynamic computation of the geostrophic current velocities and volume transports through sections perpendicular to the main axis of spreading which can only be located before with the help of core charts. The classical, dynamic method of Bjerknes, Sandström, and Helland-Hansen (1902) based on the geostrophic equation still is of importance today for the physical and dynamical description of circulation, despite certain simplifications and still uncertain deductions of a reference level as was also pointed out by Stommel (1957). This method is based on the assumption that in the greater depth a mean steady state prevails. This means that the horizontal pressure gradients, which tend to modify the distribution of properties in a variable density field, are balanced by the Coriolis force and the effects of turbulent, vertical and lateral mixing processes. The mean steady state is also a prerequisite for the core method. *To have an over-all picture of the mean steady state of stratification and permanent circulation is an indispensable supposition for any special study on the distribution of the properties* and will be used in Part II of this study. Naturally, however, the results of the mentioned two steps are only approaches to the reality.

The third step must be made by direct current measurements of long duration with the help of Swallow's neutrally buoyant float and/or parachute drogues and/or electronic recording current meters from anchored buoys. At present it is virtually impossible to distribute such anchored buoys over the entire basins and depths of the Caribbean-Antillean region like hydrographic stations. However, with the help of the core method, those crucial regions in the basins and passages can be selected where the control of the dynamic computations and of the layer of no motion would be of particular importance. Today all the direct current measurements are very time-consuming and associated with great technical difficulties. Therefore, the number of successful measurements are still very small. Such direct current measurements by various methods are to be used in one of Lamont Geological Observatory's subsequent cruises in its Antillean-Caribbean program.

All the more or less swift incoming circulation of the low temperature deep and bottom water masses must, in the face of downward diffusion of heat from above, be balanced by a very slow upward component of velocity over most of the Antillean-Caribbean Sea in order to maintain the continuity. Stommel-Arons (1958, 1960) and recently Wyrtki (1961) pointed out this idea for the thermohaline vertical circulation of the world ocean. For the lower latitudes of all oceans these authors have calculated an average for the upward velocities in the order of magnitude of 1–3×10^{-5} cm/sec. In connection with the dynamic computations of the volume transports calculations of the vertical components within the Antillean-Caribbean basins will also be made. Such computations will complete, in a quantitative manner, the picture of the deep circulation given in this paper mainly with the help of the core method. Finally the remarkable number of large water samples collected during the *Vema*-cruises will provide important contributions to Part II of this monograph by new geochemical determinations of the age of the Caribbean water masses with the help of C^{14} and other isotope methods.

Acknowledgment—This study has been largely supported by the United States Atomic Energy Commission under contract AT (30-1 2663). The author is grateful to the Ford Foundation for supporting the Visiting Professorship in Oceanography at Columbia University.

REFERENCES

Agassiz, A. 1888. Three cruises of the U.S. Coast and Geodetic Survey steamer *Blake*, Vols. 1 and 2. Bull. Mus. Comp. Zool. Harvard Coll. vols. 14 and 15. Cambridge, Mass.

Albrecht, F. 1940. Untersuchungen über den Wärmehaushalt der Erdoberfläche in verschiedenen Klimagebieten. Wiss. Abh. Reichsamt Wetterdienst VIII, 2. Berlin.

　　1949. Über die Wärme- und Wasserbilanz der Erde. Ann. d. Meteorologie 2, 129. Hamburg.

Berghaus, W. 1837. Allgemeine Länder-und Völkerkunde Bd. I Berlin-Leipzig.

Bigelow, H. B. 1917. Oceanography. Explorations of the U.S. Coast and Geodetic Survey steamer *Bache* in the Western Atlantic January–March 1914, appendix 5. Rep. U.S. Comm. Fisheries for 1915, Washington, D.C.

Böhnecke, G. 1936. Temperatur, Salzgehalt und Dichte an der Oberfläche des Atlantischen Ozeans. Wiss. Erg. Deutsch. Atlant. Exp. *Meteor*, 1925–1927, vol. 5 with Atlas.

Budyko, M. L. 1958. The heat balance of the earth's surface. Translation edited by U.S. Weather Bureau. Washington, D.C.

Carter, D. B. 1956. The water balance of the Mediterranean and Black seas. Drexel Inst. of Technology Lab. of Climatology. Centerton, N.J.

Climatological and oceanographic atlas for mariners. 1959. Vol. I North Atlantic Ocean. U.S. Weather Bureau and Navy Hydrographic Office. Washington, D.C.

Colón, F. A. 1960. On the heat balance of the troposphere and water body of the Caribbean Sea. Nat. Hurricane Res. Project report no. 41. Washington, D.C.

　　1963. Seasonal variations in heat flux from the sea surface to the atmosphere over the Caribbean Sea. Journ. Geophys. Res., 68 (5): 1421–30.

Cooper, L. H. N. 1961a. Vertical and horizontal movements in the ocean. Oceanography. Am. Ass. Adv. Sc.

　　1961b. Vertical and horizontal movements in the ocean derived from work during IGY. Rapports et Procès-Verbaux. vol. 149, pp. 111–12.

Defant, A. 1936a. Schichtung und Zirkulation das Atlantischen Ozeans. Die Troposphäre. Wiss. Ergebn. Deutsch. Atlant. Exp. *Meteor*, 1925–27, vol. 6, nos. 1, 3. Berlin

　　1936b. Ausbreitungs- und Vermischungsvorgänge im antarktischen Bodenstrom und im subantarktischen Zwischenwasser. Deutsche Atlantische Exp. *Meteor*, vol. 6, 2, 2 lief.

　　1941. Die absolute Topographie des physikalischen Meeresniveaus und der Druckflächen, sowie die Wasserbewegungen Atl. Ozean. Deutsche Atlantische Exp. *Meteor*, vol. 6, 2, 5 lief.

　　1962. Physical oceanography, vol. 1. New York.

Dietrich, G. 1937a. Fragen der Grossformen und der Herkunft des Tiefenwassers im Amerikanischen Mittelmeer. Ann. der Hydr. 65: 5, 345.

　　1937b. I. Die Lage der Meeresoberfläche im Druckfeld von Ozean und Atmosphäre. II. Über Bewegung und Herkunft des Golfstromwassers. Veröff. Inst. f. Meereskunde, Berlin, NFR. A vol. 33.

　　1939. Das Amerikanische Mittelmeer. Ein Meereskundlicher Überblick. Zeitschrift Ges. für Erdkunde zu Berlin. 1939 (3/4): 108–30.

　　1950. Kontinentale Einflüsse auf Temperatur und Salzgehalt des Oberflächenwassers. Deutsch. Hydrogr. Zeitschrift, 3, 1/2.

　　1957. Allgemeine Meereskunde. Berlin.

Drozdov, O. A. 1953. Annual amounts of precipitation. Russian Morskoi Atlas, vol. 2, chart 48b.

Ewing, J., C. B. Officer, H. R. Johnson, and R. S. Edwards. 1957. Geophysical investigations in the Eastern Caribbean; Trinidad Shelf, Tobago Trough, Barbados Ridge, Atlantic Ocean. Geol. Soc. Amer. Bull. 68: 897–912.

Ewing, J., J. Antoine, and M. Ewing. 1960. Geophysical measurements in the Western Caribbean Sea and in the Gulf of Mexico. Journ. Geophys. Res. 65: 4087–126.

Ewing, M., and B. Heezen. 1955. Puerto Rico Trench topographic and geophysical data. Geol. Soc. America, Special paper 62, pp. 255–68.

Frassetto, R., and J. Northrop. 1957. Virgin Islands bathymetric survey. Deep-Sea Res. 4 (2): 138.

Fuglister, F. C. 1947. Average monthly sea surface temperatures of the Western North Atlantic Ocean. Papers Phys. Oceanography and Meteorology. 10: 2. Woods Hole, Mass.

　　1951. Annual variations in current speeds in the Gulf Stream system. Journ. Marine Res. vol. 10.

　　1960. Atlantic Ocean atlas of temperature and salinity profiles and data from the International Geophysical Year, 1957–58. Woods Hole, Mass.

Gerard, R., M. G. Langseth, and M. Ewing. 1962. Thermal gradient measurements in the water and bottom sediment of the Western Atlantic. Journ. Geophys. Res. 67: 785–803.

Grasshoff, K. 1962. Untersuchungen über die Sauerstoffbestimmung im Meerwasser. Teil I & II Kieler Meeresforschungen, Bd. 18, heft 1 and 2.

Heezen, B. C. 1959. Some problems of Caribbean submarine geology. Trans. 2d Caribbean Geological Conference. Univ. of Puerto Rico, January, 1959.

Heezen, B. C., R. Menzies, W. S. Broecker, and M. Ewing. 1959. Stagnation of the Cariaco Trench. Abstracts Int. Oceanographical Congress. New York.

Heezen, B. C., G. L. Johnson, and R. C. Allen. 1961. Geological and oceanographic aspects of submarine cable engineering. Tech. Rep., Lamont Geol. Obs. (prepared for Bell Laboratories).

Iselin, C. O'D. 1936. A study of the circulation of the Western North Atlantic. Pap. Phys. Oceanogr. Meteorol. 4(4): 1–101.

Iselin, C. O'D, and F. C. Fuglister. 1948. Some recent developments in the study of the Gulf Stream. Journ. Mar. Res. 7(3): 317–29.

Jacobs, W. C. 1951. The energy exchange between sea and atmosphere and some of its consequences. Bull. Scripps Inst. Oceanogr. Tech. Ser. 6(2): 27–122.

Jacobsen, J. P. 1929. Contribution to the hydrography of the North Atlantic. Danish *Dana* Exp. 1920–22 Oceanog. Rep., no. 3. Copenhagen.

Krauss, W. 1958. Untersuchungen über die Mittleren Hydrographischen Verhältnisse an der Meeresoberfläche des Nördlichen Atlantischen Ozeans. Wiss. Erg. Deutsche Atlant. Exp. *Meteor*, 1925–27, 5: 3.

　　1962. Untersuchungen über die Mittlere Verteilung des Salzgehalts an der Oberfläche des Südatlantischen Ozeans und die Zonenmittelwerte der Temperatur, des Salzgehalts und der Dichte für den ganzen Atlantischen Ozean. Wiss. Erg. Deutsche Atlant. Exp. *Meteor*, 1925–27, 5: 4.

Krümmel, O. 1907. Handbuch der Ozeanographie, vol. I. Stuttgart.

Kuhlbrodt, E. *et al.* 1938. Die Meteorologischen Beobachtungen. Methoden der Bordbeobachtung, Beobachtungsmaterial und Ergebnisse, Wiss. Erg. Deutsche Atl. Exp. *Meteor* 1925–27, vol. 14. Berlin.

Leopold, L. B. 1962. Rivers. American Scientist, 50: 514

Malkus, Joanne S. V. 1962. Large-scale interactions. Chap. 4 in The Sea (ed. by M. N. Hill), vol. 1 Physical Oceanography. New York and London.

Meinardus, W. 1934. Eine neue Niederschlagskarte der Erde. Petermanns Geograph. Mitt., 80: 1–4.

Metcalf, W. G. 1959. Oceanographic data from the Caribbean Sea *Crawford* cruise 17. February–March 1958 for the International Geophysical Year of 1957–58, W.H.O.I., ref. no. 59–9. Woods Hole, Mass.

Model, F. 1950. Pillsbury's Strommessungen und der Wasserhaushalt des Amerikanischen Mittelmeeres, Deutsche Hydrographische Zeitschrift, vol. 3, heft 1/2. Hamburg.

Möller, F. 1951. Vierteljahrskarten des Niederschlags für die ganze Erde. Petermanns Geographische Mitteilungen, vol. 95, heft 1 s. 1–7.

Möller, L. 1926 .Zur Kritik und Aufbereitung der Dichte und Salzgehaltswerte älterer Expeditionen. Veröff. Inst. f. Meereskunde A, h. 15. Berlin.

Monatskarten für den Atlantischen Ozean. 1956. Deutsch. Hydrogr. Inst. Hamburg.

Montgomery, R. B. 1939. Ein Versuch den vertikalen und seitlichen Austausch in der Tiefe der Sprungschichte im Äquatorialen Atlantischen Ozean zu bestimmen. Ann. d. Hydr. u. Marit. Met. Berlin.

1938. Circulation in upper layers of southern North Atlantic deduced with use of isentropic analysis. Pap. in Physical Oceanography., 6: 2. Cambridge, Mass.

Officer, C. B., J. I. Ewing, R. S. Edwards, and H. R. Johnson. 1957. Geophysical investigations in the eastern Caribbean; Venezuelan Basin, Antilles Island Arc, and Puerto Rico Trench. Geol. Soc. Amer. Bull., 68: 359–78.

Officer, C. B., J. I. Ewing, J. F. Hennion, D. G. Harkrider, and D. E. Miller. 1959. Geophysical investigations in the eastern Caribbean: summary of 1955 and 1956 cruises. Physics and Chemistry of the Earth, 3: 17–109. London.

Parr, A. E. 1935. Hydrographic relations between the so-called Gulf Stream and the Gulf of Mexico. Transactions Am. Geophys. Union, p. 246.

1935b. Report on hydrographic observations in the Gulf of Mexico and the adjacent straits made during the Yale Oceanographic Expedition on the *Mable Taylor* in 1932. Bull. Bingham Oceanog. Coll., vol. 5, art. 1. New Haven.

1937a. A contribution to the hydrography of the Caribbean and Cayman Seas. Bulletin to the Bingham Oceanographic Collection, vol. 5, art. 4, pp. 1–110.

1937b. On the longitudinal variations in the dynamic elevation of the surface of the Caribbean currents. Bulletin of the Bingham Oceanographic Collection, vol. 6 art. 2, pp. 1–20.

1937c. Analysis of evidence relating to eddy diffusion processes at mid-depths in the eastern Caribbean. Conseil Permanent International pour l'Exploration de la Mer. Journal du Conseil, 14(3): 347–56.

1938. Further observations on the hydrography of the eastern Caribbean and adjacent Atlantic waters. Bulletin of the Bingham Oceanographic Collection, vol. 6, art. 4, pp. 1–29.

Pillsbury, J. 1886. Report on deep-sea current work in the Gulf Stream. Rep. Supt. U.S. Coast and Geodetic Survey, 1885, app. 14. Washington, D.C.

1887. A report of Gulf Stream explorations. Observations of currents 1886. Rep. Supt. U.S. Coast and Geodetic Survey, 1886, App. no. 11. Washington, D.C.

1889. Gulf Stream explorations. Observations of currents 1887. Rep. Supt. U.S. Coast and Geodetic Survey, App. no. 18. Washington, D.C.

1890. Gulf Stream explorations. Observations of currents, 1888 and 1889. Report of Supt. U.S. Coast and Geodetic Survey, 1889, pp. 467–77. Washington, D.C.

1891. The Gulf Stream—a description of the methods employed in the investigation and the results of research. Rep. Supt. U.S. Coast and Geodetic Survey, 1890. Washington, D.C.

Rakestraw, N. W., and H. P. Smith. 1936. A contribution to the chemistry of the Caribbean and Cayman seas. Bull. Bingham Oceanographic Collection, vol. 6, art. I.

Rakestraw, N. W. 1947. Oxygen consumption in sea water over long periods. J. of Marine Research, 6(3): 259–63.

Redfield, A. C. 1942. The processes determining the concentration of oxygen phosphate and other organic derivatives within the depths of the Atlantic Ocean. Pap. Phys. Oceanogr. Meteorol, vol. 9, no. 2.

Richards, F. A., and R. F. Vaccaro. 1956. The Cariaco Trench, an anaerobic basin in the Caribbean Sea. Deep-sea Res., 3(3): 214–28.

Richards, F. A. 1957a. Oxygen in the ocean. Geol. Soc. Amer. Mem., 67(1): 185–238.

1957b. Some current aspects of chemical oceanography. Physics and Chemistry of the Earth, vol. 2. London.

1958. Dissolved silicate and related properties of some western North Atlantic and Caribbean waters. J. of Marine Research, 17: 449–65.

1960. Some chemical and hydrographic observations along the north coast of South America Cabo Tres Puntas to Curacao including the Cariaco Trench and the Gulf of Cariaco. Deep-sea Res., 7(3): 163–82.

Richards, F. A., and A. C. Redfield. 1955. Oxygen-density relationships in the western North Atlantic. Deep-sea Res., 182–99.

Rochford, D. J. 1963. SCOR-UNESCO chemical intercalibration tests. Results of 2d series, R. S. *Vityaz*, Aug. 2–9, 1962, International Indian Ocean Expedition. Cronulla (C.S.I.R.O. Div. of Fish. and Oceanography). Sydney.

Samoylov, I. V. 1956. Die Flussmündungen. Gotha.

Schott, G. 1942. Geographie des Atlantischen Ozeans, 3 Auflage. Hamburg.

Schubert, O. 1932. Die Strommesungen Pillsbury's im moderner Bearbeitung. Ann. d. Hydr. und Marit. Meterologie, 60: 378–385. Berlin.

Seiwell, H. R. 1938. Application of the distribution of oxygen to the physical oceanography of the Caribbean Sea region. Papers in Physical Oceanography and Meteorology, 6(1): 1–60.

1939. Atlantis cruise to the tropical North Atlantic. January–March, 1939. Trans. Am. Geophys. Union.

Stommel, H. 1957. Florida straits transports, 1952–56. Bulletin of Marine Science of the Gulf and Caribbean, vol. 7, no. 3.

1958. The Gulf Stream. A physical and dynamical description. Berkeley-London.

Stommel, H., and A. B. Arons. 1960. On the abyssal circulation. Deep-sea Res., 6: 140–54. 219–33.

Sverdrup, H. U. 1951. Evaporation from the oceans. Compendium of Meteorology. Ed. by T. F. Malone. Boston.

Sverdrup, H. U., M. W. Jonhson, and R. H. Fleming. 1942. The oceans, their physics, chemistry and general biology. New York.

Swallow, J. C. and L. V. Worthington. 1961. An observation of a deep counter current in the Western North Atlantic. Deep-sea Res. 8: 1–19.

Swallow, J. C. 1962. Ocean circulation. Proc. R. Soc. A., 265: 326–28.

Tanner, Z. L. 1897. Deep-sea exploration. A general description of the steamer *Albatross*, her appliances and methods. Washington, D.C.

U.S. Coast and Geodetic Survey. 1933. Deep-sea soundings, Atlantic and Pacific oceans and Caribbean Sea, Spec. pub. 97. Washington, D.C.

Wattenberg, H. 1933. Das chemische Beobachtungsmaterial und seine Gewinnung. Wiss. Erg. D. Atl. Exp. *Meteor*, Bd. 8. Berlin.

1938. Die Verteilung des Sauerstoffs im Atlantischen Ozean. Deutsche Atlantische Exp. *Meteor* Werk, 9. Lief 1 with Atlas. Berlin.

Worthington, L. V. 1954. A preliminary note on the time scale in North Atlantic circulation. Deep-sea Res., 1954, 1: 244–51.

1955. A new theory on Caribbean bottom water formation. Deep-sea Res., 3: 82–87.

1956. The temperature increase in Caribbean deep water since 1933. Letter to the editor. Deep-sea Res., 3(1): 234–35.

1959. Oceanographic data from the R.R.S. *Discovery II* International Geophysical Year Cruise 3, 1958. W.H.O.I. Ref. no. 59–54. Woods Hole, Mass.

Wüst, G. 1924. Florida- und Antillenstrom, eine hydrodynamische Untersuchung. Veröff. Inst. f. Meereskunde. Berlin N.F.A., vol. 12.

1936a. Schichtung und Zirkulation des Atlantischen Ozeans. Die Stratosphäre. Wiss. Erg. D. Atl. Exp. *Meteor*, 6: 1 with Atlas, Berlin.

1936b. Oberflächensalzgehalt, Verdunstung und Niederschlag auf dem Weltmeere. Landeskundliche Forschung. Festschrift N. Krebs. Stuttgart.

1950a. Blockdiagramme der atlantischen Zirkulation auf Grund der *Meteor* Ergebnisse. Kieler Meeresforschungen, 7: 24–34.

1950b. Wasserdampf und Niederschlag auf dem Meere als Glieder des Wasserkreislaufs (unter besonderer Berücksichtigung von Ergebnissen der *Meteor* Expedition und neuerer Arbeiten). Deutsche Hydrographische Zeitschrift 1950, 3: 111–27.

1951. Über die Fernwirkungen Antarktischer und Nordatlantischer Wassermassen in den Tiefen des Weltmeeres. Naturwissenschaftliche Rundschau., pp. 97–108.

1952. Der Wasserhaushalt des Mittelländischen Meeres und der Ostsee in vergleichender Betrochtung. Riv. Geofis. pura e applic., vol. 21. Geneva.

1954a. Gesetzmässige Wechselbeziehungen zwischen Ozean und Atmosphäre in der zonalen Verteilung von Oberflächensalzgehalt, Verdunstung und Niederschlag. Archiv. f. Meteorologie, Geophysik u. Bioklimatologie, ser. A, vol. 7. Vienna.

1955. Stromgeschwindigkeiten im Tiefen- und Bodenwasser des Atlantischen Ozeans auf Grund dynamischer Berechnung der *Meteor*-Profile. Deep-sea Res., suppl. to vol. 3, pp. 373–97.

1957. Stromgeschwindigkeiten und Strommengen in den Tiefen des Atlantischen Ozeans. Wiss. Erg. d. Atl. Exp. *Meteor* 1925–27, 6(2): 261–420. Berlin.

1960. Die Tiefenzirkulation des Mittelländischen Meeres in den Kernschichten des Zwischen- und Tiefenwassers. Deutsche Hydrogr. Zeitschr., 13(3): 105–31.

1961a. Das Bodenwasser und die Vertikalzirkulation des Mittelländischen Meeres. Deutsche Hydrogr. Zeitschr. 14(3): 81–92.

1961b. On the vertical circulation of the Mediterranean Sea. J. Geophys. Res., 66(10): 3261–71.

1963. On the stratification and the circulation in the cold water sphere of the Antillean-Caribbean basins. An abstract. Deep-sea Res., 10(3): 165–87.

Wüst, G., G. Böhnecke, and H. H. F. Meyer. 1932. Ozeanographische Methoden und Instrumente. Wiss. Erg. D. Atl. *Meteor* 1925–27, 4: 1. Berlin.

Wüst, G., W. Brogmus, and E. Noodt. 1954. Die zonale Verteilung von Salzgehalt, Niederschlag. Verdunstung, Temperatur und Dichte an der Oberfläche der Ozeane. Kieler Meeresforschungen 1954, pp. 137–61.

Wyrtki, K. 1961a. Physical oceanography of southeast Asian waters. NAGA Rep., vol. 2. La Jolla.

1961b. The thermohaline circulation in relation to the general circulation in the oceans. Deep-sea Res. 8(1): 39–64.

1962. The oxygen minima in relation to oceanic circulation. Deep-sea Res., 9: 11–28.

Oceanographic Atlas

PLATES I–LI

I. Averages of surface salinity in one-degree quadrangles for Winter–Spring (December–May, 1931–1961)

II. Averages of surface salinity in one-degree quadrangles for Summer–Autumn (June–November, 1931–1961)

III. Distribution of surface salinity in Winter–Spring (December–May, 1931–1961)

IV. Distribution of surface salinity in Summer–Autumn (June–November, 1931–1961)

V. Distribution of precipitation (after Fritz Möller's "Vierteljahrskarten für die ganze Erde," 1951, and averaged by Stanley Jacobs for the two half-years) for Winter–Spring (December–May)

VI. Distribution of precipitation (after Fritz Möller's "Vierteljahrskarten für die ganze Erde," 1951) for Summer–Autumn (June–November)

VII. Surface currents (based on "Climatological and Oceanographic Atlas for Mariners," Vol. I, North Atlantic Ocean, Washington, D.C., 1959, and "Monatskarten für den Nordatlantischen Ozean," Hamburg, 1956) for January

VIII. Surface currents (based on "Climatological and Oceanographic Atlas for Mariners," Vol. I, North Atlantic Ocean, Washington, D.C., 1959, and "Monatskarten für den Nordatlantischen Ozean," Hamburg, 1956) for April

IX. Surface currents (based on the "Climatological and Oceanographic Atlas for Mariners," Vol. I, North Atlantic Ocean, Washington, D.C., 1959, and "Monatskarten für den Nordatlantischen Ozean," Hamburg, 1956) for July

X. Surface currents (based on the "Climatological and Oceanographic Atlas for Mariners," Vol. I, North Atlantic Ocean, Washington, D.C., 1959, and "Monatskarten für den Nordatlantischen Ozean," Hamburg, 1956) for October

XI. Basins and ridges of the Caribbean–Antillean region

XII. Hydrographic stations in Caribbean–Antillean region (1873–1961) with observations deeper than 200 meters

XIII. Spreading of the Subtropical Underwater within its core (Intermediate Salinity Maximum) in 50–200 meters depth

XIV. Distribution of oxygen in the core of the main O_2 Minimum (1932–37)

XV. Distribution of oxygen in the core of the main O_2 Minimum (1954–58)

XVI. Spreading of the Subantarctic Intermediate Water within its core (Intermediate Salinity Minimum) in 700–850 meters

XVII. Percentage amount and depth of the core layer of the Subantarctic Intermediate Water and the T/S correlation in this layer (700–850 meters)

XVIII. Positions of the longitudinal and cross sections of temperature and salinity

XIX. Longitudinal section along the axis of the Subantarctic Intermediate Current

XX. Cross section II of salinity—64° 30′ W

XXI. Cross section II of temperature (°C)—64° 30′ W

XXII. Cross section III of salinity—68° 30′ W

XXIII. Cross section III of temperature (°C)—68° 30′ W

XXIV. Cross section IV of salinity—73° 50′ W

XXV. Cross section IV of temperature (°C)—73° 50′ W

XXVI. Cross section V of salinity—79° 10′ W

XXVII. Cross section V of temperature (°C)—79° 10′ W

XXVIII. Cross section VI of temperature (°C)—through the Yucatan Straits

XXIX. Cross section VI of salinity—through the Yucatan Straits

XXX. Cross section VII of salinity—66° 08′ W

XXXI. Cross section VII of temperaure (°C)—66° 08′ W

XXXII. Oxygen-salinity correlation within the core layer of the North Atlantic Deep Water outside the Antillean Arc, during six periods between 1921 and 1961

XXXIII. Oxygen-salinity correlation within the core layer of the North Atlantic Deep Water inside the Antillean Arc, during various periods between 1921 and 1961

XXXIV. Distribution of oxygen in the core of the Intermediate O_2 Maximum in about 2000 meters, 1921–22

XXXV. Distribution of oxygen in the core of the Intermediate O_2 Maximum in about 2000 meters, 1932–37

XXXVI. Distribution of oxygen in the core of the Intermediate O_2 Maximum in about 1950 meters, 1939

XXXVII. Distribution of oxygen in the core of the Intermediate O_2 Maximum in about 2000 meters, 1952

XXXVIII. Distribution of oxygen in the core of the Intermediate O_2 Maximum in about 2000 meters, 1954–58

XXXIX. Distribution of oxygen in the core of the Intermediate O_2 Maximum in about 2000 meters, 1960–61

XL. Positions of stations along the vertical T_p and O_2 sections

XLI. Variability of average oxygen content found by various expeditions (1921–61) in the core layer of the North Atlantic Deep Water (Upper Oxygen Maximum) within the basins of the Antillean–Caribbean region (suspicious and not comparable averages included)

XLII. Representative averages of oxygen content in the core layer of the North Atlantic Deep Water (Upper Oxygen Maximum) within the basins of the Antillean-Caribbean region (suspicious averages and averages of less than nine observations excluded)

XLIII. Longitudinal oxygen section along axis of North Atlantic Deep Water inside the Windward Passage and distribution of oxygen outside Antillean Arc (1932–34)

XLIV. Oxygen section through Jamaica and Windward passages and the Central Colombia and East Cayman basins, 1933

XLV. Oxygen section through the Grenada and Tobago basins and their sills

XLVI. T_p-S diagram for the Antarctic Bottom Water outside and of the Caribbean Bottom Water inside the Antillean Arc

XLVII. Distribution of potential temperature in the Near Bottom Water of the deep basins (>2000 meters) in the Caribbean-Antillean region

XLVIII. Distribution of salinity in the Near Bottom Water of the deep basins (>2000 meters) in the Caribbean-Antillean region

XLIX. Longitudinal T_p section along the axis of the bottom currents outside and inside the Windward passages

L. Longitudinal T_p section along the axis of the deep and bottom currents outside and inside the Virgin Islands passages

LI. Longitudinal T_p section through the South Aves and Dominica passages

PLATE I

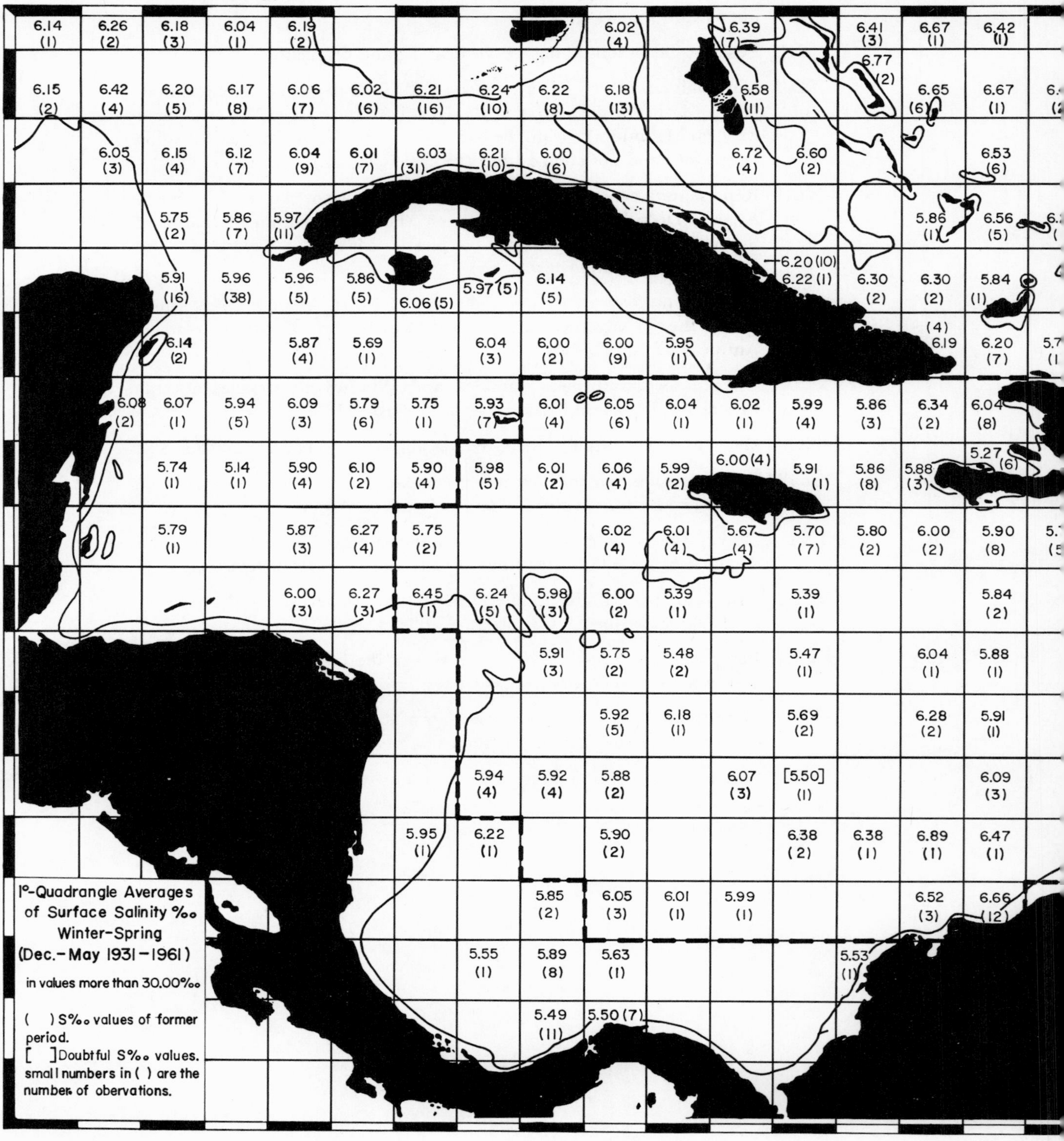

85°   80°   75°

25°

20°

15°

10°

1°-Quadrangle Averages
of Surface Salinity ‰
Winter-Spring
(Dec.-May 1931-1961)

in values more than 30.00‰

( ) S‰ values of former
period.
[ ] Doubtful S‰ values.
small numbers in ( ) are the
number of obervations.

6.14 (1)   6.26 (2)   6.18 (3)   6.04 (1)   6.19 (2)   6.02 (4)   6.39 (7)   6.41 (3)   6.67 (1)   6.42 (1)

6.15 (2)   6.42 (4)   6.20 (5)   6.17 (8)   6.06 (7)   6.02 (6)   6.21 (16)   6.24 (10)   6.22 (8)   6.18 (13)   6.58 (11)   6.77 (2)   6.65 (6)   6.67 (1)

6.05 (3)   6.15 (4)   6.12 (7)   6.04 (9)   6.01 (7)   6.03 (31)   6.21 (10)   6.00 (6)   6.72 (4)   6.60 (2)   6.53 (6)

5.75 (2)   5.86 (7)   5.97 (11)   5.86 (1)   6.56 (5)

5.91 (16)   5.96 (38)   5.96 (5)   5.86 (5)   6.06 (5)   5.97 (5)   6.14 (5)   6.20 (10)   6.22 (1)   6.30 (2)   6.30 (2)   5.84 (1)

6.14 (2)   5.87 (4)   5.69 (1)   6.04 (3)   6.00 (2)   6.00 (9)   5.95 (1)   6.19 (4)   6.20 (7)

6.08 (2)   6.07 (1)   5.94 (5)   6.09 (3)   5.79 (6)   5.75 (1)   5.93 (7)   6.01 (4)   6.05 (6)   6.04 (1)   6.02 (1)   5.99 (4)   5.86 (3)   6.34 (2)   6.04 (8)

5.74 (1)   5.14 (1)   5.90 (4)   6.10 (2)   5.90 (4)   5.98 (5)   6.01 (2)   6.06 (4)   5.99 (2)   6.00 (4)   5.91 (1)   5.86 (8)   5.88 (3)   5.27 (6)

5.79 (1)   5.87 (3)   6.27 (4)   5.75 (2)   6.02 (4)   6.01 (4)   5.67 (4)   5.70 (7)   5.80 (2)   6.00 (2)   5.90 (8)

6.00 (3)   6.27 (3)   6.45 (1)   6.24 (5)   5.98 (3)   6.00 (2)   5.39 (1)   5.39 (1)   5.84 (2)

5.91 (3)   5.75 (2)   5.48 (2)   5.47 (1)   6.04 (1)   5.88 (1)

5.92 (5)   6.18 (1)   5.69 (2)   6.28 (2)   5.91 (1)

5.94 (4)   5.92 (4)   5.88 (2)   6.07 (3)   [5.50] (1)   6.09 (3)

5.95 (1)   6.22 (1)   5.90 (2)   6.38 (2)   6.38 (1)   6.89 (1)   6.47 (1)

5.85 (2)   6.05 (3)   6.01 (1)   5.99 (1)   6.52 (3)   6.66 (12)

5.55 (1)   5.89 (8)   5.63 (1)   5.53 (1)

5.49 (11)   5.50 (7)

[58]

6.36 (1)	6.58 (1)	6.65 (1)			6.49 (1)		6.78 (1)				[6.07] (1)					25°
30 (1)		6.71 (1)	6.43 (3)	6.76 (1)	6.46 (1)			6.67 (1)				6.62 (2)		6.73 (2)		6.98 (3)
	6.39 (1)		641 (4)				6.69 (1)		6.01 (1)	6.33 (1)	6.61 (2)	6.56 (1)	6.90 (2)	6.73 (3)	7.01 (2)
56 (1)	6.28 (2)	6.30 (2)	6.04 (2)	6.49 (2)				6.42 (2)	6.74 (2)	6.35 (1)	6.68 (2)	6.84 (1)	6.62 (6)	6.81 (1)	7.03 (2)
2 (3)	6.04 (5)		6.18 (3)	6.08 (2)	6.28 (3)		6.15 (2)	6.00 (1)	6.40 (3)	6.26 (4)	6.49 (3)	6.51 (2)	6.74 (2)	6.83 (1)	6.89 (3)
		6.24 (1)	6.22 (1)	5.87 (2)		6.20 (1)	6.13 (1)	6.20 (5)	6.23 (5)	6.00 (1)	[4.83] (1)		6.57 (1)	6.99 (1)	20°
	5.76 (1)	5.82 (2)	5.90 (1)	6.04 (9)	5.76 (5)	6.31 (6)		6.20 (5)		6.08 (1)	6.39 (3)	6.24 (1)		6.27 (2)	6.31 (4)
	5.51 (4)	5.87 (8)	5.86 (1)	5.98 (5)	5.95 (8)	6.09 (6)	6.22 (4)	5.76 (2)	6.29 (1)	5.81 (1)	6.05 (3)	6.24 (1)	6.61 (1)	6.43 (7)
5.57 (3)	5.40 (1)	5.90 (9)	5.48 (5)	5.95 (1)	5.78 (17)	5.90 (13)	5.80 (4)	6.04 (2)	6.18 (2)	5.79 (4)	6.25 (2)		6.36 (1)	6.49 (9)	6.19 (9)
		5.40 (3)	5.52 (3)	5.81 (1)		6.05 (3)	6.07 (2)	5.89 (7)	5.98 (2)	6.18 (2)		5.86 (2)	5.36 (3)	5.58 (13)	6.04 (10)
97 (1)		5.66 (8)	5.83 (8)	6.00 (2)	5.53 (1)	5.92 (6)	5.84 (5)	5.84 (2)	5.92 (13)	5.70 (2)		[4.22] (2)	5.18 (5)	5.54 (17)	5.44 (8)	15°
		5.41 (4)	5.65 (3)	5.70 (1)		5.91 (6)	5.32 (1)	5.53 (4)	5.71 (14)	5.75 (10)	5.48 (4)	5.58 (4)	4.94 (18)	5.46 (3)	5.71 (1)
02 (1)	6.36 (1)	6.00 (1)	5.68 (3)			5.92 (7)		5.63 (2)	5.77 (2)	5.70 (3)	5.53 (9)	5.68 (29)	5.46 (2)	5.55 (4)	5.51 (3)
0 (14)	5.92 (8)	5.88	6.37 (4)	5.84 (2)		5.85 (11)	5.55 (2)	5.74 (2)	5.58 (2)	5.14 (9)	5.23 (10)	4.81 (4)		5.19 (2)	
		6.80 (1)	6.61 (3)		6.66 (9)	6.24 (4)	5.84 (9)	5.77 (3)	5.78 (8)	5.54 (6)	5.12 (1)	6.00 (1)		5.31 (1)	
		6.74 (1)		6.60 (5)	6.76 (4)								5.55 (1)	5.31 (1)	
															33.64 (1)	10°
											4.24 (1)	4.28 (1)	32.00 (3)	28.12 (3)

PLATE II

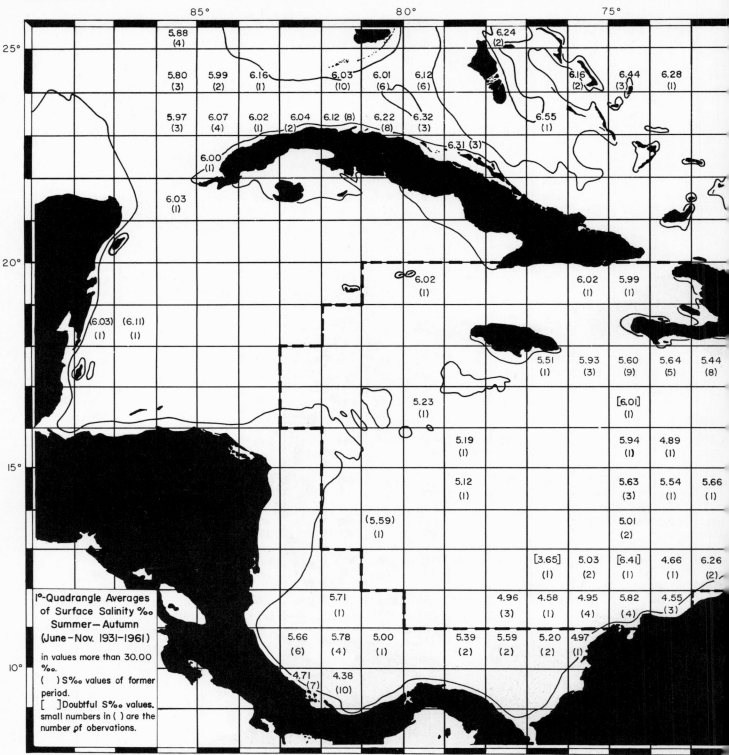

1°-Quadrangle Averages
of Surface Salinity ‰
Summer—Autumn
(June–Nov. 1931–1961)

in values more than 30.00
‰.
( ) S‰ values of former
period.
[ ] Doubtful S‰ values.
small numbers in ( ) are the
number of obervations.

	70°			65°				60°							
										6.54 (2)			7.17 (2)		
45 (2)	6.31 (1)		6.28 (1)	6.60 (1)	6.23 (1)	6.89 (1)	6.28 (1)		[5.87] (1)	6.50 (1)		6.66 (2)	6.81 (2)	6.20 (2)	6.55 (3)	6.97 (3)
	6.33 (1)			6.46 (1)	6.48 (1)	7.01 (1)		6.59 (1)				6.99 (3)	6.51 (3)	6.50 (5)	6.56 (2)	6.19 (1)
				6.44 (1)	6.29 (4)		6.82 (1)		6.51 (2)	6.07 (1)	6.50 (4)	6.42 (3)	6.29 3	[5.69] (1)	6.66 (1)	[5.79] (1)
7	6.11 (2)		6.42 (1)		6.40 (13)		[4.91] (1)	6.49 (1)	6.17 (2)	6.03 (6)	6.18 (1)	6.29 (1)			6.87 (1)	6.51 (1)
	6.19 (2)		6.32 (1)	5.52 (1)	6.10 (1)		5.80 (3)	5.93 (8)	5.80 (4)					[4.51] (1)	6.13 (2)
				5.34 (3)	5.75 (13)	5.60 (6)	5.75 (4)					[6.74] (1)	[4.26] (1)		6.64 (1)
				4.91 (3)	5.67 (4)	5.17 (1)					4.73 (1)	4.55 (3)		[6.38] (1)	4.48 (6)
(3)	5.81 (5)	4.95 (2)	5.07 (8)	4.62 (3)	5.70 (3)	5.12 (3)	4.93 (4)	5.01 (1)		4.88 (2)	4.74 (2)		4.71 (3)	4.39 (7)
			4.52 (1)			4.31 (2)				4.53 (3)	4.77 (1)	4.87 (2)	5.03 (8)	3.88 (7)	5.21 (4)
			4.945 (1)	4.825 (4)		3.96 (1)	4.76 (1)	3.62 (1)	3.99 (2)	4.53 (2)		5.61 (1)	4.20 (4)	4.65 (11)	5.28 (3)
	[5.42] (1)	4.41 (1)	4.12 (2)			4.72 (2)		[2.79] (1)	4.76 (2)	4.96 (3)	4.67 (13)	5.08 (5)	5.19 (3)	4.39 (2)
23]	5.26 (2)		5.55 (1)		4.32 (1)		5.18 (3)		[5.43] (1)	4.12 (12)	4.11 (5)	5.03 (3)	4.63 (1)	[6.50] (1)
(5)	6.30 (2)	5.68 (4)	6.24 (4)			5.04 (1)		4.57 (1)		4.43 (3)	4.59 (4)	4.76 (1)		
			6.31 (2)	6.43 (4)	5.83 (2)	6.37 (10)	5.85 (4)	5.24 (7)	3.55 (2)	4.02 (2)	[5.48] (1)	3.45 (1)		
			6.06 (3)	5.82 (1)	5.94 (9)	6.23 (4)							5.59 (2)	5.44 (1)
												5.74 (2)	5.31 (1)
										5.25 (1)			

PLATE III

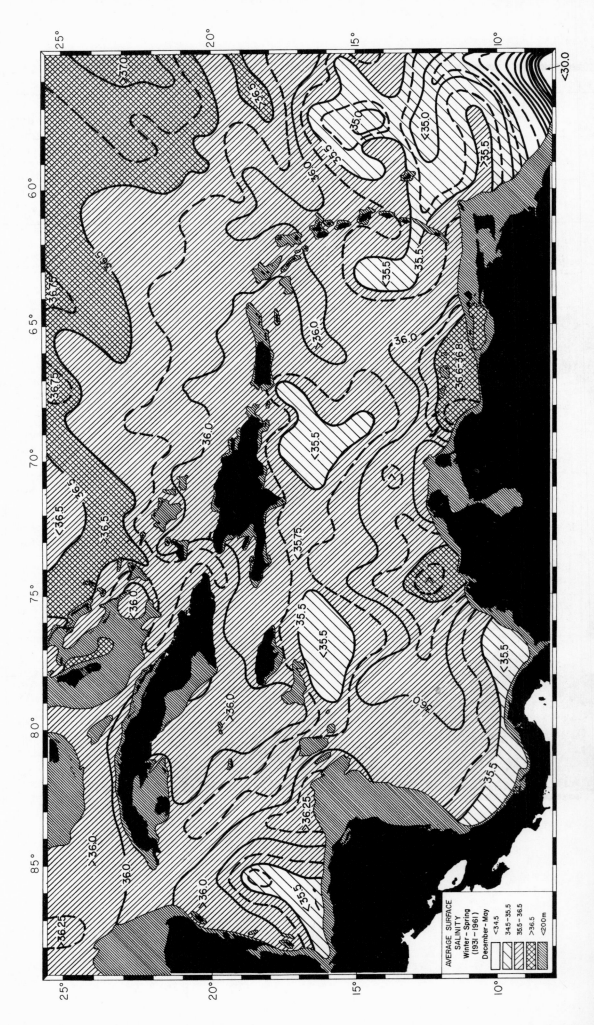

AVERAGE SURFACE
SALINITY
Winter – Spring
(1931–1961)
December – May

<34.5
34.5–35.5
35.5–36.5
>36.5
<200m

PLATE IV

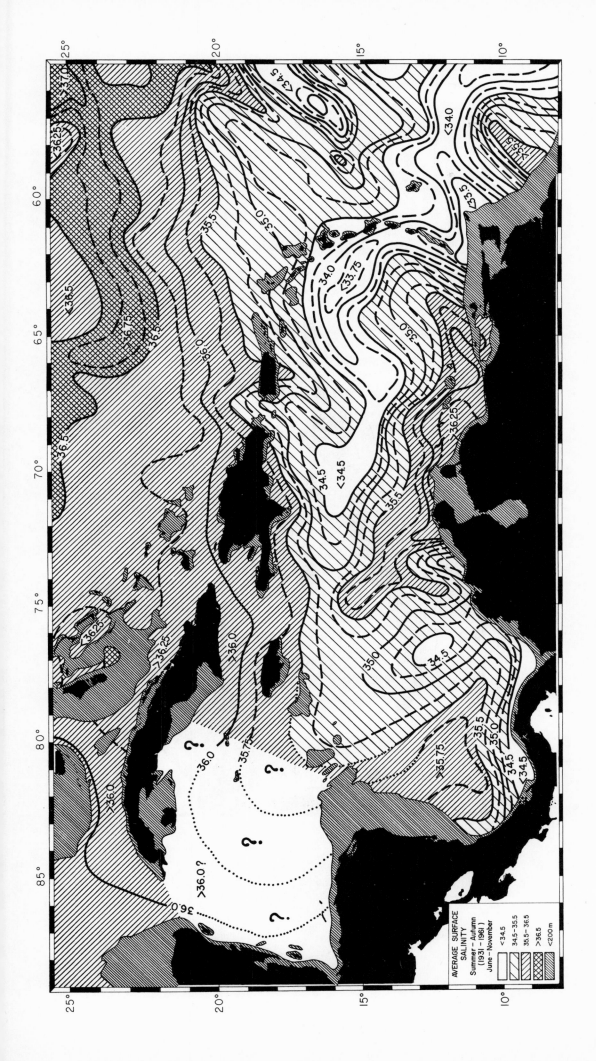

AVERAGE SURFACE
SALINITY
Summer – Autumn
(1931 – 1961)
June – November

<34.5
34.5 – 35.5
35.5 – 36.5
>36.5
<200 m

PLATE V

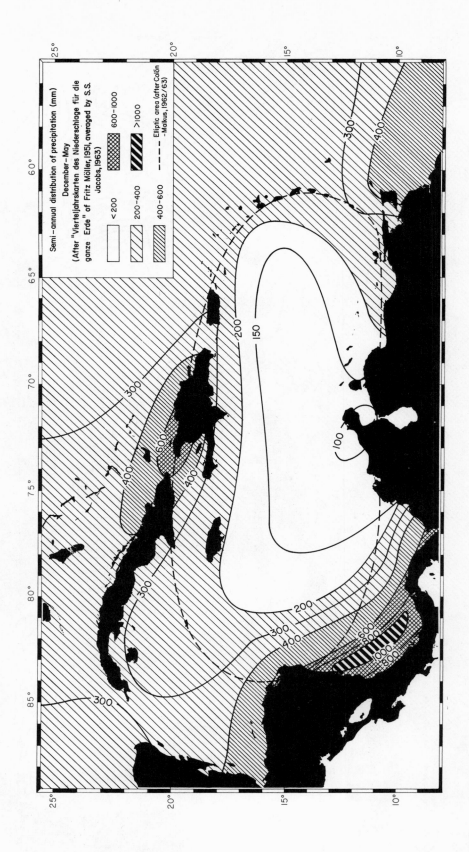

Semi-annual distribution of precipitation (mm)
December–May
(After "Vierteljahrskarten des Niederschlage für die ganze Erde" of Fritz Möller, 1951, averaged by S.S. Jacobs, 1963)

PLATE VI

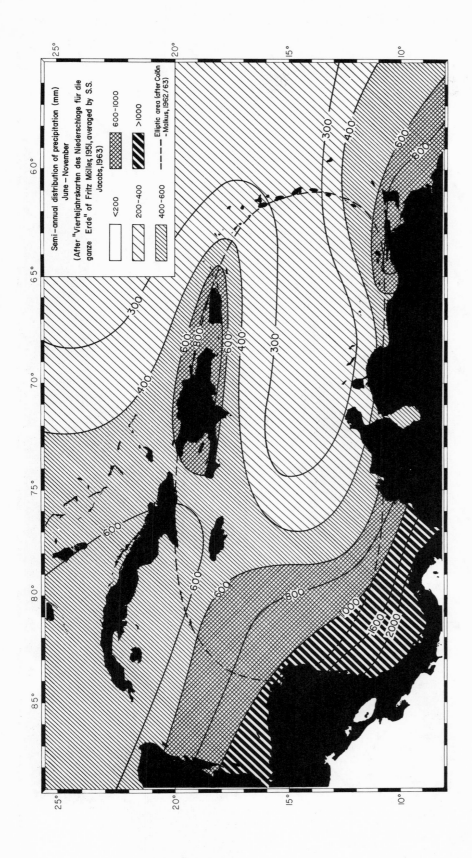

Semi-annual distribution of precipitation (mm)
June – November

(After "Vierteljahrskarten des Niederschlage für die
ganze Erde" of Fritz Möller, 1951, averaged by S.S.
Jacobs, 1963)

<200
200-400
400-600
600-1000
>1000
Elliptic area (after Colón
– Malkus, 1962/'63)

PLATE VII

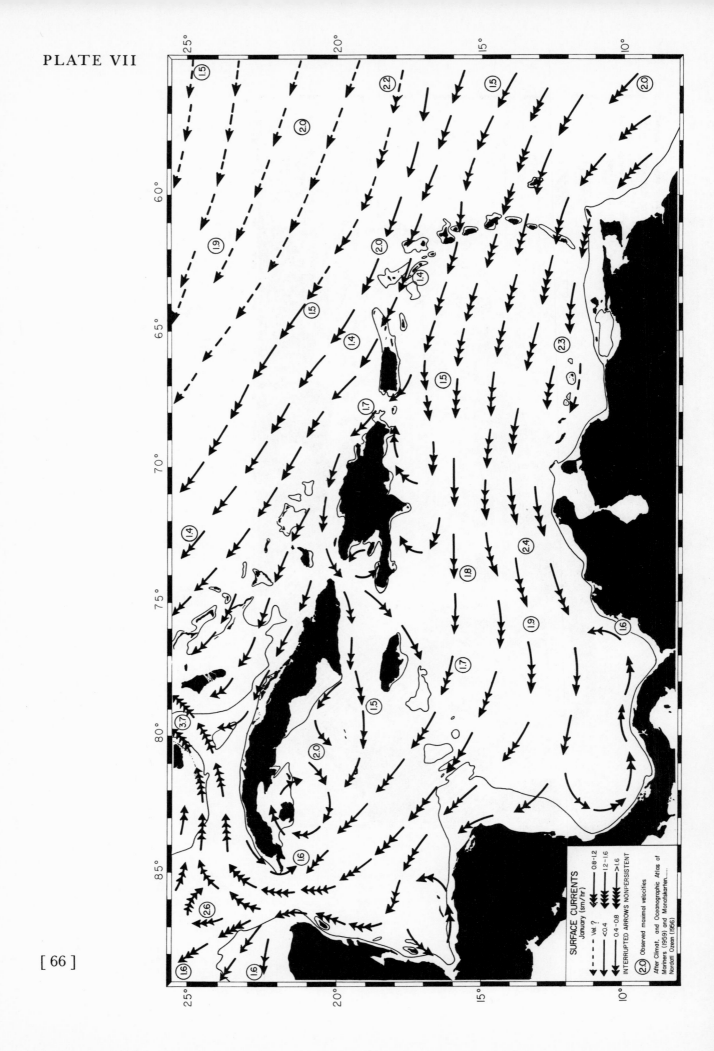

SURFACE CURRENTS
January (sm/hr)

Vel.?
<0.4
0.4–0.8
0.8–1.2
1.2–1.6
>1.6

INTERRUPTED ARROWS NONPERSISTENT

2.0 Observed maximal velocities

After Climat. and Oceanographic Atlas of
Mariners (1959) and Monatskarten.......
Nordatl Ozean (1956).

PLATE VIII

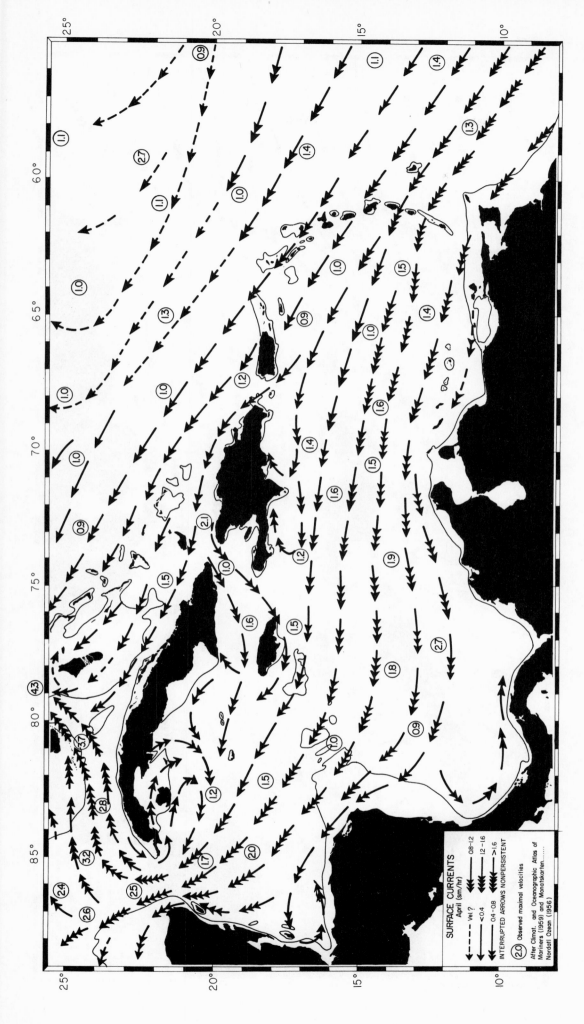

SURFACE CURRENTS
April (sm/hr)

Vel.?
<0.4
0.4–0.8
0.8–1.2
1.2–1.6
>1.6
INTERRUPTED ARROWS NONPERSISTENT

2.0 Observed maximal velocities

After Climat. and Oceanographic Atlas of
Mariners (1959) and Monatskarten.......
Nordatl Ozean (1956)

PLATE IX

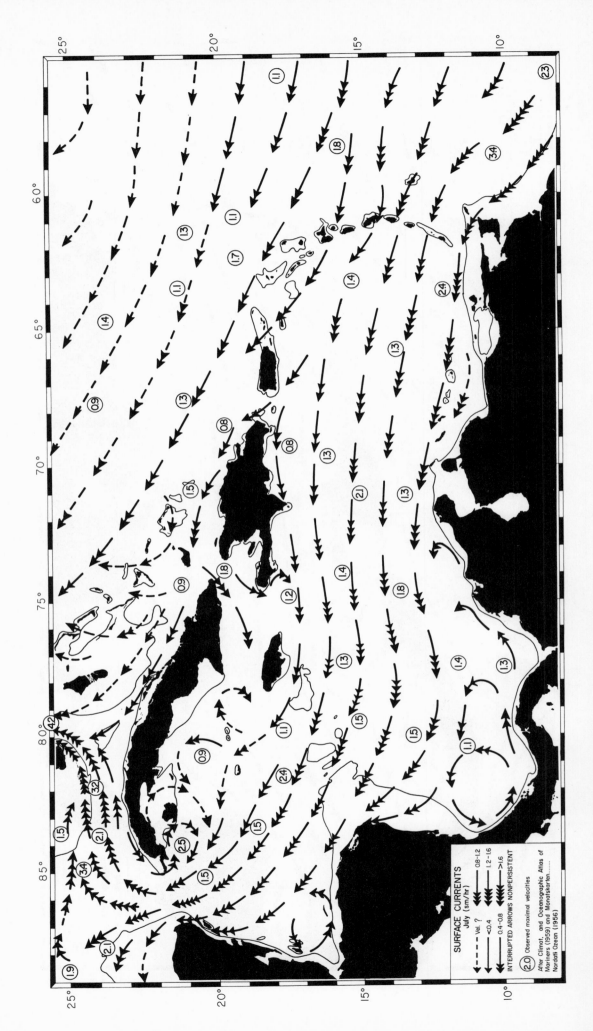

SURFACE CURRENTS
July (sm/hr)
Vel. ?
0.8-1.2
<0.4
1.2-1.6
0.4-0.8
>1.6
INTERRUPTED ARROWS NONPERSISTENT
2.0 Observed maximal velocities
After Climat, and Oceanographic Atlas of
Mariners (1959) and Monatskarten........
Nordatl Ozean (1956)

PLATE X

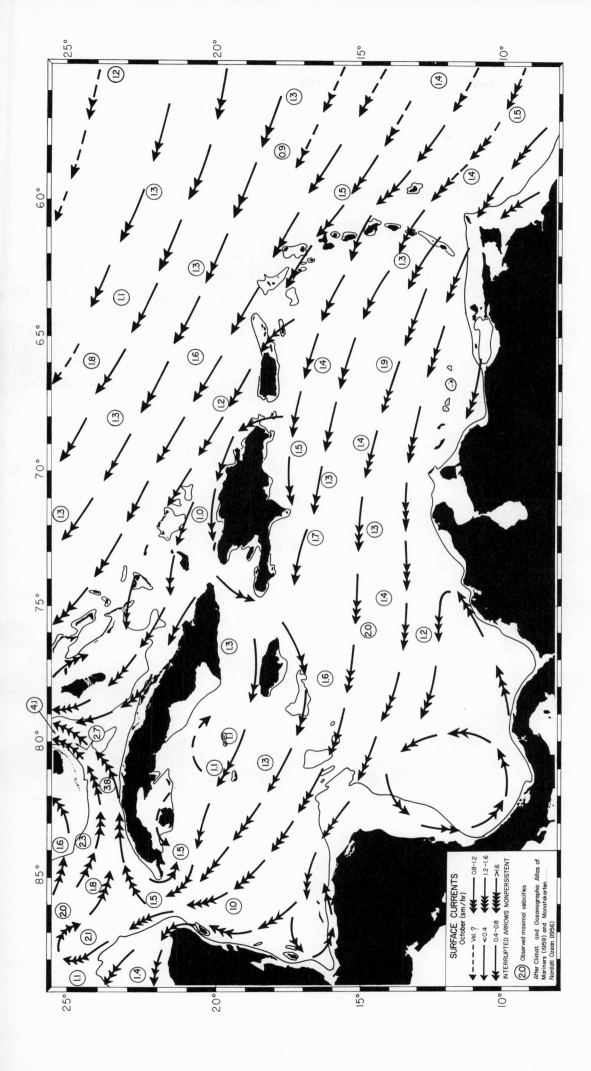

SURFACE CURRENTS
October (sm/hr)

Vel.?
<0.4   0.4-0.8
0.8-1.2
1.2-1.6
>1.6

INTERRUPTED ARROWS NONPERSISTENT

20 Observed maximal velocities

After Climat. and Oceanographic Atlas of
Mariners (1959) and Monatskarten.
Nordatl Ozean (1956)

PLATE XI

Mexico Basin

Yucatan Basin

Cayman Ridge

Cayman Trench

Cayman Basin

Jamaica Ridge

Colombia Basin

Beata Rise

Aruba

Hispani

85° 80° 75°

25°
20°
15°
10°

<55
<55

Basins and Ridges
of the
Caribbean–Antillean Region

Generalized Contour lines for
1000m, 2000m, 3000m, 4000m,
6000m, and 8000m (in special
areas for 5000m, and 5500m),
all Given in Hectometers.

The Symbols Concern the Near
Bottom Observations of Temp.
and Salinity.

<2000m

For Explanation of Symbols see Table I.

[70]

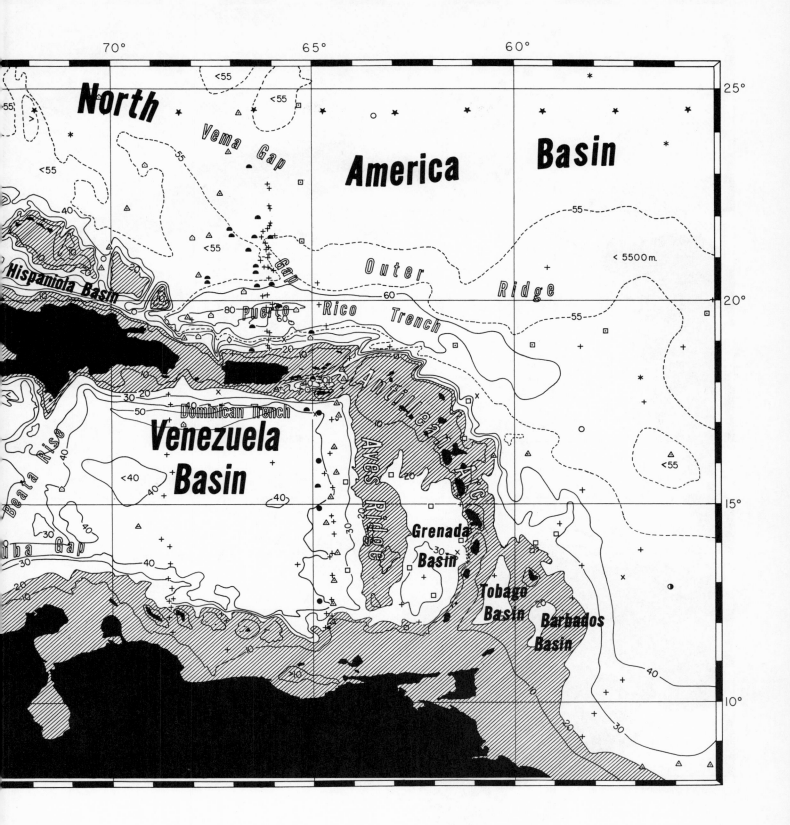

North **America** **Basin**

Vema Gap

Hispaniola Basin

Beata Rise

Cuba Gap

Venezuela **Basin**

Dominican Trench

Puerto Rico Trench

Outer Ridge

< 5500 m.

Anegada Passage

Aves Ridge

Grenada **Basin**

Tobago **Basin**

Barbados **Basin**

[71]

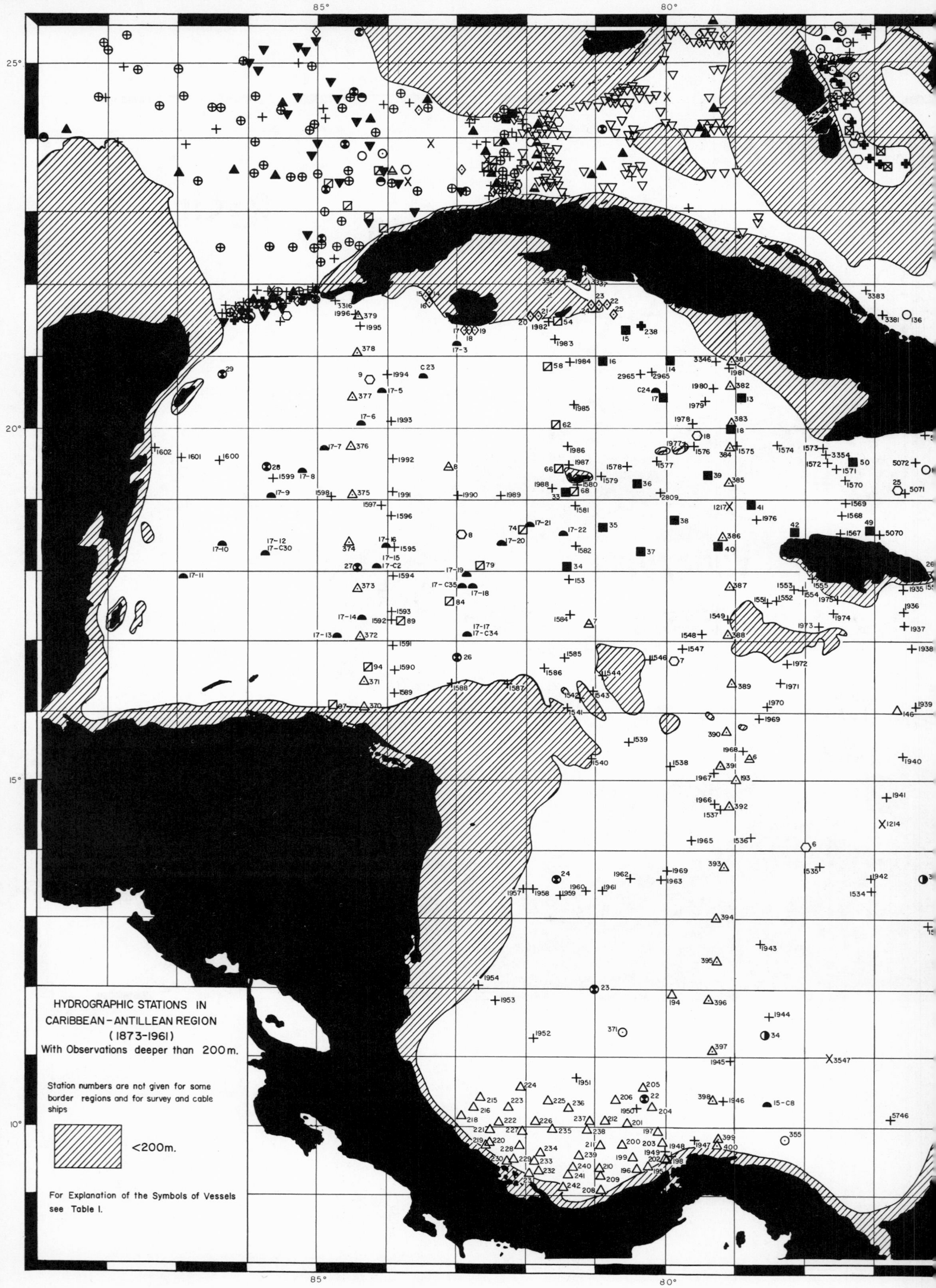

HYDROGRAPHIC STATIONS IN
CARIBBEAN-ANTILLEAN REGION
(1873-1961)
With Observations deeper than 200 m.

Station numbers are not given for some
border regions and for survey and cable
ships.

<200 m.

For Explanation of the Symbols of Vessels
see Table I.

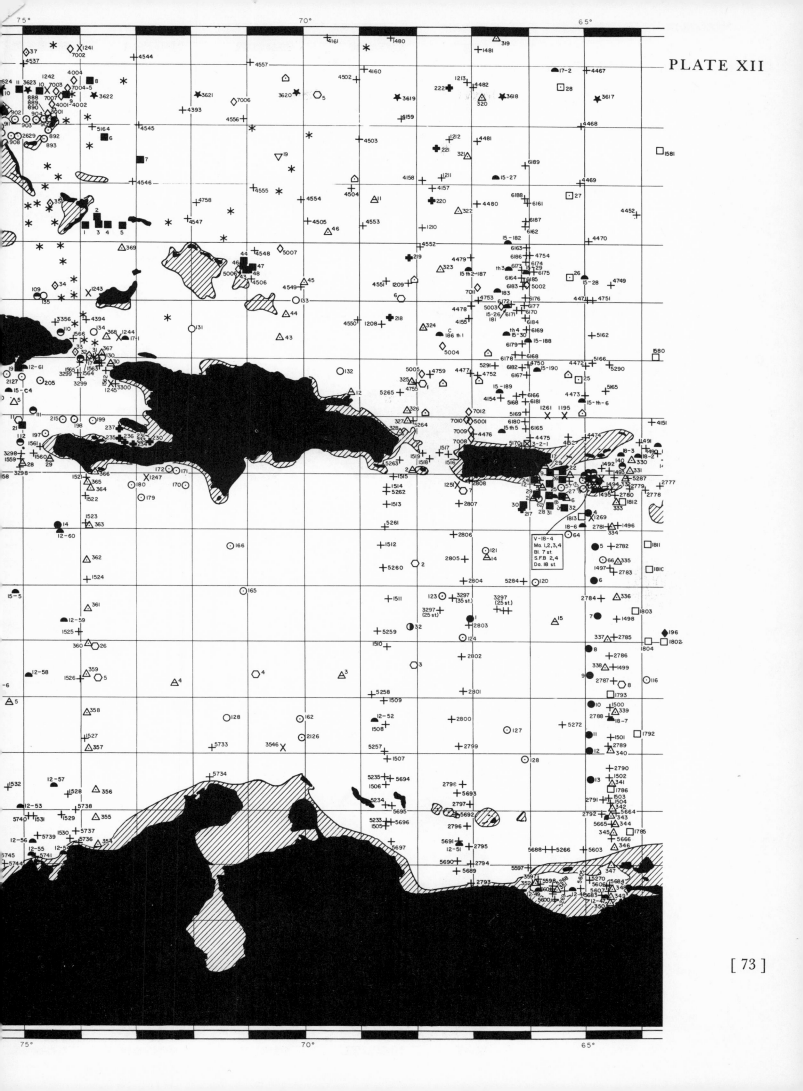

PLATE XII

PLATE XII (Continued)

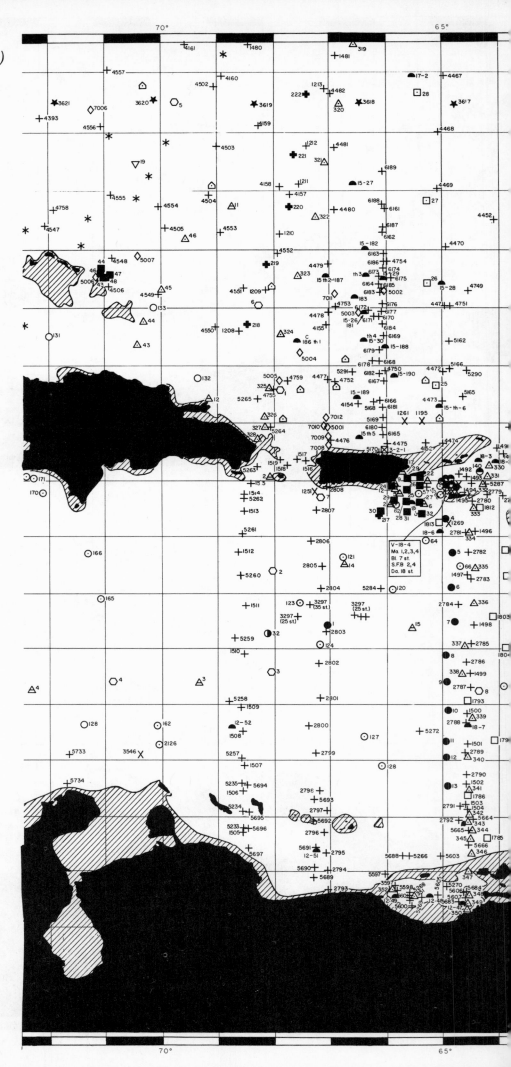

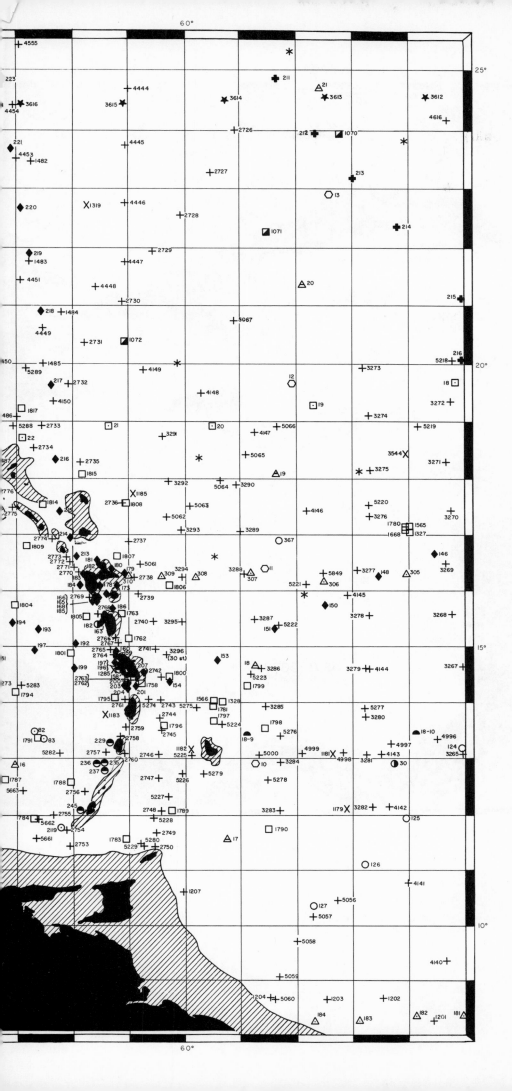

PLATE XIII

70°   65°   60°

25°

36.8

<36.8
(100-150m)

36.8
36.9
37.0
37.1

(~100m)

36.8

36.9

37.15

>37.0

<36.8
(100-150m)

(90-140m)

37.2

37.0

37.1

37.2

37.15

37.1

20°

(~150m)

<37.0
(120-150m)

(~100-140m)

>36.9
(150m)

<37.0
(150m)

?   <36.8
(150m)

36.9

37.0

>37.0
(90-100m)

<37.0

37.0

15°

<37.0
(150m)

37.10 (100-130)

>36.8
(120-150m)

37.0
(100-140m)

>37.0
(100-140m)

37.0

36.9

36.72-36.79
(90-100m)

36.9

36.8

37.0?

36.71-36.79
(50-100m)

36.4

36.7

<36.6
36.6?

10°

[77]

PLATE XIV

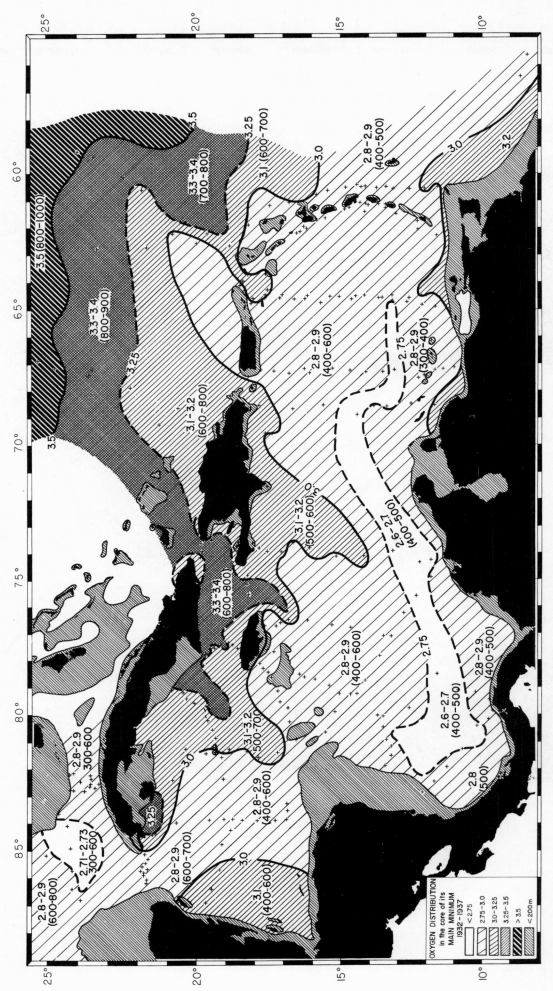

OXYGEN DISTRIBUTION
in the core of its
MAIN MINIMUM
1932–1937

PLATE XV

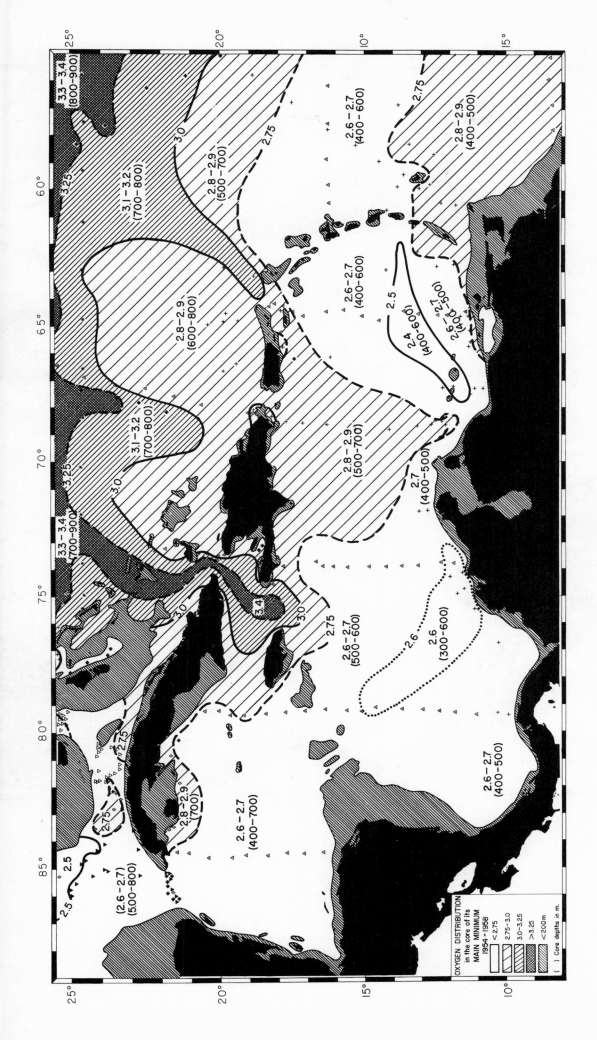

OXYGEN DISTRIBUTION
in the core of its
MAIN MINIMUM
1954 - 1958

< 2.75
2.75 - 3.0
3.0 - 3.25
> 3.25
< 200 m.

( ) Core depths in m.

PLATE XVI

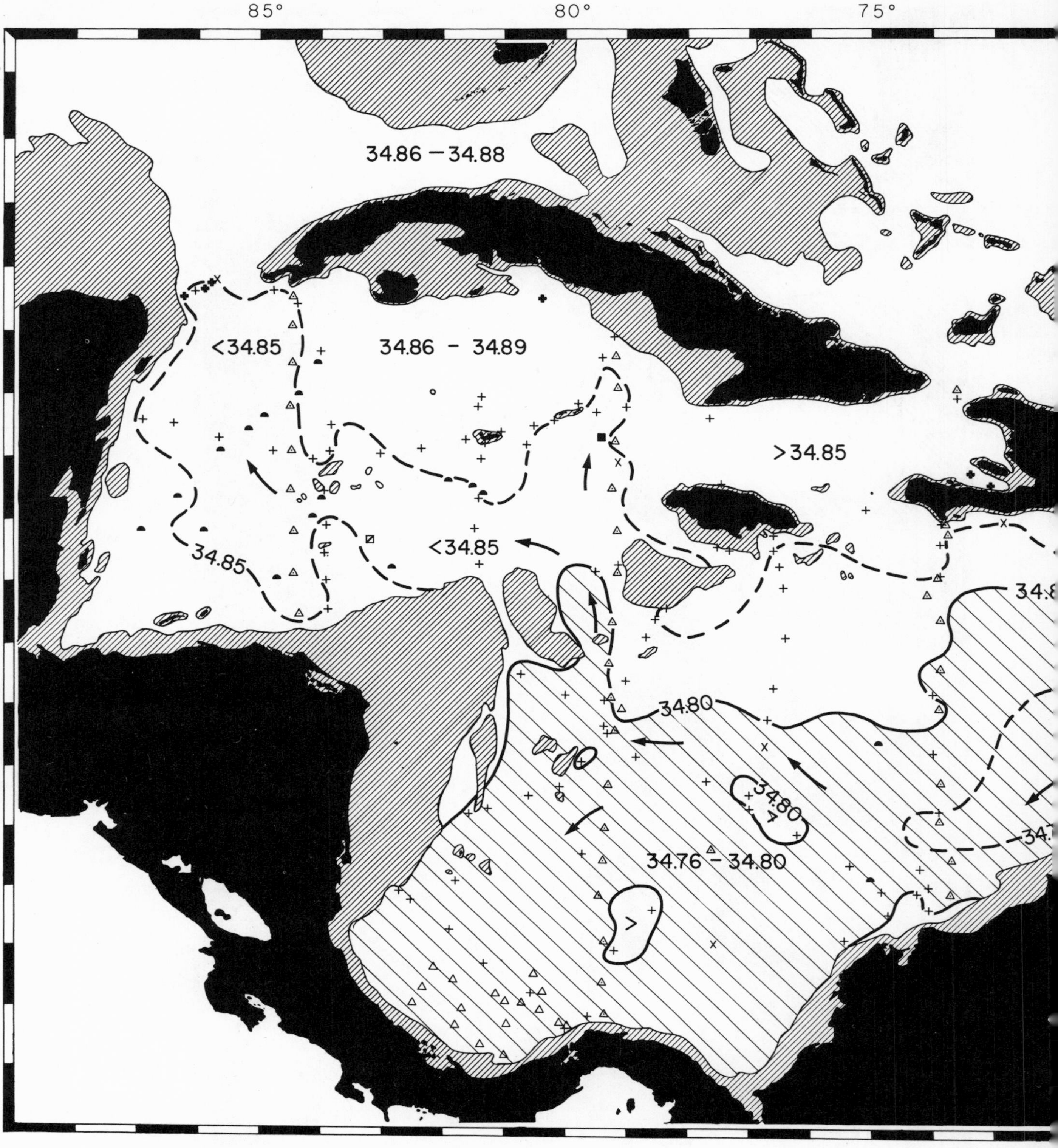
85°
80°
75°
25°
20°
15°
10°
34.86 – 34.88
<34.85
34.86 - 34.89
>34.85
34.85
<34.85
34.80
34.80
34.76 - 34.80
>

Spreading of the Subantarctic Intermediate Water within its core (Intermediate Salinity Minimum) in 700-850 meter depth

0-500 m.		< 34.60	
34.60-.70		34.70-.80	

← MAIN SPREADING

FOR EXPLANATION OF SYMBOLS SEE TABLE I.

No Well-Defined Minimum

> 34.85   34.85
34.80
34.75
34.80   34.70
34.85

34.85
34.75
34.70
34.70   34.70
34.67-   34.71 - 34.74
34.69
34.65
34.70
34.60
< 34.60

PLATE XVII

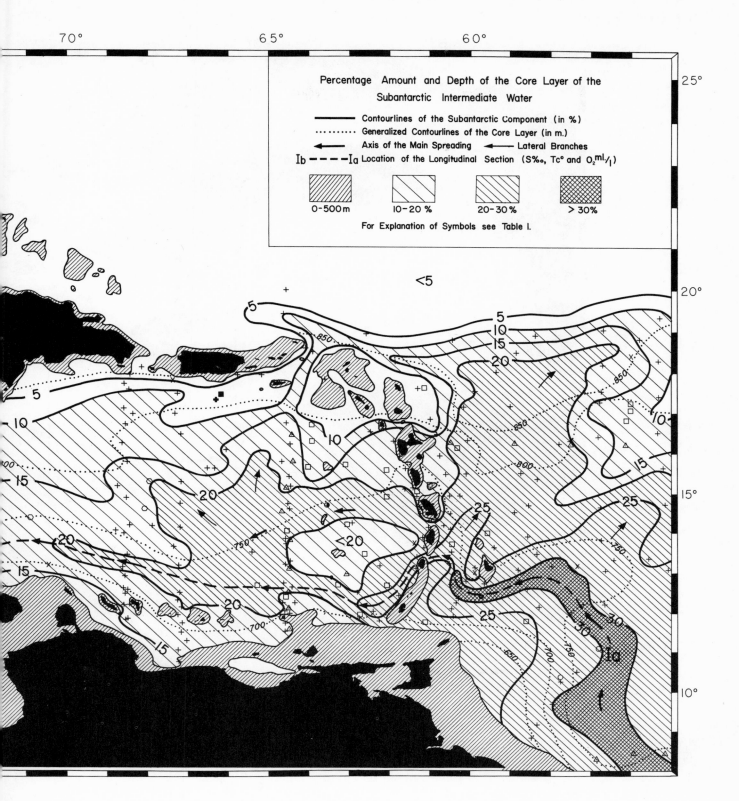

Percentage Amount and Depth of the Core Layer of the
Subantarctic Intermediate Water

——— Contourlines of the Subantarctic Component (in %)
.... Generalized Contourlines of the Core Layer (in m.)
◄——— Axis of the Main Spreading   ◄——— Lateral Branches
Ib ─ ─ ─ ─ Ia Location of the Longitudinal Section (S‰, Tc° and O_2 ml./l)

0-500 m   10-20 %   20-30 %   > 30%

For Explanation of Symbols see Table I.

PLATE XVIII

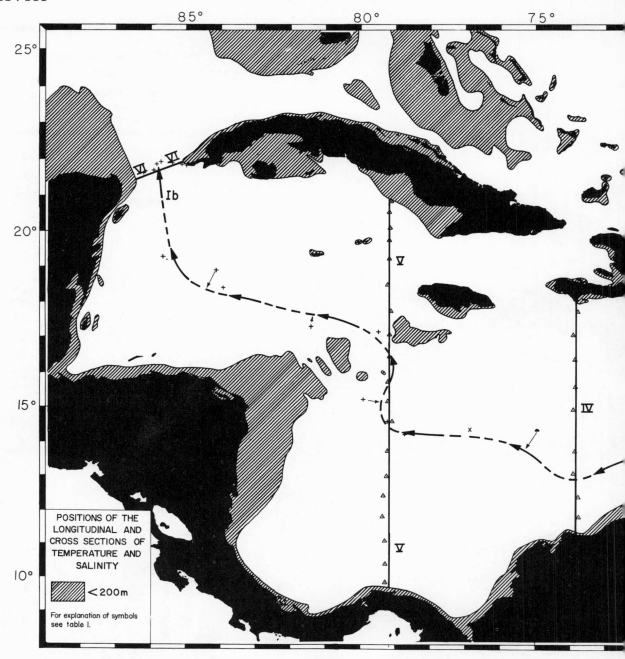

POSITIONS OF THE
LONGITUDINAL AND
CROSS SECTIONS OF
TEMPERATURE AND
SALINITY

▨ <200m

For explanation of symbols
see table I.

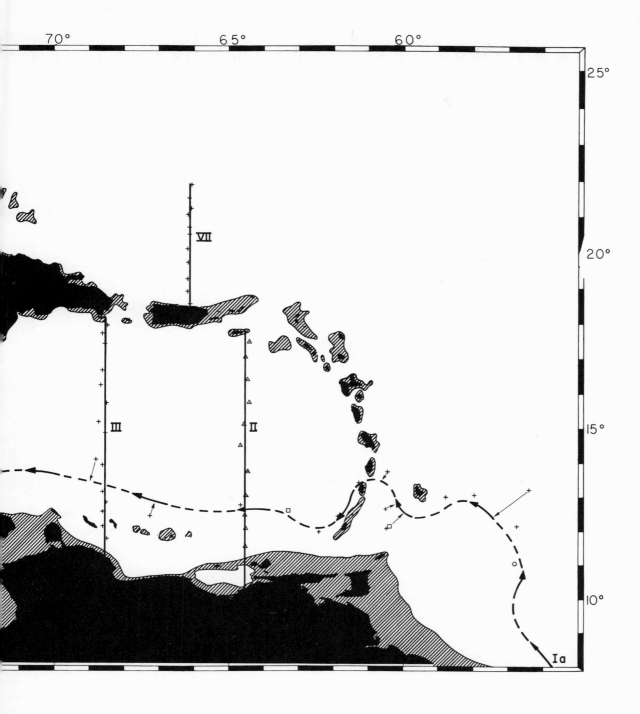

PLATE XIX

LONGITUDINAL SECTION ALONG AXI

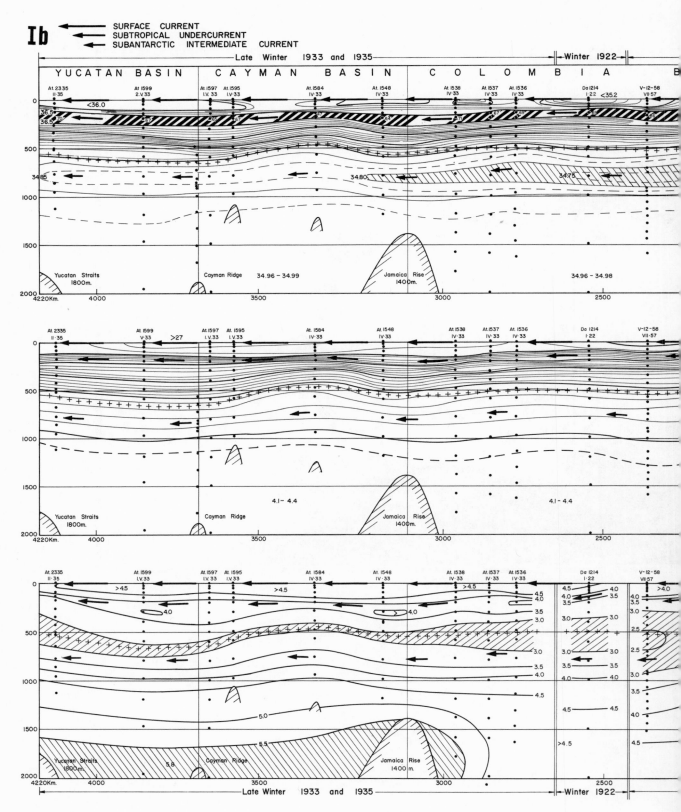

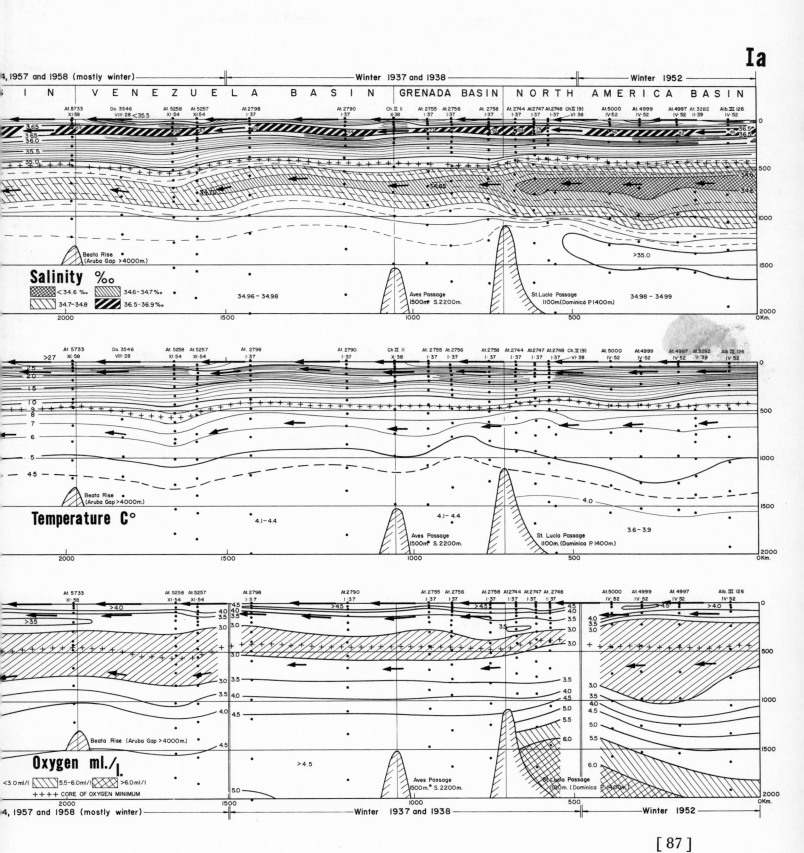

PLATE XX

V E N E Z U E L A   B A S I N

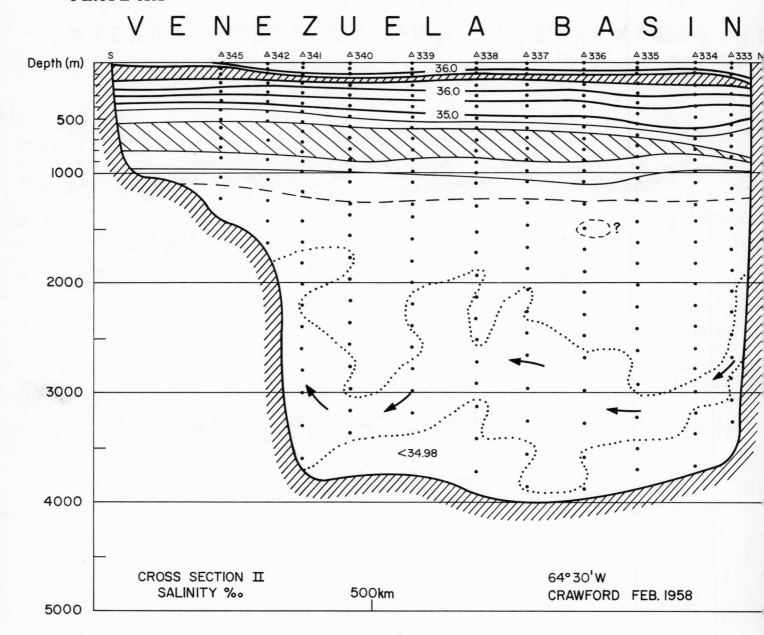

CROSS SECTION II
SALINITY ‰

500km

64°30'W
CRAWFORD FEB. 1958

PLATE XXI

VENEZUELA BASIN

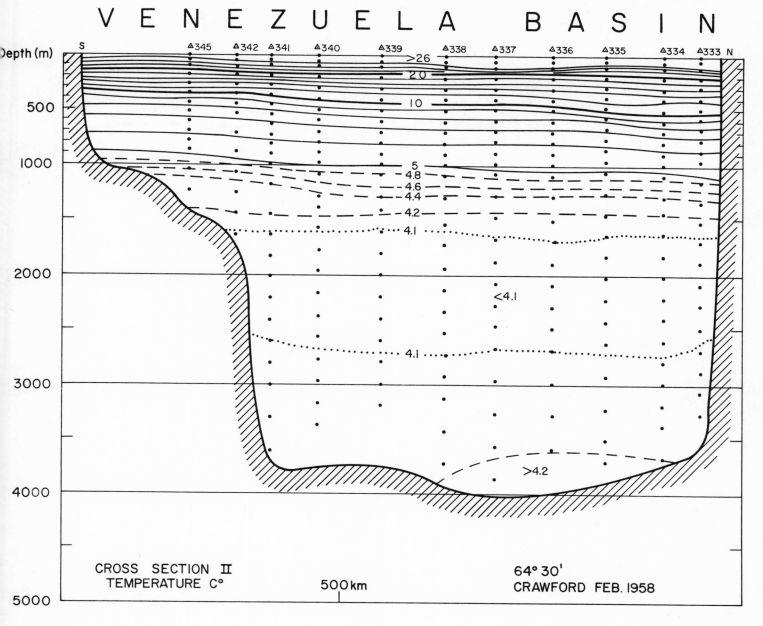

CROSS SECTION II
TEMPERATURE C°

500 km

64° 30'
CRAWFORD FEB. 1958

PLATE XXII

VENEZUELA BASIN

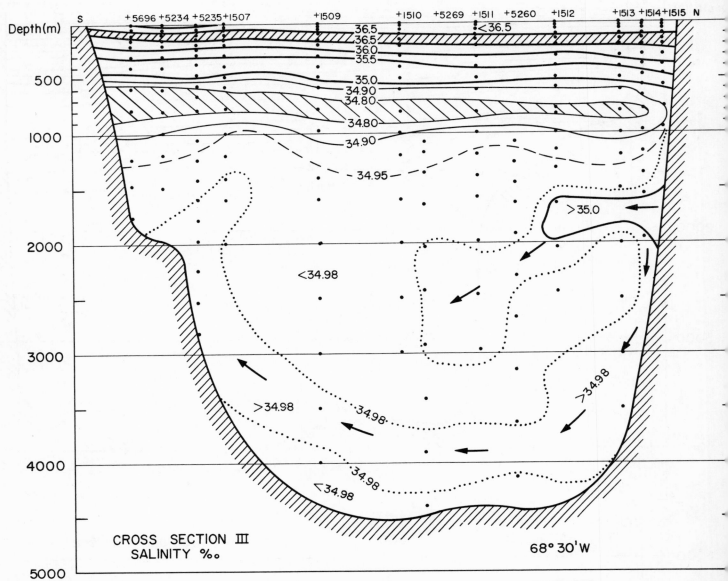

CROSS SECTION III
SALINITY ‰

68° 30'W

ATLANTIS
5696 NOV. 1958
5234, 5235 DEC. 1954
5259, 5260 DEC. 1954
1507–1515 MAR. 1933

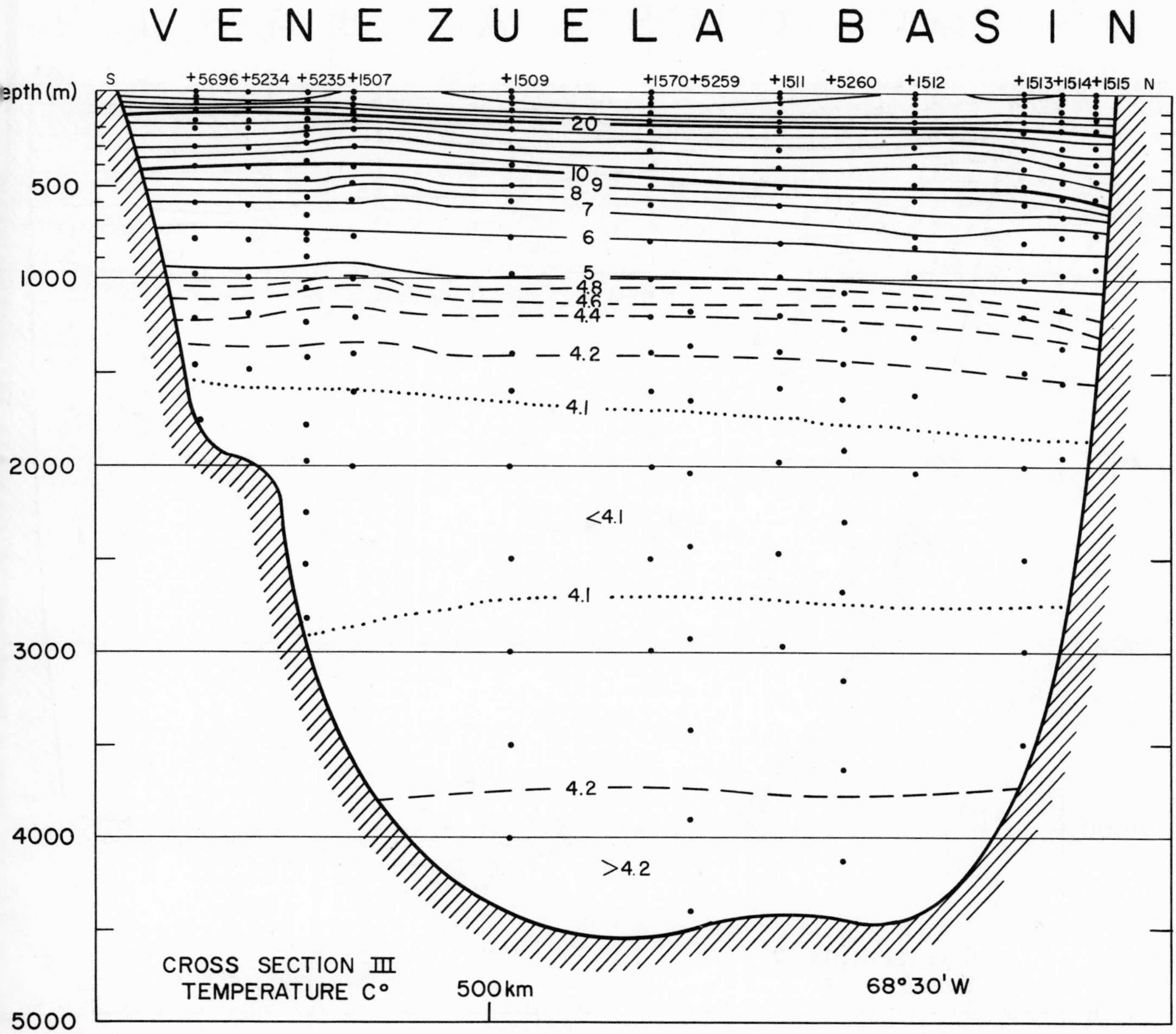

PLATE XXIII

V E N E Z U E L A   B A S I N

CROSS SECTION III
TEMPERATURE C°

500 km

68° 30' W

ATLANTIS
5696 NOV. 1958
5234, 5235 DEC. 1954
5259, 5260 DEC. 1954
1507-1515 MAR. 1933

PLATE XXIV

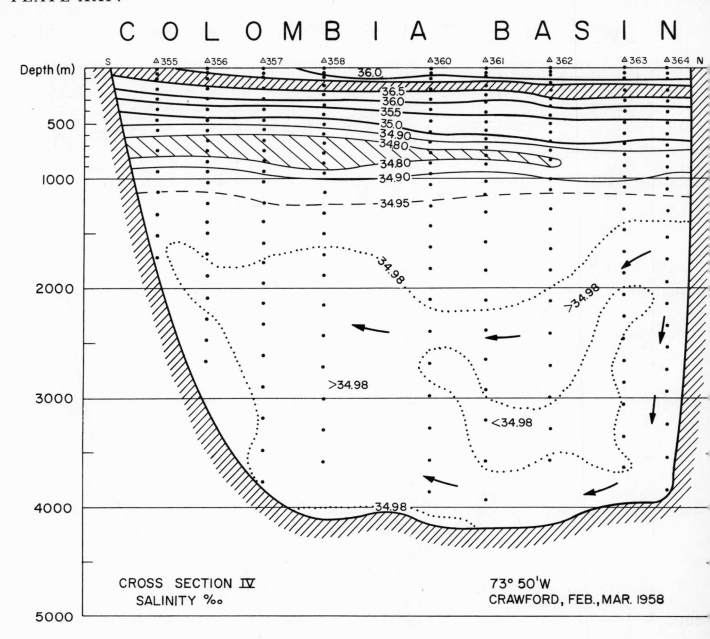

COLOMBIA BASIN

CROSS SECTION IV
SALINITY ‰

73° 50'W
CRAWFORD, FEB., MAR. 1958

PLATE XXV

COLOMBIA BASIN

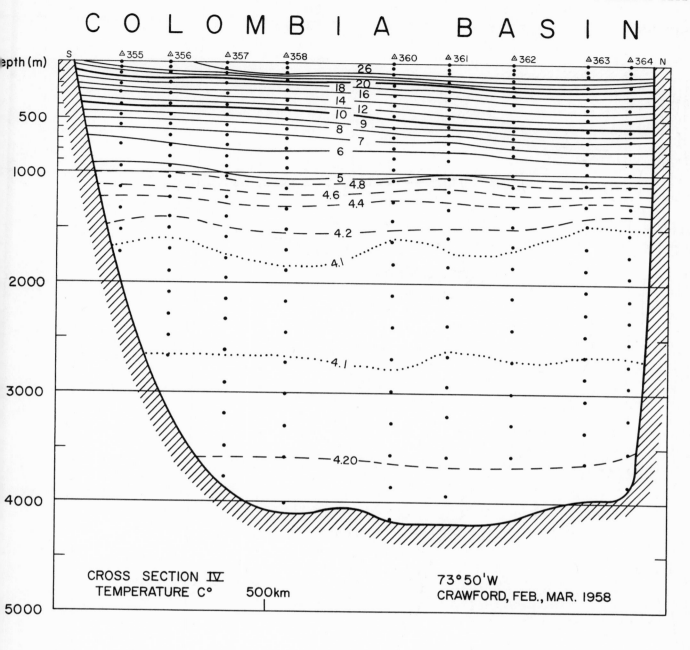

CROSS SECTION IV
TEMPERATURE C°   500km

73°50'W
CRAWFORD, FEB., MAR. 1958

PLATE XXVI

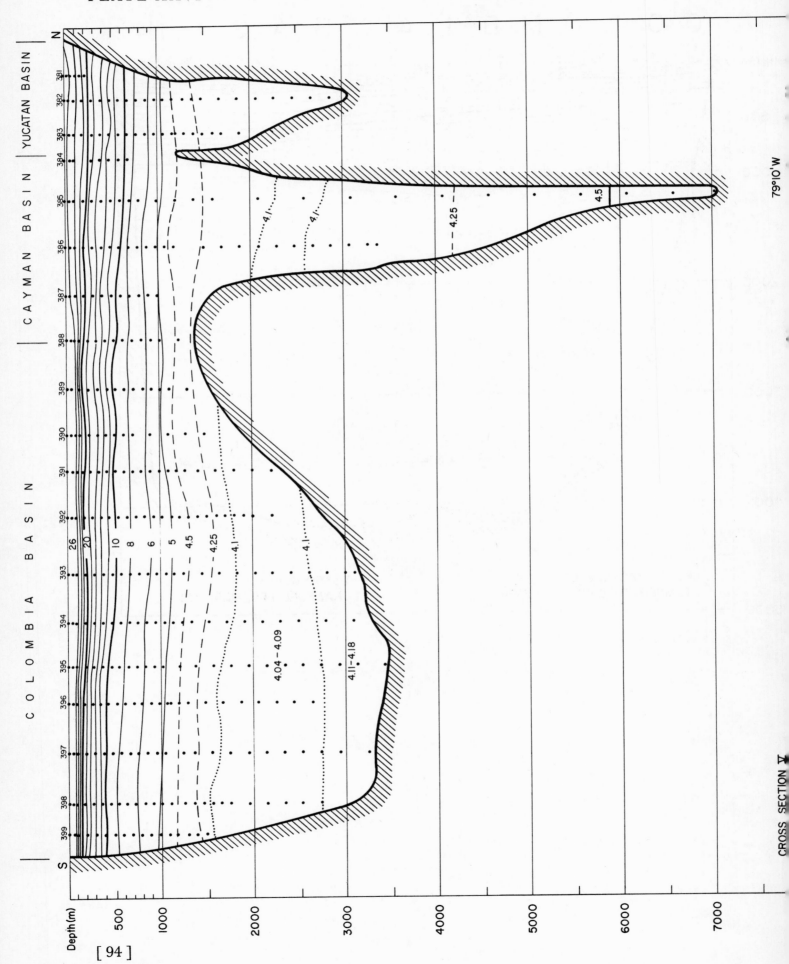

PLATE XXVII

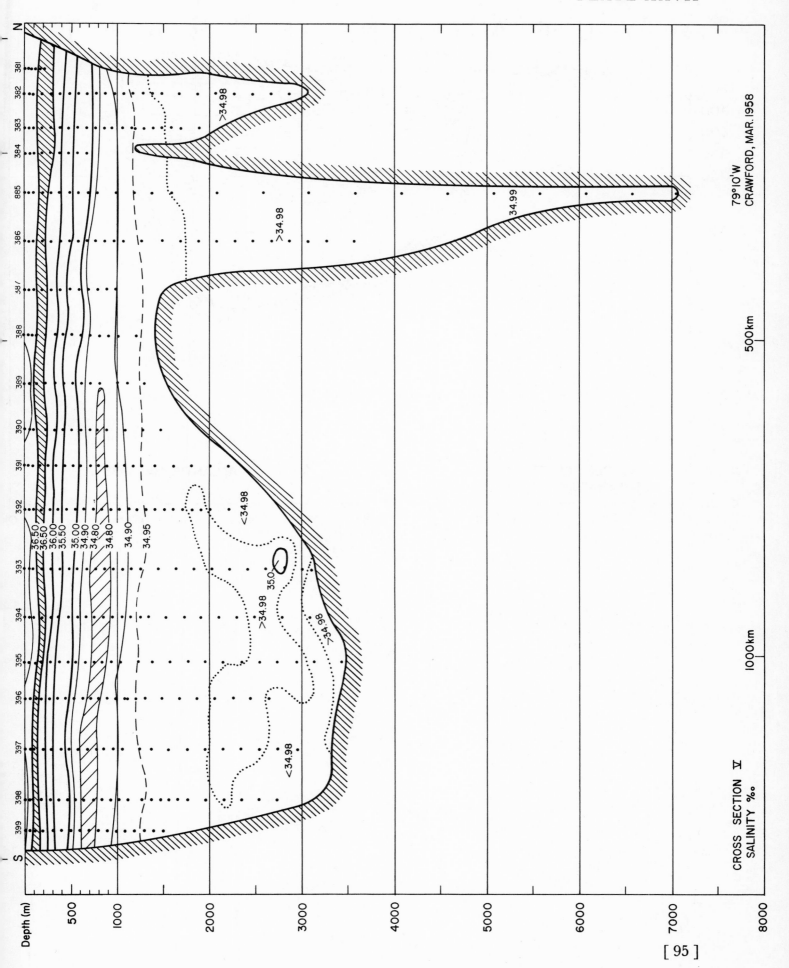

CROSS SECTION Ⅴ
SALINITY ‰

79°10'W
CRAWFORD, MAR. 1958

PLATE XXVIII

YUCATAN STRAIT

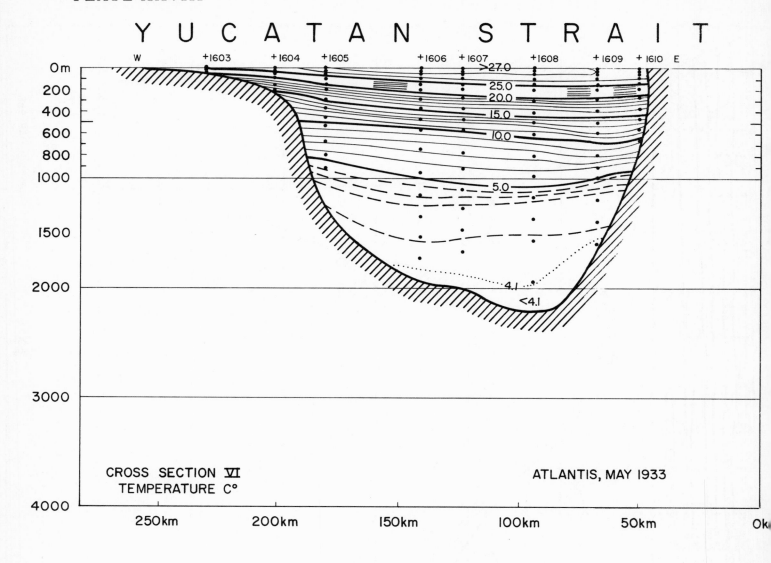

CROSS SECTION VI
TEMPERATURE C°

ATLANTIS, MAY 1933

PLATE XXIX

YUCATAN STRAIT

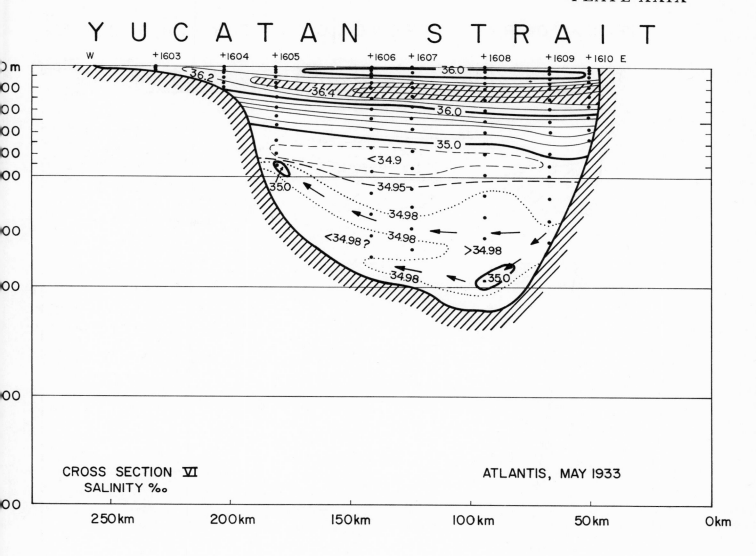

CROSS SECTION VI
SALINITY ‰

ATLANTIS, MAY 1933

PLATE XXX

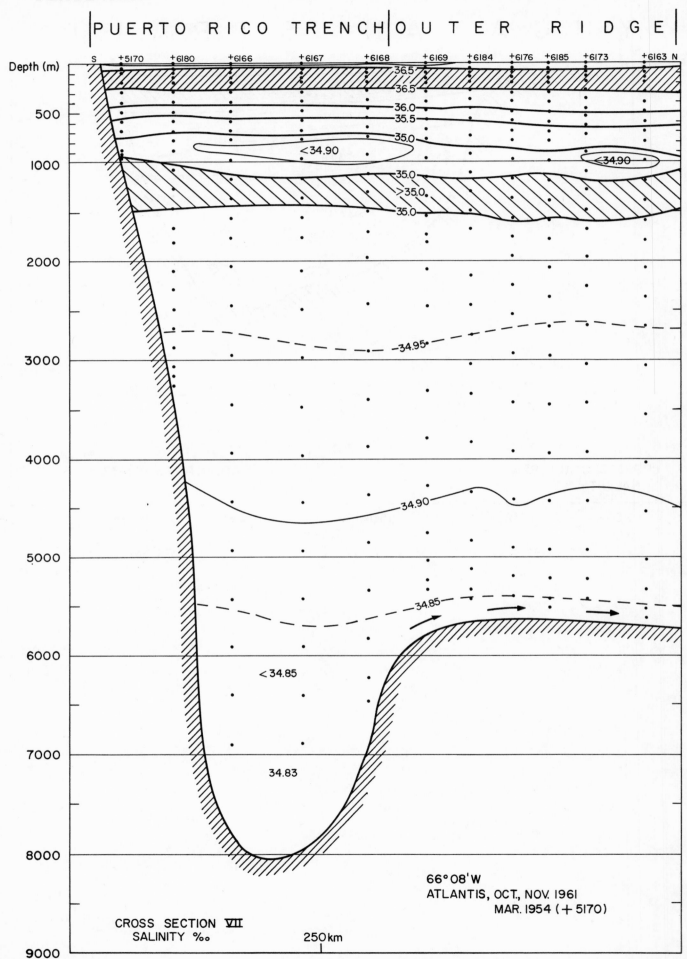

PUERTO RICO TRENCH OUTER RIDGE

CROSS SECTION VII
SALINITY ‰

250km

66°08'W
ATLANTIS, OCT., NOV. 1961
MAR. 1954 (+5170)

PLATE XXXI

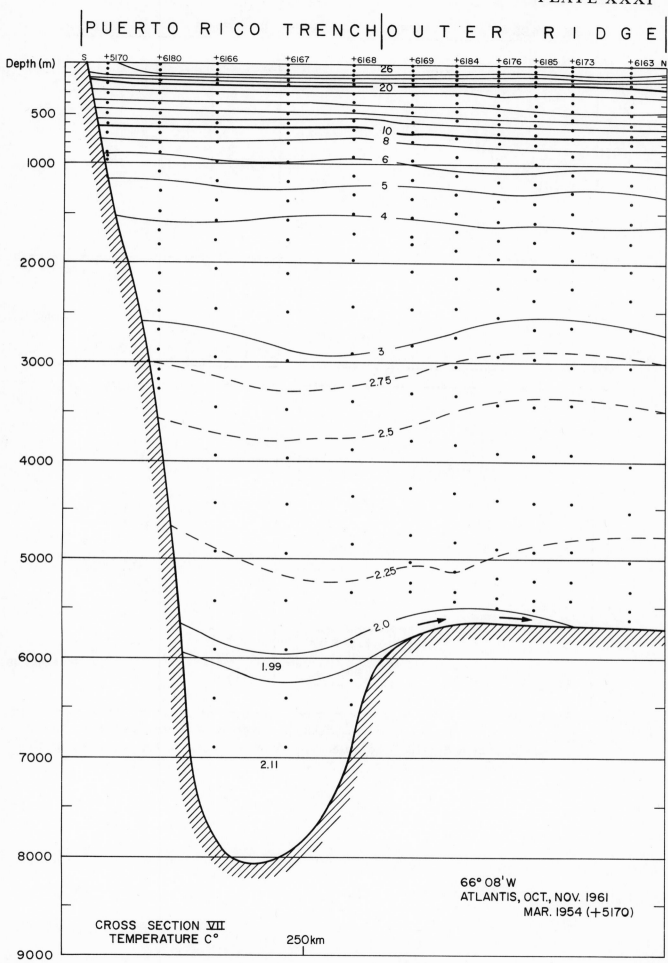

PUERTO RICO TRENCH|OUTER RIDGE

CROSS SECTION VII
TEMPERATURE C°

250km

66° 08' W
ATLANTIS, OCT., NOV. 1961
MAR. 1954 (+5170)

PLATE XXXII

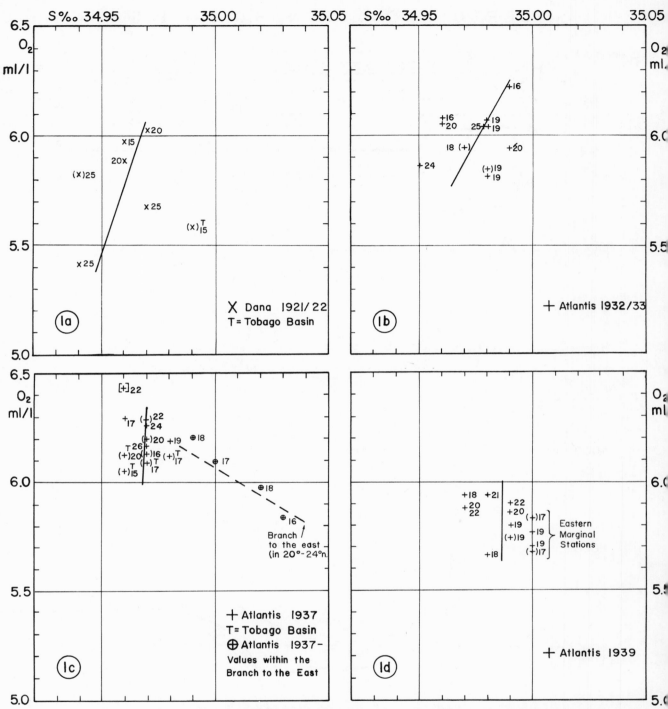

Ia–Id   Oxygen–Salinity Correlation (upper oxygen maximum) within the
Core–layer of N. Atlantic Deep Water in the Antillean Sector of the N.–American Basin

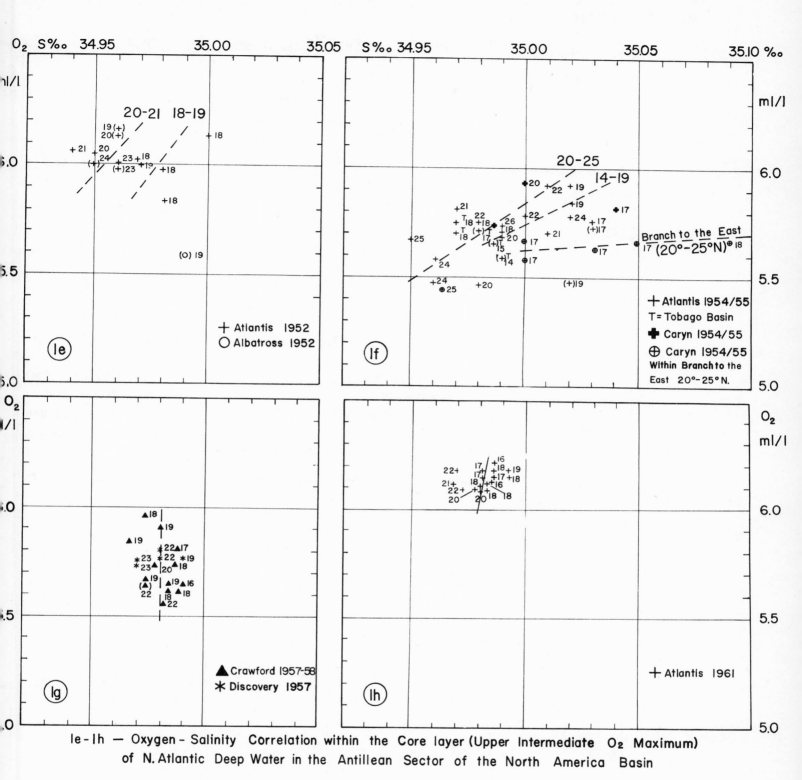

le-lh — Oxygen - Salinity Correlation within the Core layer (Upper Intermediate O₂ Maximum) of N. Atlantic Deep Water in the Antillean Sector of the North America Basin

PLATE XXXIII

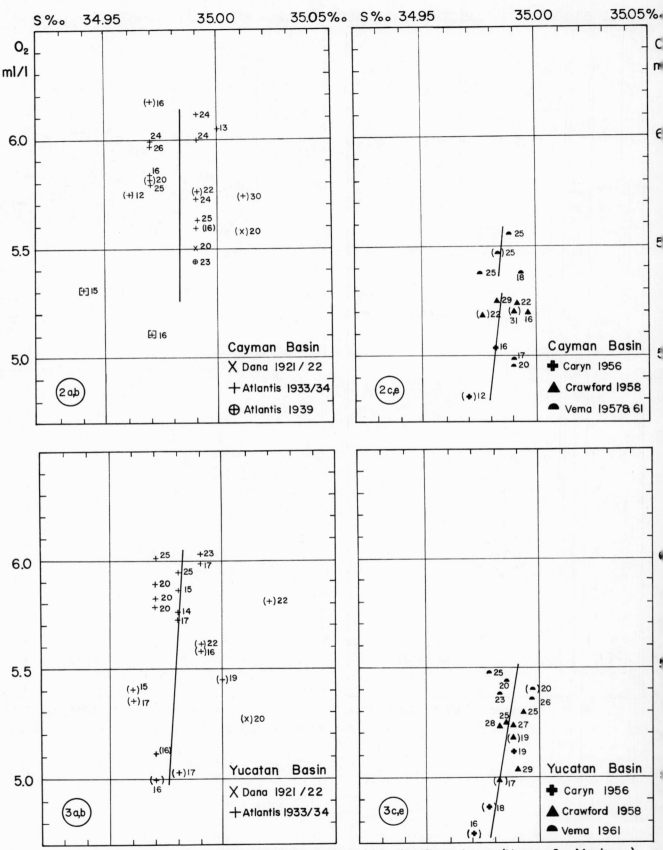

2a-2e, 3a-3e   Oxygen-Salinity Correlation within the Core-Layer (Upper O$_2$ Maximum) of N. Atlantic Deep Water in the Cayman and Yucatan Basin

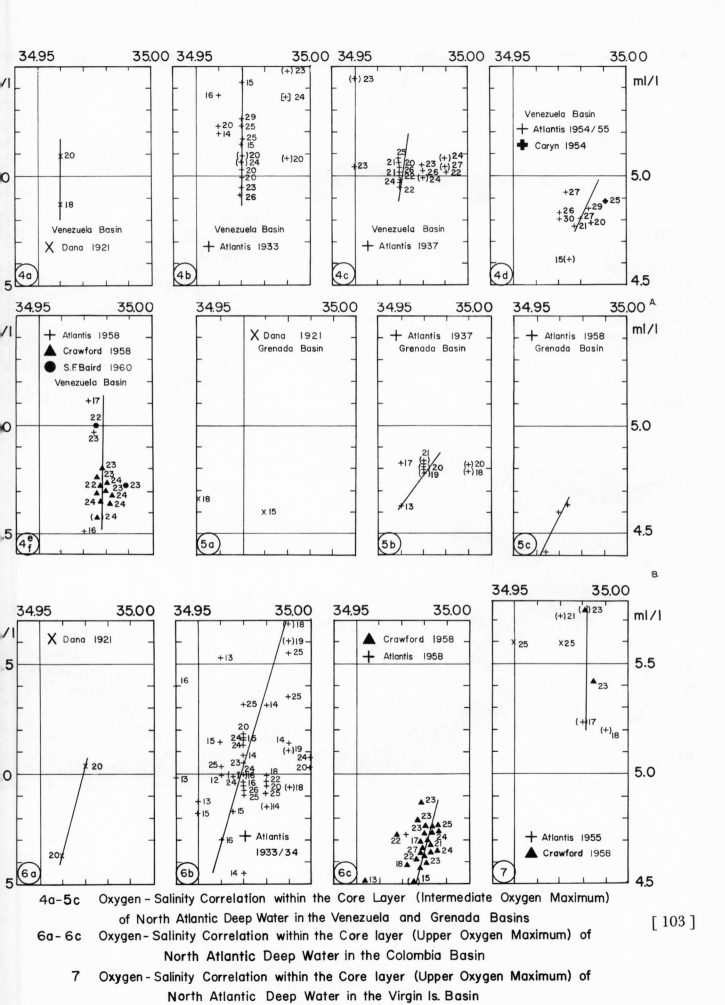

4a–5c   Oxygen – Salinity Correlation within the Core Layer (Intermediate Oxygen Maximum) of North Atlantic Deep Water in the Venezuela and Grenada Basins

6a– 6c   Oxygen – Salinity Correlation within the Core layer (Upper Oxygen Maximum) of North Atlantic Deep Water in the Colombia Basin

7   Oxygen – Salinity Correlation within the Core layer (Upper Oxygen Maximum) of North Atlantic Deep Water in the Virgin Is. Basin

[103]

PLATE XXXIV

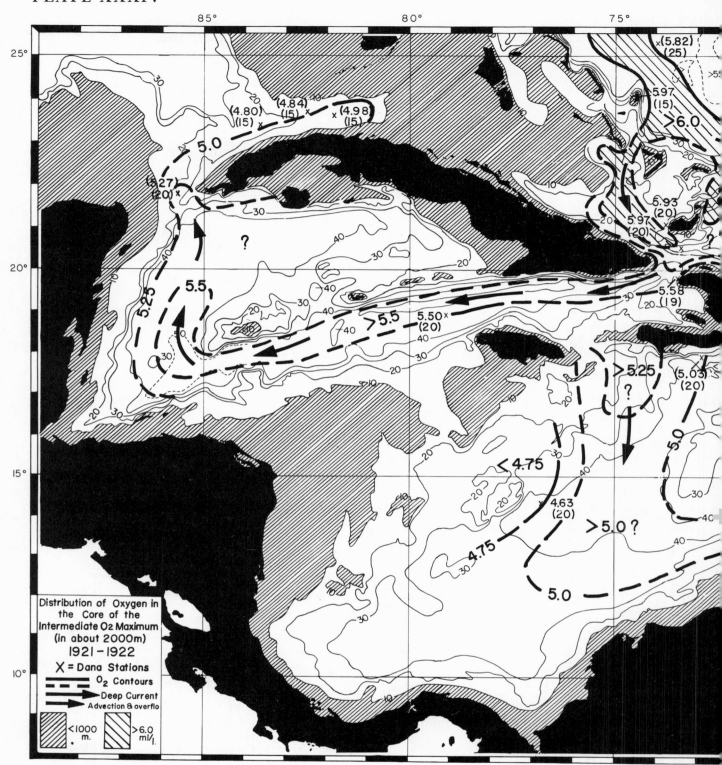

Distribution of Oxygen in
the Core of the
Intermediate O₂ Maximum
(in about 2000m)
1921–1922
X = Dana Stations
O₂ Contours
Deep Current
Advection & overflo
<1000 m.
>6.0 ml/l.

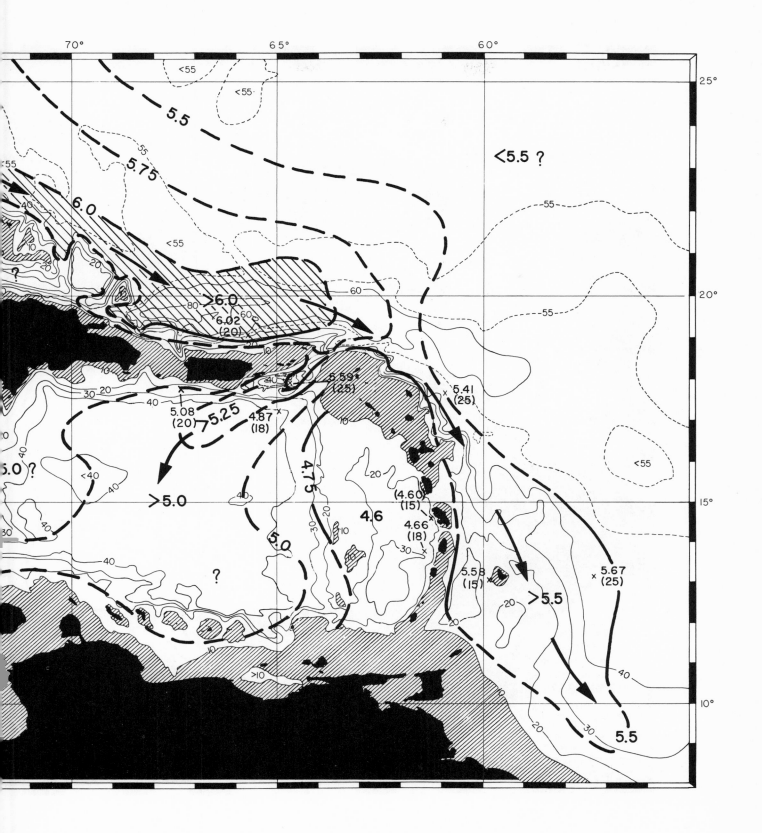

PLATE XXXV

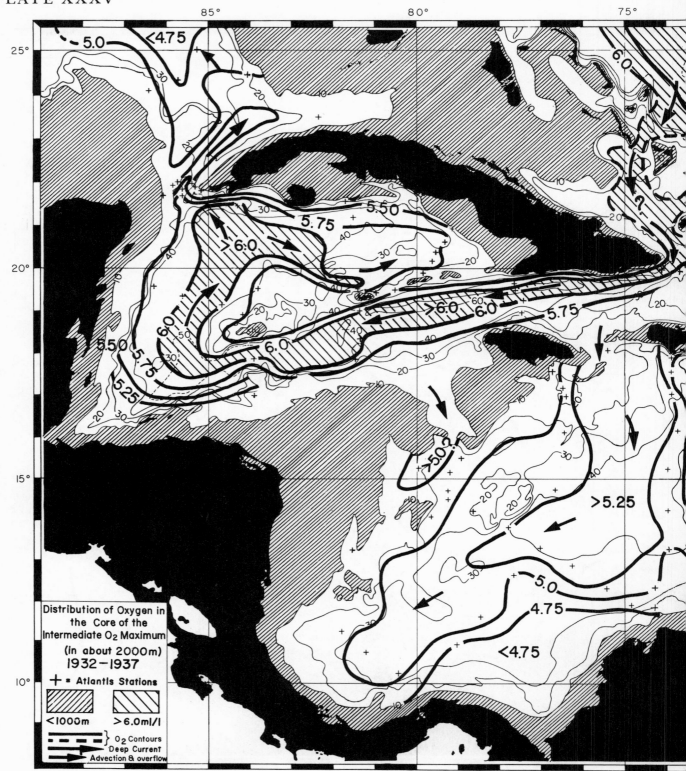

Distribution of Oxygen in
the Core of the
Intermediate O₂ Maximum
(in about 2000m)
1932–1937
+ = Atlantis Stations

<1000m   >6.0ml/l

O₂ Contours
Deep Current
Advection & overflow

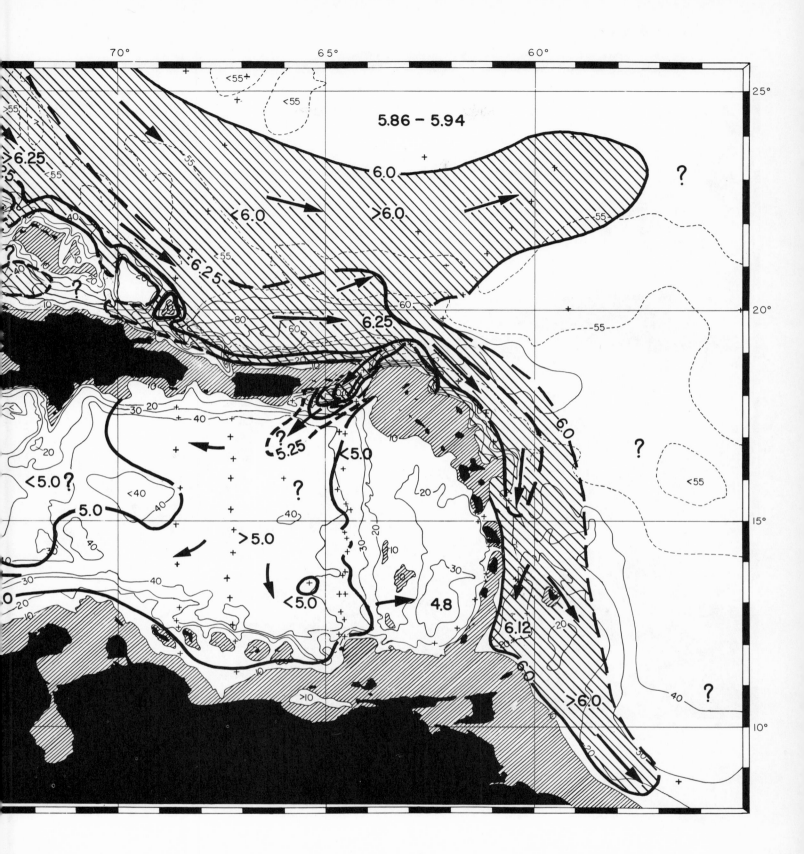

PLATE XXXVI

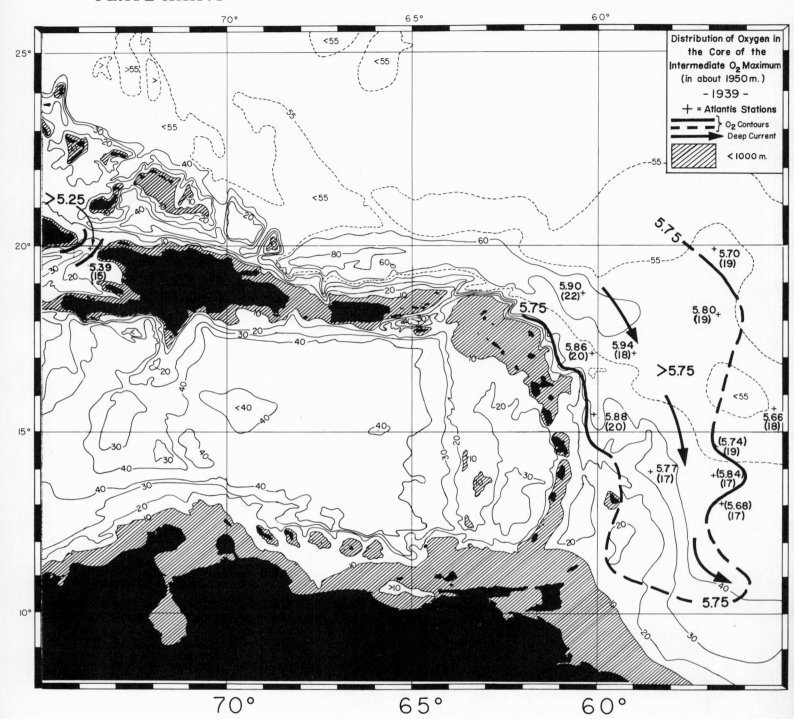

Distribution of Oxygen in
the Core of the
Intermediate O₂ Maximum
(in about 1950 m.)
- 1939 -
+ = Atlantis Stations
O₂ Contours
Deep Current
< 1000 m.

PLATE XXXVII

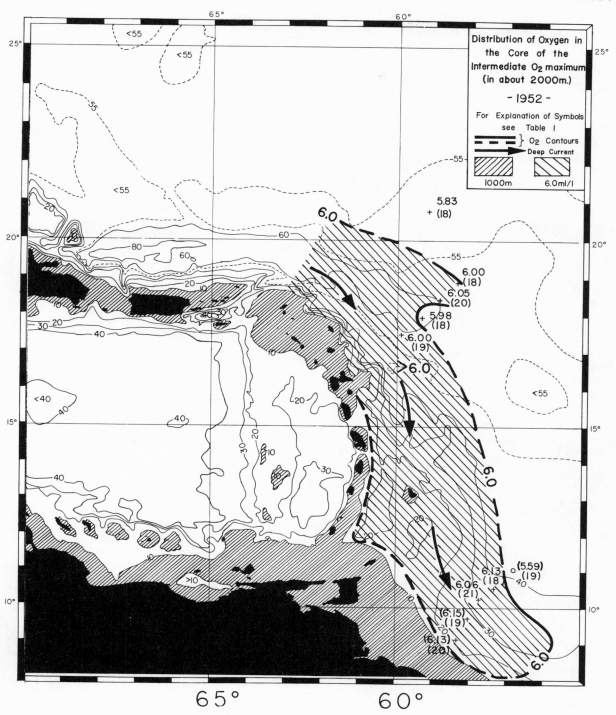

PLATE XXXVIII

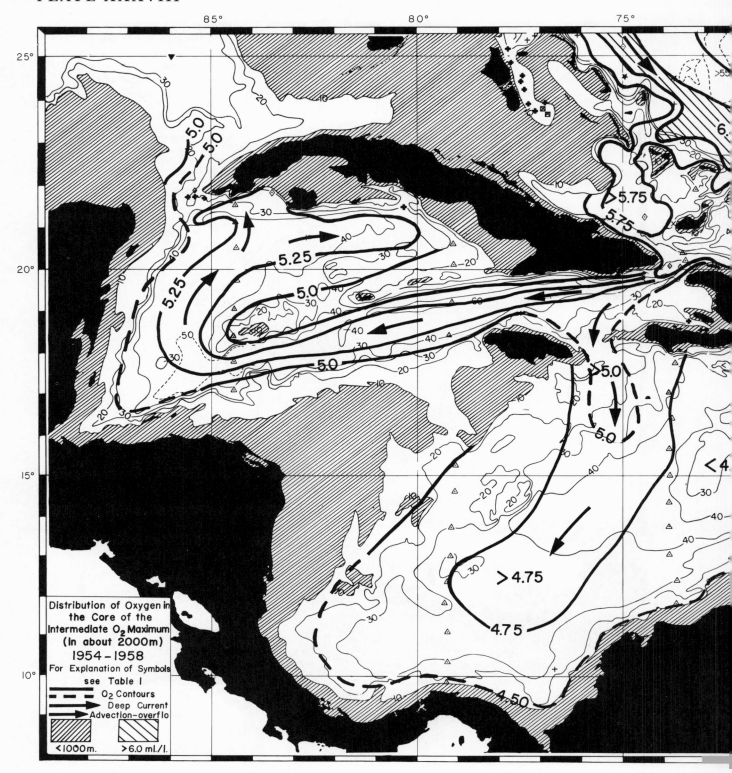

Distribution of Oxygen in
the Core of the
Intermediate O₂ Maximum
(In about 2000m)
1954–1958
For Explanation of Symbols
see Table I
— — — O₂ Contours
——▶ Deep Current
——▶ Advection-overflo
〈1000m.   〉6.0 ml./l.

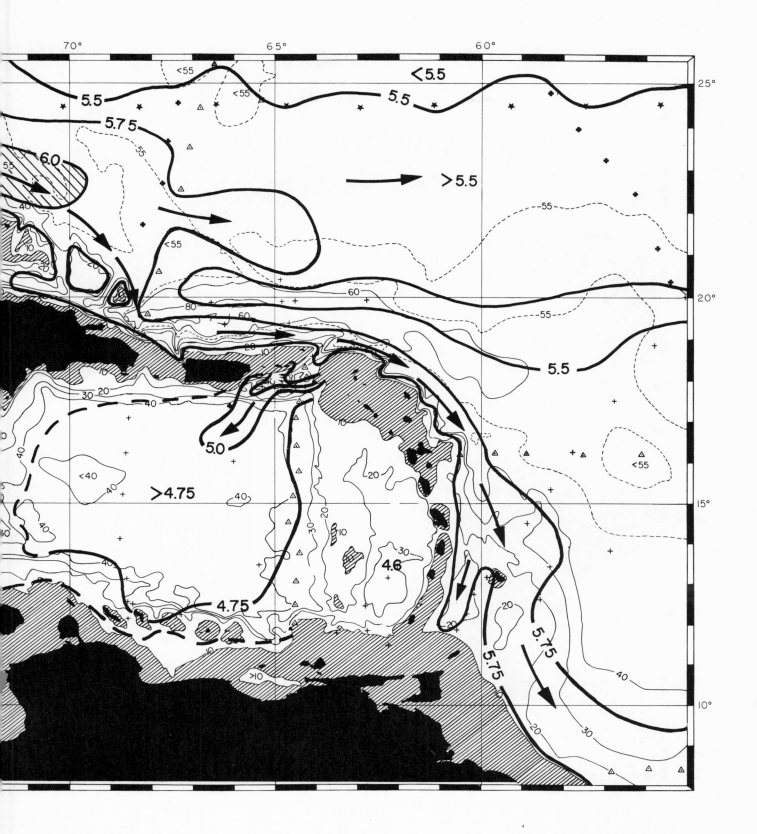

[111]

PLATE XXXIX

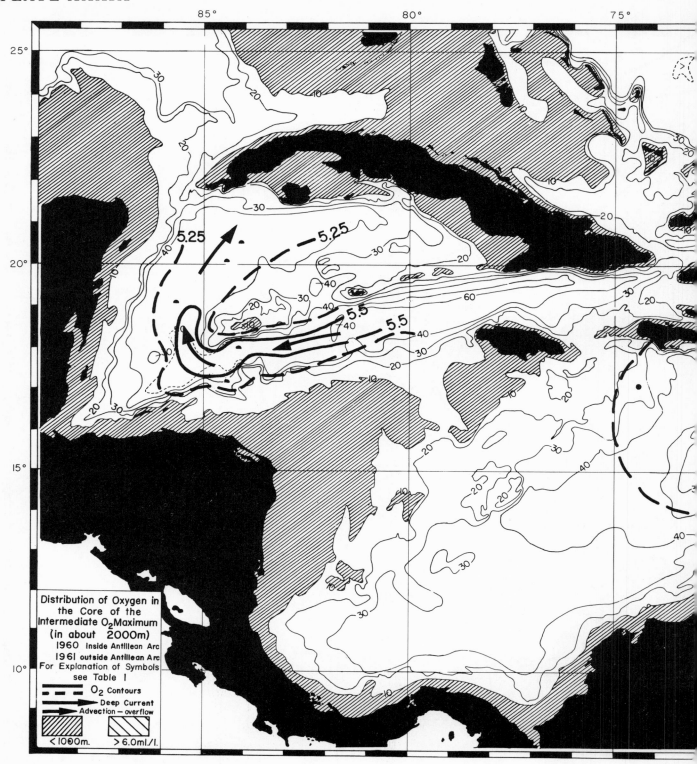

Distribution of Oxygen in
the Core of the
Intermediate O₂ Maximum
(in about 2000m)
1960 Inside Antillean Arc
1961 outside Antillean Arc
For Explanation of Symbols
see Table 1

O₂ Contours
Deep Current
Advection — overflow
< 1000m.   > 6.0 ml./l.

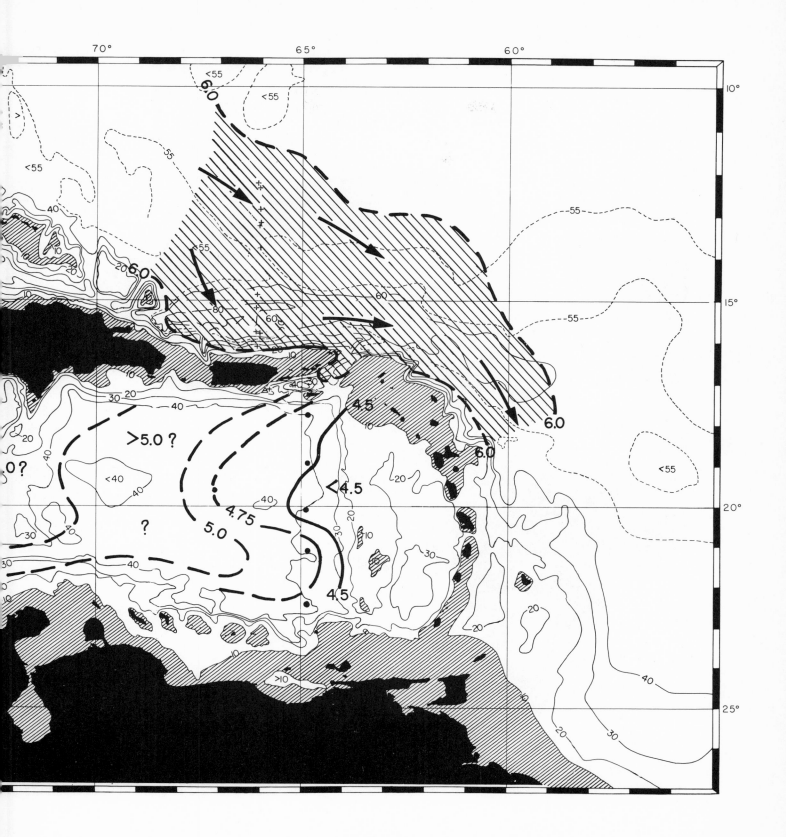

PLATE XL

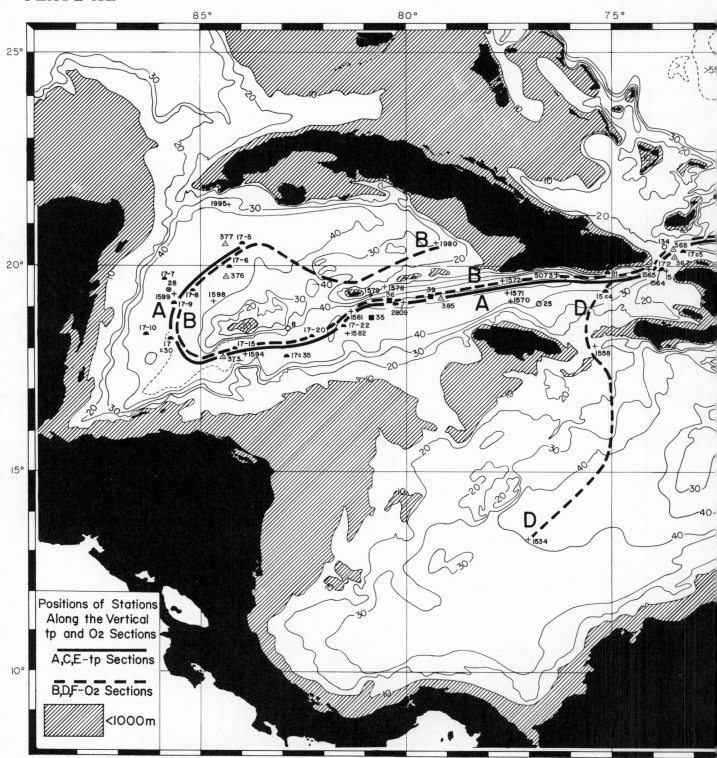

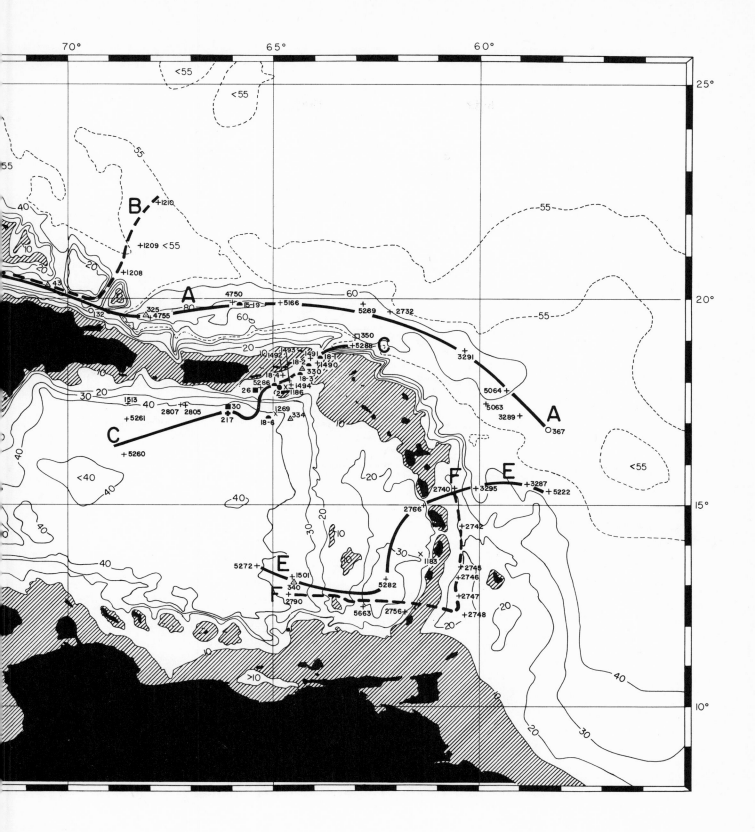

PLATE XLI

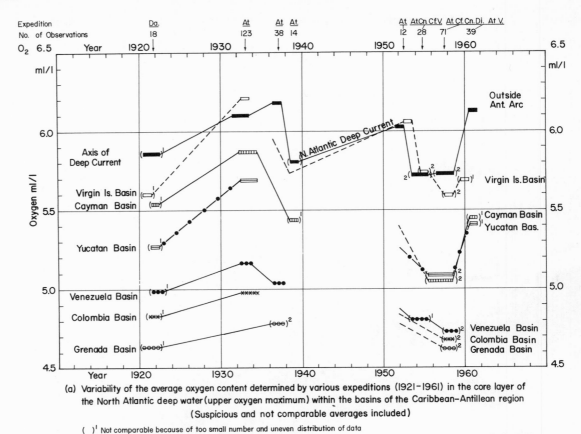

(a) Variability of the average oxygen content determined by various expeditions (1921–1961) in the core layer of the North Atlantic deep water (upper oxygen maximum) within the basins of the Caribbean–Antillean region

(Suspicious and not comparable averages included)

( )[1] Not comparable because of too small number and uneven distribution of data
( )[2] Suspicious averages because of analytic difficulties

G. Wüst 1962

PLATE XLII

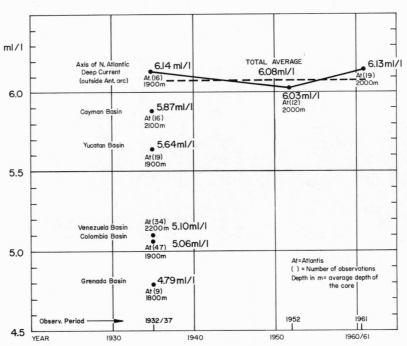

Representative averages of oxygen content in the core layer of the North Atlantic deep water (upper oxygen maximum) within the basins of the Caribbean–Antillean region (suspicious averages and averages of less than 9 observations excluded)

Des. by Wüst 1963

PLATE XLIII

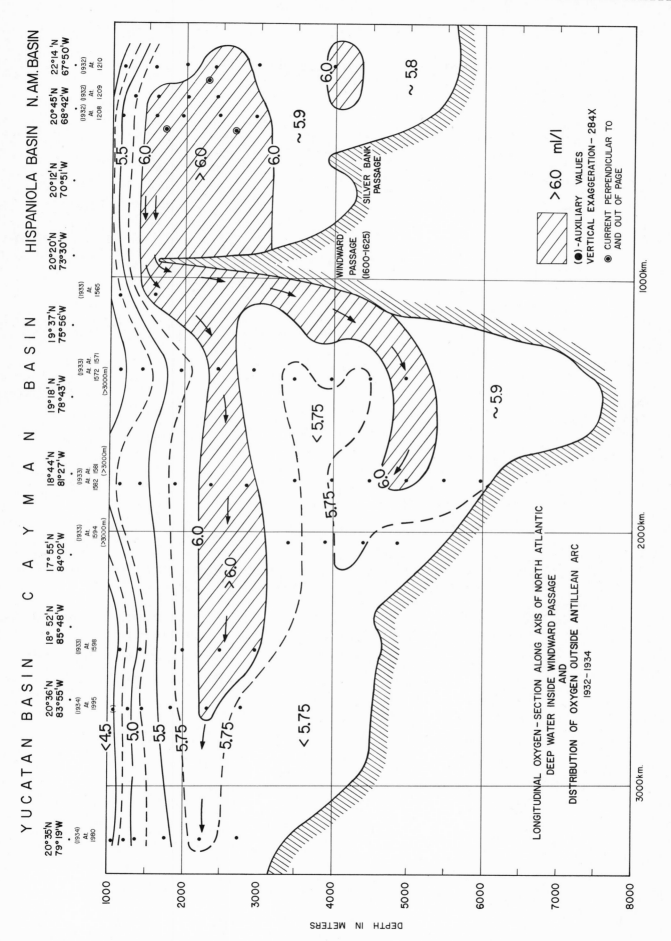

LONGITUDINAL OXYGEN–SECTION ALONG AXIS OF NORTH ATLANTIC
DEEP WATER INSIDE WINDWARD PASSAGE
AND
DISTRIBUTION OF OXYGEN OUTSIDE ANTILLEAN ARC
1932–1934

PLATE XLIV

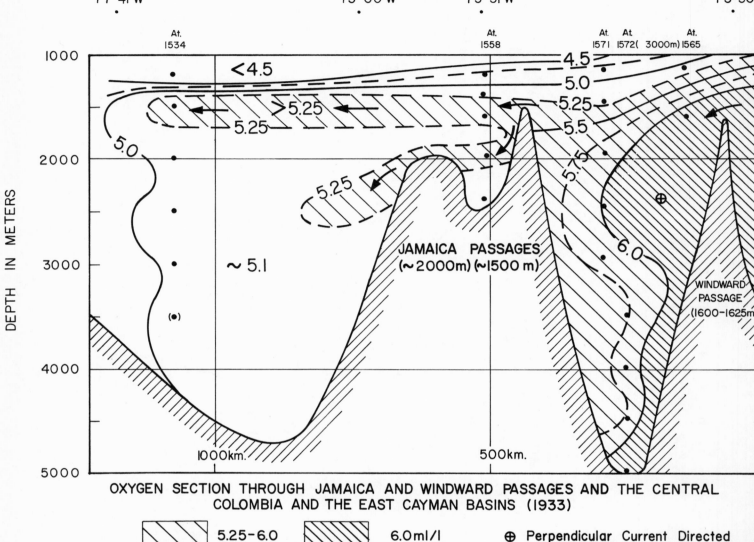

OXYGEN SECTION THROUGH JAMAICA AND WINDWARD PASSAGES AND THE CENTRAL
COLOMBIA AND THE EAST CAYMAN BASINS (1933)

PLATE XLV

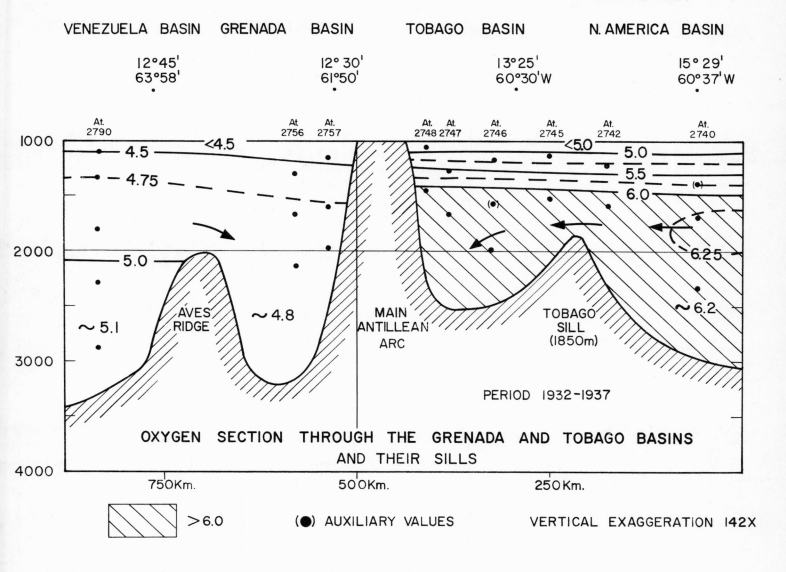

VENEZUELA BASIN   GRENADA   BASIN   TOBAGO   BASIN   N. AMERICA BASIN

OXYGEN SECTION THROUGH THE GRENADA AND TOBAGO BASINS
AND THEIR SILLS

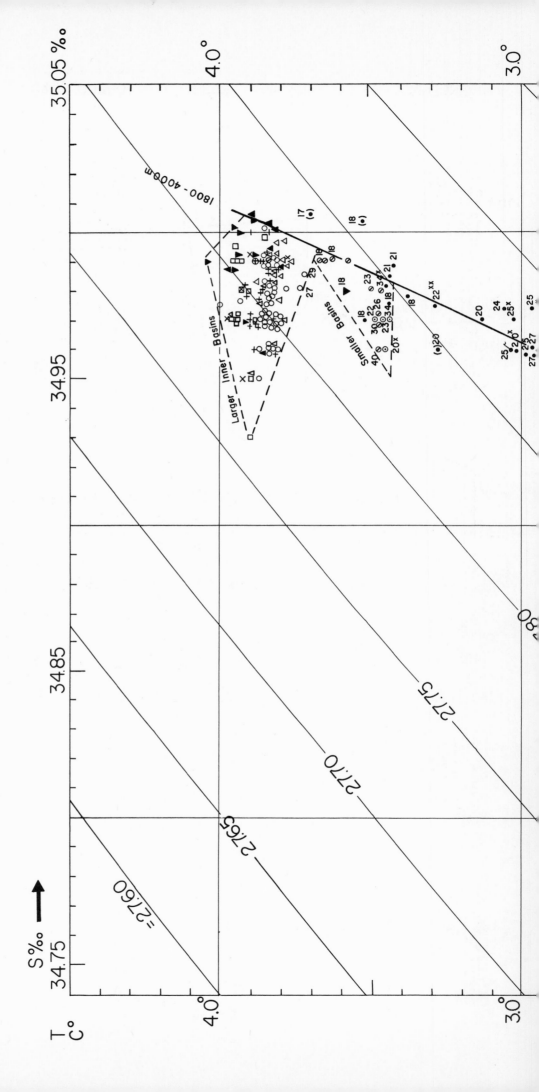

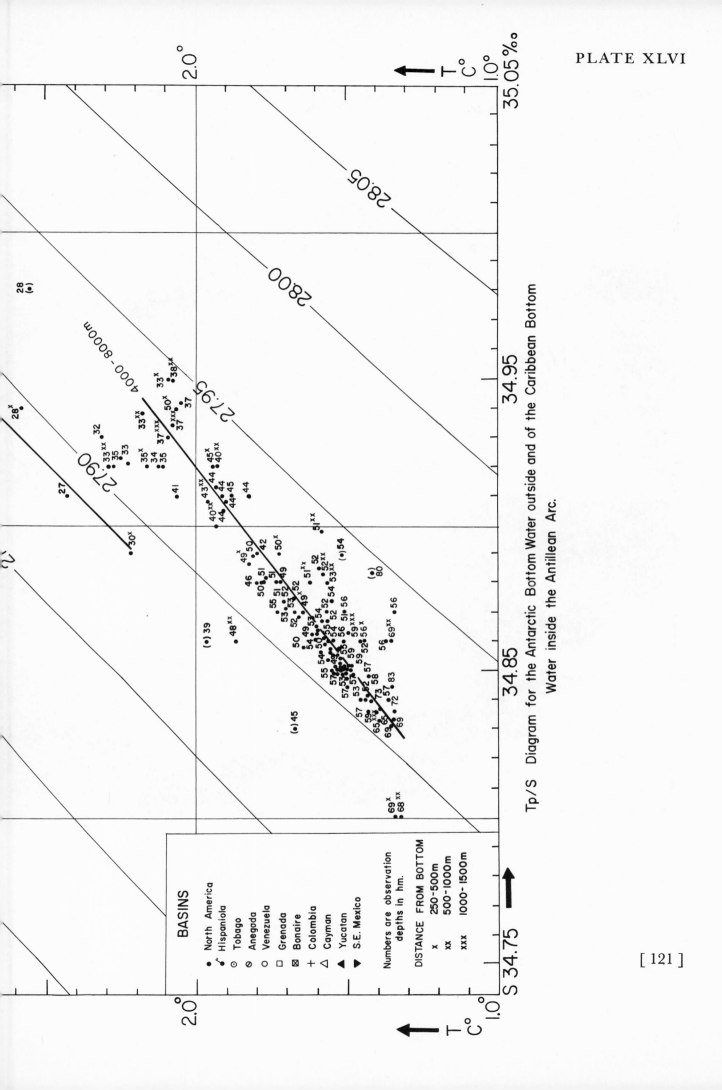

PLATE XLVI

Tp/S Diagram for the Antarctic Bottom Water outside and of the Caribbean Bottom
Water inside the Antillean Arc.

PLATE XLVII

Distribution of Potential Temperature
in the Near Bottom Waters of
the Deep Basins (>2000m)
in the Caribbean-Antillean Region

Contour Lines (generalized) for 1000m.,
2000m., 3000m., 4000m., 6000m.,
8000m., and in special areas 5000m.
and 5500m. given in hectometers

Isotherms of Potential
Bottom Temperature
Auxiliary Isotherms
Axis of Bottom Current
Axis of Advection in
the Bottom Water

< 2000m   < 1.60°

For Explanation of Symbols see Table I

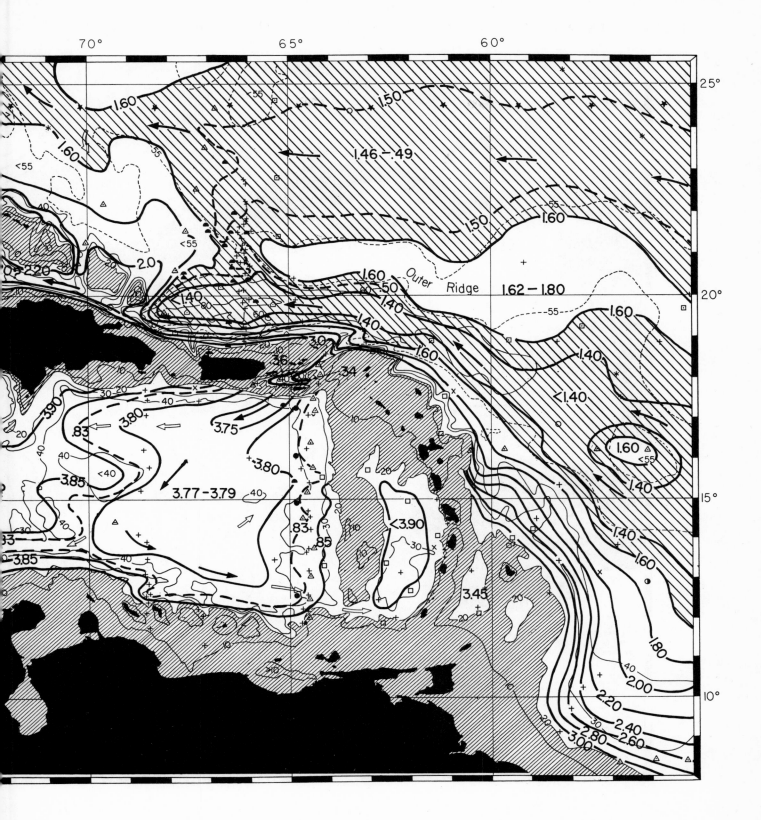

PLATE XLVIII

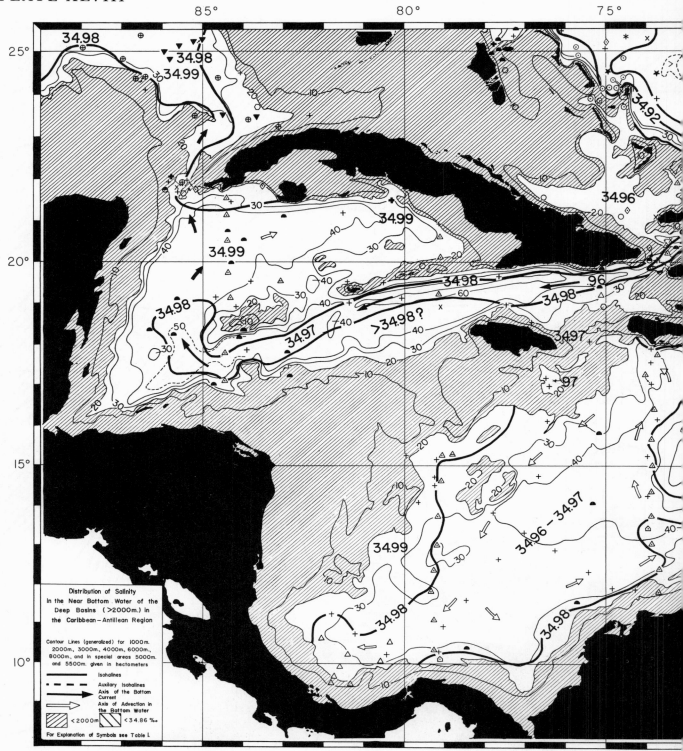

Distribution of Salinity
in the Near Bottom Water of the
Deep Basins (>2000m.) in
the Caribbean — Antillean Region

Contour Lines (generalized) for 1000 m.
2000m., 3000m., 4000m., 6000m.,
8000m., and in special areas 5000m.
and 5500m. given in hectometers

―――――――― Isohalines

– – – – – Auxiliary Isohalines

←――――― Axis of the Bottom
Current

⇨ Axis of Advection in
the Bottom Water

<2000m   <34.86 ‰

For Explanation of Symbols see Table I.

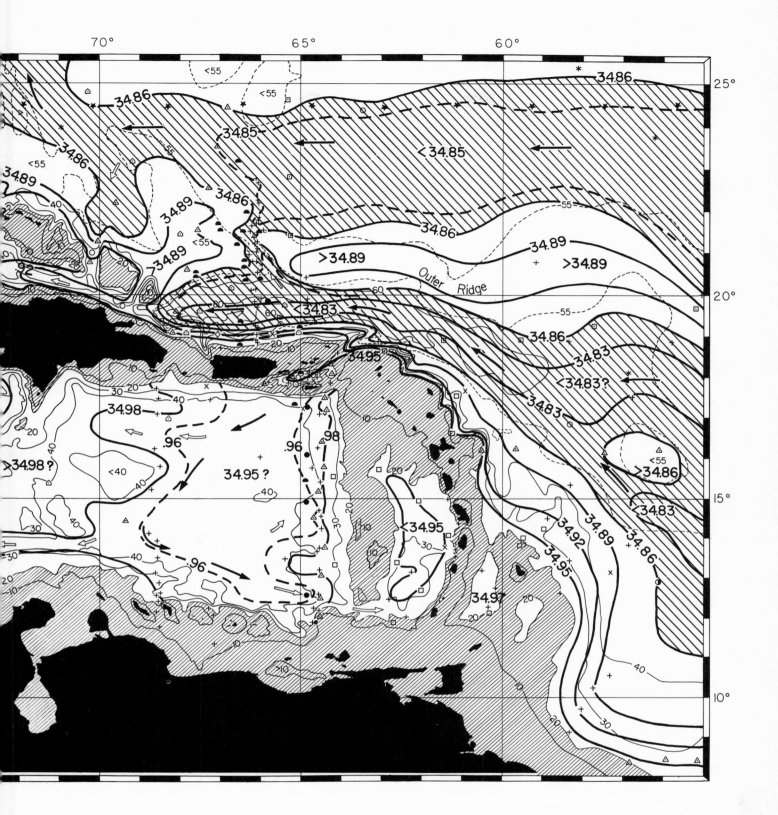

PLATE XLIX

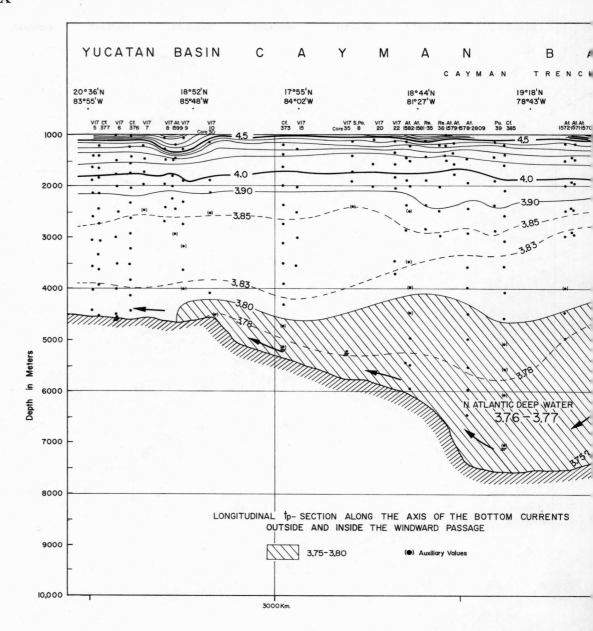

LONGITUDINAL tp- SECTION ALONG THE AXIS OF THE BOTTOM CURRENTS
OUTSIDE AND INSIDE THE WINDWARD PASSAGE

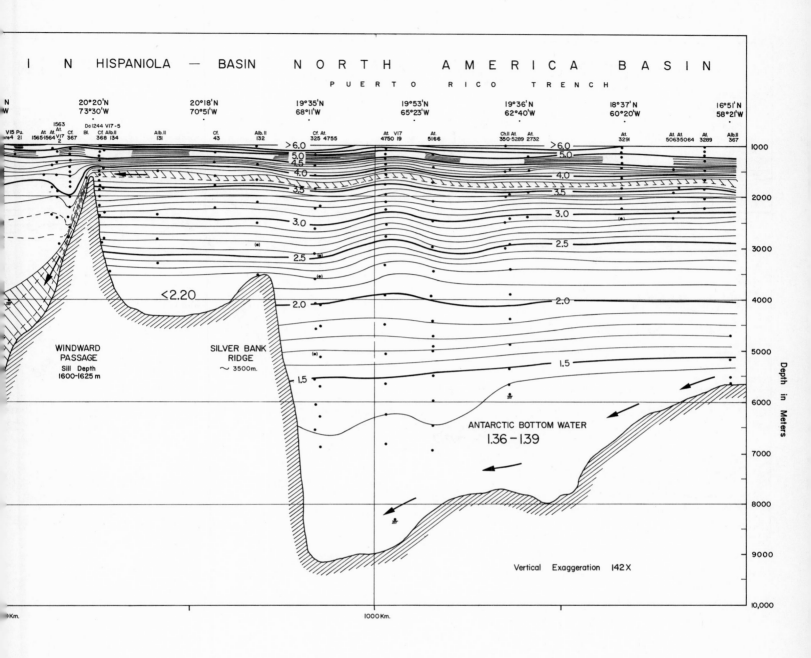

20°20'N
73°30'W

20°18'N
70°51'W

19°35'N
68°11'W

19°53'N
65°23'W

19°36'N
62°40'W

18°37'N
60°20'W

16°51'N
58°21'W

>6.0

5.0
4.5
4.0

3.5

3.0

2.5

2.0

>6.0

5.0

4.0

3.5

3.0

2.5

2.0

1.5

<2.20

WINDWARD
PASSAGE
Sill Depth
1600-1625 m

SILVER BANK
RIDGE
~ 3500m.

1.5

1.5

ANTARCTIC BOTTOM WATER
1.36 – 1.39

Vertical Exaggeration 142 X

Depth in Meters

1000

2000

3000

4000

5000

6000

7000

8000

9000

10,000

1000 Km.

[127]

PLATE L

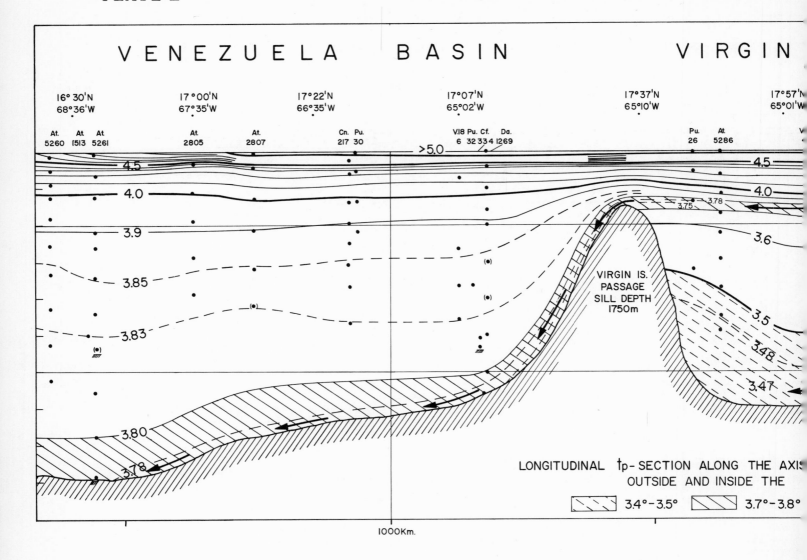

VENEZUELA BASIN   VIRGIN

LONGITUDINAL †p-SECTION ALONG THE AXIS
OUTSIDE AND INSIDE THE

VIRGIN IS.
PASSAGE
SILL DEPTH
1750m

1000Km.

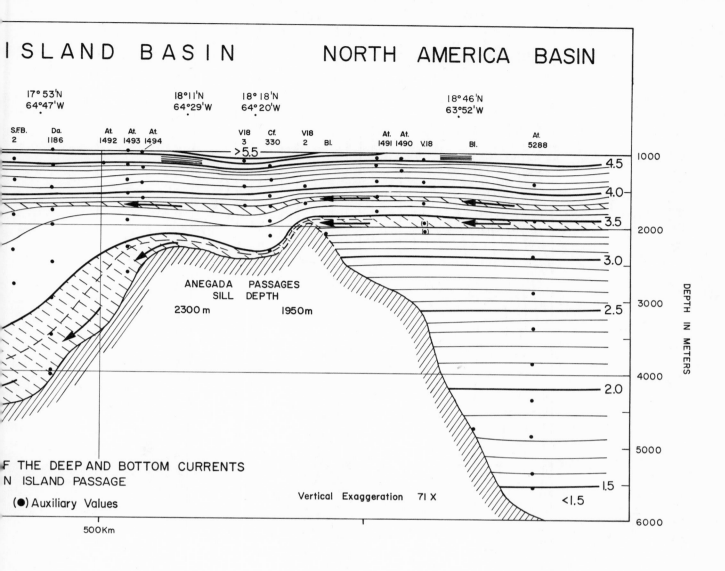

ISLAND BASIN NORTH AMERICA BASIN

17° 53'N
64°47'W

18°11'N
64°29'W

18° 18'N
64°20'W

18° 46'N
63°52'W

S.F.B.
2

Da.
1186

At.
1492

At.
1493

At.
1494

VI8
3

Cf.
330

VI8
2

Bl.

At.
1491

At.
1490

V.18

Bl.

At.
5288

>5.5

4.5

4.0

3.5

3.0

2.5

2.0

1.5

<1.5

1000

2000

3000

4000

5000

6000

DEPTH IN METERS

ANEGADA PASSAGES
SILL DEPTH

2300 m   1950m

F THE DEEP AND BOTTOM CURRENTS

N ISLAND PASSAGE

(●) Auxiliary Values

Vertical Exaggeration 71 X

500Km

PLATE LI

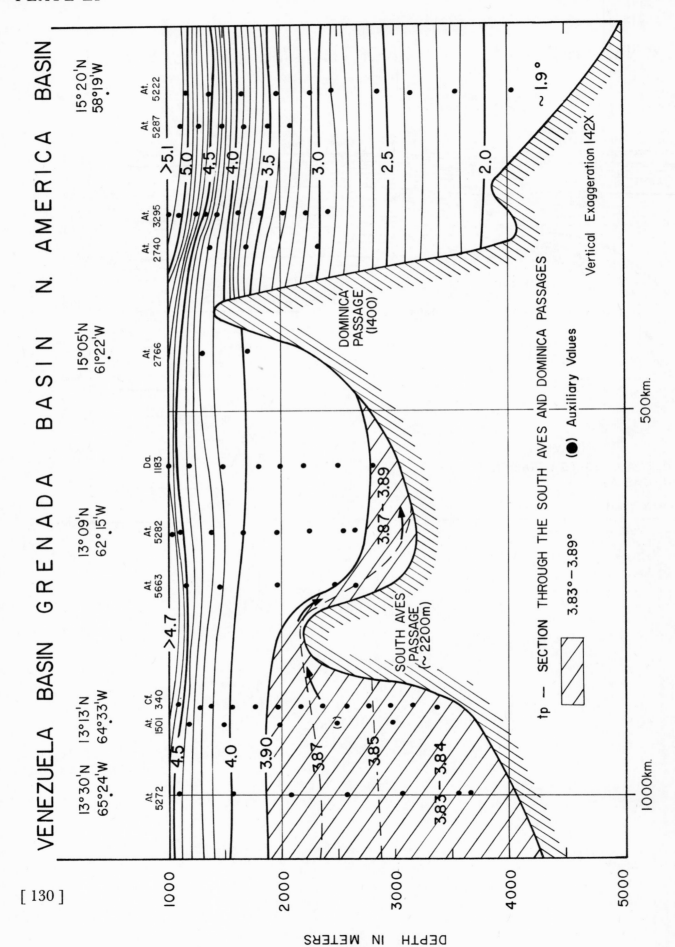

tp — SECTION THROUGH THE SOUTH AVES AND DOMINICA PASSAGES

Appendix. Data Used in the Construction of Core Charts and Sections

TABLES I–VI

I. Vessels Contributing Oceanographic Data from Depths >200 meters

II. Selected Observations in the Core of the Subtropical Underwater (Intermediate Salinity Maximum)

IIIa. Observations in the Core of the Main Oxygen Minimum, 1932–1937

IIIb. Observations in the Core of the Main Oxygen Minimum, 1954–1958

IV. Observations in the Core of the Subantarctic Intermediate Water (Intermediate Salinity Minimum)

V. Observations in the Core of the North Atlantic Deep Water (Intermediate Oxygen Maximum)

VI. The Observations in the Core of the Antarctic Bottom Water and the Caribbean Bottom Water (Potential Temperature and Bottom Salinity)

TABLE I

VESSELS CONTRIBUTING OCEANOGRAPHIC DATA FROM DEPTHS > 200 M

A. Stations in Caribbean-Antillean Basins

NO.	INST-TUTION*	NAME OF VESSEL	NATION	PERIOD OF OBS.	ABBREV. OF VESSEL	SYMBOL OF VESSEL	NUMBER OF STATIONS	TOTAL
1	WHOI	Atlantis	USA	1932-61	At	+	682	
		Crawford	USA	1956-58	Cf	△	90	821
		Caryn	USA	1954-56	Cn	✚	34	
		Albatross III	USA	1948-52	Alb III	○	15	
2	HO	Pursuit	USA	1953	Pu	■	44	
		San Pablo	USA	1950-60	S Pa	○	36	130
		Rehoboth	USA	1950-53	Re	△	31	
		Sheldrake	USA	1952-53	Sh	◇	19	
3	LGO	Vema	USA	1955-61	V	●	75	75
4	BF	Albatross I	USA	1884-86, 1919	Alb I	⊙	58	58
5	SI	Hannibal	USA	1934-36	Ha	△	45	57
		Sp. F. Baird	USA	1960	SFB	●	12	
6	CL	Dana II	Denmark	1921-28	DA	✕	51	51
7	ADM	Challenger II	UK	1933-39	Ch II	□	45	45
8	STPM	Th. Tissier	France	1951	TT	◆	44	44
9	CGS	Blake	USA	1877-83	Bl	◓	20	32
		Explorer	USA	1960	Ex	◉	12	
10	MIAMI	Physalia	USA	1954	Ph	⊘	17	17
11	NIO	Discovery II	UK	1957	Di	✶	13	13
12	CHO	Challenger I	UK	1873	Ch I	⊡	8	8
13	KH	Margrethe	Denmark	1913-14	Ma	◩	7	7
14	CI	Carnegie	USA	1928	Ca	◑	6	6
15	RSS	Albatross II	Sweden	1947-48	Alb II	○	2	2

B. Stations Mainly in Southeastern Gulf of Mexico and Southern Straits of Florida

NO.	INST-TUTION*	NAME OF VESSEL	NATION	PERIOD OF OBS.	ABBREV. OF VESSEL	SYMBOL OF VESSEL	NUMBER OF STATIONS	TOTAL
10	MIAMI	Gerda	USA	1955-60	Ge	▽	115	115
16	TEXAS	Alaska	USA	1951-61	Al	⊕	63	114
		Hidalgo	USA	1958	Hd	◇	30	
		Jakkula	USA	1954-55	Ja	▼	21	
17	FWS	Gill	USA	1952-54	Gi	⊠	53	53
18	YALE	Mable Taylor	USA	1932-33	MT	▲	23	23
4	BF	Bache	USA	1914	Ba	▲	6	6

C. Additional Bottom Observations (outside Antillean Arc)

NO.	INST-TUTION*	NAME OF VESSEL	NATION	PERIOD OF OBS.	ABBREV. OF VESSEL	SYMBOL OF VESSEL	NUMBER OF STATIONS	TOTAL
9	CGS	Lydonia	USA	1922	Ly	∗	--	
		Pioneer	USA	1922	Pi	∗	--	
		Surveyor	USA	1919	Su	∗	--	
--	--	Britannia	UK	1897-1900	Br	∗	--	39
--	--	Goldfinch	UK	1902-1903	Go	∗	--	
--	--	Rambler	UK	1895-1896	Ra	∗	--	
--	--	Anonymous	--	1927	An	∗	--	
5	SI	Guide	USA	1923	Gu	⌂	9	9

Total Number of Vessels	Total Period of Observations	Total Number of Stations
38	1873-1961	1725

1) Woods Hole Oceanographic Institution, Woods Hole, Massachusetts
2) U. S. Navy Hydrographic Office, Washington, D. C.
3) Lamont Geological Observatory, Palisades, New York
4) U. S. Bureau of Fisheries, Washington, D. C.
5) Scripps Institution of Oceanography, La Jolla, California
6) Carlsberg Physiological Laboratory, Copenhagen (J. Schmidt)
7) British Admiralty
8) Institut Scientifique et Technique des Pêches Maritimes, Paris
9) U. S. Coast and Geodetic Survey, Washington, D. C.
10) University of Miami, Miami, Florida
11) National Institute of Oceanography, Wormley, Godalming, Surrey
12) Challenger Office, Edinburgh
13) Komm. f. Havundersgelser, Copenhagen
14) Carnegie Institution of Washington, Washington, D. C.
15) Royal Scientific Society, Göteborg
16) Agricultural and Mechanical College of Texas, College Station, Texas
17) U. S. Fish and Wildlife Service, Washington, D. C.
18) The Bingham Oceanographic Collection, Yale University, New Haven, Connecticut

TABLE II

SELECTED OBSERVATIONS IN THE CORE OF THE SUBTROPICAL UNDERWATER

(Intermediate Salinity Maximum)

North America Basin

SHIP AND STATION NUMBER	LAT. N	LONG. W	DEPTH OF SAL. MAX.	SAL. MAX.	NOTE
At 5060	8° 47'	58° 28'	87	36.81	
At 1202	8° 41'	56° 30'	101	37.05	
Cf 181	8° 25'	55° 10'	90	36.714	
At 5059	9° 08'	58° 20'	86	36.83	
At 5058	9° 41'	58° 00'	88	36.72	
At 5056	10° 31'	57° 20'	92	36.70	
At 5229	11° 29'	60° 49'	99	36.608	
At 2749	11° 41'	60° 31'	97	36.86	
At 2750	11° 28'	60° 31'	71	36.71	
At 5227	12° 17'	60° 21'	99	36.829	
At 5226	12° 45'	60° 07'	83	36.978	
At 5278	12° 36'	58° 34'	96	36.97	
At 3284	12° 55'	58° 17'	133	36.91	
Da II 1179	12° 05'	57° 04'	100	36.81	
At 4142	12° 10.5'	56° 26.1'	121	36.89	
At 2746	13° 11'	60° 31'	95	37.12	
At 2744	13° 47'	60° 28'	100	36.84	
At 2745	13° 30'	60° 28'	85	36.98	
Ch II 1796	13° 40'	60° 26'	100	36.98	
Da II 1182	13° 03'	59° 50'	125	37.00	
At 5275	13° 54'	59° 47'	97	37.01	
Ch II 1797	13° 41'	59° 32'	100	37.03	
Ch II 1798	13° 35'	58° 39'	100	36.94	
At 3280	13° 49'	56° 49'	95	36.95	
At 4143	13° 01'	56° 33.3'	121	37.03	
At 4996	13° 19'	55° 35'	119	36.97	
At 3265	13° 02'	55° 05'	83	36.96	
At 5274	14° 08'	60° 42'	140	37.09	
At 2743	14° 07'	60° 29'	133	36.86	
At 3296A	14° 56'	60° 16'	171	36.80	
Ch II 1800	14° 27'	60° 14'	100	37.01	
Ch II 1799	14° 18'	58° 59'	100	37.10	
Re 59 18	14° 44'	58° 45'	130	37.14	
At 3279	14° 39'	56° 46'	105	37.01	
At 3267	14° 42'	55° 08'	108	36.91	
At 2739	15° 55'	60° 48'	103	37.13	
At 2740	15° 29'	60° 37'	117	37.09	
At 3287	15° 30'	58° 45'	115	37.06	
T T 151	15° 17'	58° 26'	100	37.09	
At 3278	15° 32'	56° 42'	121	37.05	
At 3268	15° 39'	55° 13'	111	37.00	
Ch II 1807	16° 37'	61° 15'	150	37.08	
At 2737	16° 50'	61° 00'	131	37.21	
At 2738	16° 15'	60° 52'	118	37.07	
Cf 309	16° 15'	60° 28'	145	37.048	
Ch II 1806	16° 07'	60° 20'	100	37.06	
At 3294	16° 18'	60° 05'	126	37.00	

SHIP AND STATION NUMBER	LAT. N	LONG. W	SAL. MAX.	SAL. MAX.	NOTE
At 5221	16° 12'	57° 49'	94	37.034	
At 3277	16° 23'	56° 50'	118	37.01	
Cf 305	16° 14'	56° 08'	100	37.059	
At 3269	16° 29'	55° 19'	100	36.99	
At 2736	17° 32'	61° 10'	129	37.11	
Da II 1185	17° 41'	60° 58'	100	37.11	
At 3292	17° 58'	60° 17'	127	37.07	
At 3293	17° 08'	60° 10'	118	37.03	
At 3290	17° 53'	59° 01'	131	37.01	
At 3289	17° 09'	59° 00'	141	37.03	
At 4146	17° 27.9'	57° 48.4'	141	37.00	
At 3276	17° 13'	56° 48'	115	37.03	
Ch II 1668	17° 05'	56° 00'	100	37.10	
At 3270	17° 23'	55° 19'	115	37.03	
At 5264	18° 50'	68° 10'	95	36.95	
At 1518	18° 22'	67° 45'	146	37.00	
At 1517	18° 24'	67° 38'	120	36.97	
Sh 5001	18° 59'	67° 07'	136	36.94	
Sh 7008	18° 39'	67° 07'	150	36.96	
Sh 7009	18° 47'	67° 06'	150	36.96	
Sh 7010	18° 57'	67° 04'	150	36.92	
At 6165	18° 51'	66° 08'	195	36.914	
Gi 3	18° 38'	66° 06'	99	36.96	
Gi 2	18° 36'	66° 06'	100	36.92	
At 4152	18° 41.7'	65° 17.5'	169	36.89	
At 1491	18° 35'	64° 05'	115	36.98	
At 4151	18° 59'	63° 54'	143	36.96	
At 5288	18° 52'	63° 05'	142	37.10	
At 2734	18° 34'	62° 46'	115	37.07	
At 2733	18° 59'	62° 37'	117	37.14	
At 2735	18° 15'	61° 52'	97	37.11	
At 3291	18° 47'	60° 25'	95	36.98	
At 4147	18° 48.8'	58° 47'	136	36.92	
At 5066	18° 53'	58° 22'	174	36.97	
At 3275	18° 11'	56° 46'	115	37.04	
At 5219	18° 50'	55° 49'	157	37.085	
At 3271	18° 17'	55° 19'	127	37.06	
Re 59-12	19° 24'	68° 13'	146	37.00	
S Pa 62-1	19° 33'	67° 55'	135	37.03	
At 5291	19° 52'	66° 35'	175	37.12	
At 6167	19° 44'	66° 07'	145	37.109	
At 5169	19° 02'	66° 05'	95	36.94	
At 4750	19° 56'	66° 01'	149	36.96	
Da II 1261	19° 04'	65° 43'	150	36.91	
Da II 1195	19° 01'	65° 23'	150	37.01	
At 5289	19° 56'	62° 50'	122	37.09	
At 2732	19° 40'	62° 12'	121	37.06	
At 4149	19° 51.1'	60° 47'	130	36.92	
At 4148	19° 29.4'	59° 42.9'	118	36.94	
At 3273	19° 52'	56° 51'	120	37.05	
At 3274	19° 02'	56° 42'	138	37.05	
At 3272	19° 19'	55° 17'	115	37.01	
At 3356	20° 38'	74° 25'	137	36.95	
Da II 1244	20° 23'	73° 24'	200	36.92	
At 4506	20° 52'	71° 00'	170	36.75	
Cf 44	20° 48'	70° 17'	119	36.84	
Cn 218	20° 45'	68° 28'	179	36.90	

SHIP AND STATION NUMBER		LAT. N	LONG. W	DEPTH OF SAL. MAX.	SAL. MAX.	NOTE
Sh	5004	20° 13'	67° 31'	160	37.00	
At	4155	20° 42'	67° 11'	140	36.88	
At	6172	20° 59'	66° 19'	145	36.740	
At	6178	20° 09'	66° 15'	145	36.781	
At	6177	20° 50'	66° 09'	142	36.742	
At	6171	20° 50'	66° 13'	186	36.753	
At	6168	20° 09'	66° 09'	141	36.945	
At	6170	20° 58'	66° 08'	182	36.752	
At	6184	20° 47'	66° 07'	138	36.736	
At	6169	20° 31'	66° 06'	144	36.787	
At	2731	20° 24'	61° 45'	142	37.14	
At	5218	20° 01'	55° 02'	178	37.073	
At	3383	21° 50'	77° 10'	164	36.79	
Alb III 136		21° 33.5'	76° 35'	193	36.77	
Da II 1243		21° 04'	73° 48'	150	36.83	
Pu	43	21° 36'	71° 10'	147	36.83	
Pu	46	21° 34'	71° 06'	147	36.82	
Sh	5006	21° 37'	71° 02'	150	36.82	
Pu	48	21° 33'	71° 00'	184	36.85	
Pu	47	21° 38'	70° 59'	196	36.83	
Cf	45	21° 17'	70° 03.6'	149	37.095	
Cn	219	21° 43'	68° 11'	192	36.90	
At	6173	21° 31'	66° 08'	136	36.777	
At	6176	21° 03'	66° 08'	146	36.745	
At	6183	21° 16'	66° 07'	144	36.758	
At	6186	21° 47'	66° 06'	97	36.706	
At	6185	21° 17'	66° 05'	148	36.742	
At	6163	21° 52'	66° 04'	148	36.752	
At	6174	21° 39'	66° 04'	98	36.833	
At	6175	21° 31'	65° 57'	143	36.751	
At	4751	21° 01'	64° 55'	149	36.97	
At	4749	21° 20'	64° 38'	94	37.00	
At	2730	21° 11'	61° 11'	91	36.96	
At	2729	21° 50'	60° 33'	118	36.98	
Re	59-20	21° 24'	57° 54'	146	37.17	
Cn	215	21° 04'	55° 41'	92	37.26	
Pu	1	22° 16'	73° 52'	100	36.92	
Pu	2	22° 28'	73° 43'	200	36.85	
Pu	4	22° 20'	73° 30'	100	36.89	
Pu	5	22° 20'	73° 18'	150	36.82	
At	4547	22° 27'	72° 02'	156	36.76	
At	4758	22° 42'	71° 51'	197	36.79	
At	4505	22° 21'	69° 50'	200	37.05	
Re	59-11	22° 47'	68° 44'	149	37.02	
At	1210	22° 14'	67° 50'	100	36.82	
Cn	220	22° 43'	67° 47'	98	36.80	
At	4157	22° 58'	67° 44.5'	155	36.74	
At	6188	22° 47'	66° 09'	90	36.729	
At	6162	22° 14'	66° 06'	147	36.727	
At	6161	22° 41'	66° 04'	146	36.734	
Da II 1319		22° 43'	61° 43'	125	36.98	
At	2728	22° 32'	60° 03'	90	36.94	
Cn	214	22° 25'	56° 15'	96	37.19	
At	5164	23° 55'	73° 46'	194	36.75	
At	4546	23° 01'	73° 02'	187	36.78	
Pu	7	23° 20'	72° 59'	197	36.71	
At	4158	23° 05.8'	67° 55'	89	36.89	

North America Basin (continued)

SHIP AND STATION NUMBER		LAT. N	LONG. W	SAL. MAX.	SAL. MAX.	NOTE
Cn	221	23° 40'	67° 38'	131	36.79	
At	1211	23° 10'	67° 34'	84	36.73	
At	6189	23° 19'	66° 08'	98	36.963	
At	2727	23° 17'	59° 31'	140	36.98	
Cn	212	23° 57'	57° 39'	98	37.29	
Cn	213	23° 10'	57° 00'	96	37.15	
Di II	3624	24° 31'	75° 28'	198	36.70	
Pu	12	24° 30'	75° 28'	98	36.87	
Pu	10	24° 34'	74° 44'	98	36.71	
Da II	1242	24° 05'	74° 36'	150	36.78	
Sh	4001	24° 19'	74° 29'	150	36.71	
Sh	7003	24° 34'	74° 25'	188	36.80	
Sh	7007	24° 26'	74° 24'	100	36.73	
Sh	7004	24° 34'	74° 17'	139	36.78	
Sh	7005	24° 30'	74° 14'	142	36.76	
Pu	9	24° 31'	74° 13'	150	36.71	
Sh	4004	24° 44'	74° 08'	195	36.74	
Pu	8	24° 36'	73° 50'	150	36.74	
Di II	3622	24° 30'	73° 47'	195	36.81	
Di II	3621	24° 33'	71° 53'	197	36.73	
Sh	7006	24° 24'	71° 14'	148	36.82	
Di II	3620	24° 29'	70° 10'	199	36.78	
At	4502	24° 47'	69° 01'	96	36.82	
At	4160	24° 53'	68° 48'	126	36.80	
At	4159	24° 05.5'	68° 24.7'	108	36.74	
Cn	222	24° 36'	67° 22'	140	36.80	
Di II	3617	24° 30'	64° 47'	100	36.74	
Di II	3616	24° 27'	62° 57'	194	36.75	
Di II	3615	24° 31'	61° 08'	99	36.77	
Di II	3614	24° 29'	59° 18'	100	36.84	
At	2726	24° 00'	59° 03'	99	37.03	
Cn	211	24° 48'	58° 20'	83	37.03	
Re	59-21	24° 38'	57° 35'	178	37.00	
Di II	3612	24° 31'	55° 41'	100	36.90	
At	5163	25° 28'	76° 05'	152	36.74	
Sh	7002	25° 15'	74° 13'	92	36.74	
Da II	1241	25° 18'	74° 00'	200	36.80	
At	4161	25° 29'	69° 34'	120	36.85	

Colombia and Venezuela Basins

Ha	227	9° 52'	82° 04'	96	36.76	
Ha	233	9° 30'	81° 49'	96	36.62	
Ha	234	9° 40'	81° 44'	97	36.76	
Ha	240	9° 29'	81° 20'	96	36.62	
Ha	239	9° 38'	81° 16'	88	36.69	
Ha	200	9° 42'	80° 32'	129	36.71	
Ha	199	9° 34'	80° 28'	98	36.71	
Ha	197	9° 55'	80° 09'	100	36.73	
At	1949	9° 48'	80° 04'	(99)	36.71	
Ha	202	9° 37'	80° 01'	100	36.69	
At	1948	9° 39'	79° 54'	97	36.65	
Cf	399	9° 51'	79° 17'	100	36.736	
Cf	400	9° 45'	79° 16'	100	36.688	
Ha	225	10° 26'	81° 44'	82	36.73	
Ha	201	10° 01'	80° 38'	94	36.73	
Ha	205	10° 32'	80° 24'	96	36.73	

SHIP AND STATION NUMBER	LAT. N	LONG. W	DEPTH OF SAL. MAX.	SAL. MAX.	NOTE
At 1946	10° 19'	79° 17'	94	36.71	
At 5746	10° 10'	76° 40'	99	36.758	
At 5689	10° 46'	67° 16'	50	36.654	
At 5596	10° 52'	66° 00'	120	36.677	6)
At 5597A	10° 48'	65° 52'	100	36.741	1)
At 5598	10° 44'	65° 52'	100	36.79	1)
At 5231	10° 40'	65° 36'	90	36.67	1)
At 5686	10° 38'	65° 36'	50	36.666	1)
At 5600	10° 28'	65° 34'	99	36.65	1)
At 5685	10° 23'	65° 34'	80	36.707	1), 6)
At 5602	10° 52'	65° 33'	73	36.74	1)
At 5601	10° 37'	65° 32'	100	36.65	1)
At 5605	10° 38'	65° 08'	91	36.708	1)
At 5684	10° 41'	64° 40'	50	36.712	1)
At 5607	10° 32'	64° 40'	100	36.703	1)
At 5606	10° 32'	64° 40'	95	36.645	1)
At 1953	11° 48'	82° 28'	115	36.67	
At 1952	11° 15'	81° 50'	100	36.76	
Cf 397	11° 03'	79° 18'	95	36.741	
At 1944	11° 38'	78° 30'	87	36.73	
Da II 3547	11° 00'	77° 40'	50	36.79	
At 5745	11° 04'	75° 29'	91	36.749	
At 5744	11° 00'	75° 26'	92	36.700	
At 5740	11° 51'	74° 54'	95	36.750	
At 5741	11° 10'	74° 50'	94	36.767	
At 5739	11° 31'	74° 47'	88	36.741	
At 5737	11° 38'	74° 07'	100	36.765	
At 5736	11° 24'	74° 06'	92	36.730	
Cf 355	11° 51'	73° 46'	90	36.729	
At 5697	11° 26'	68° 30'	50	36.749	
At 5691	11° 28'	67° 13'	97	36.691	
At 2796	11° 42'	67° 11'	76	36.72	
At 2795	11° 21'	67° 08'	50	36.74	
At 2794	11° 00'	67° 05'	42	36.71	
At 5688	11° 16'	65° 41'	50	36.698	
At 5266	11° 18'	65° 39'	75	36.71	
Cf 346	11° 18'	64° 32'	65	36.731	
Cf 345	11° 34'	64° 31'	95	36.729	
At 5662	11° 52'	62° 44'	99	36.646	
At 2754	11° 44'	62° 13'	84	36.88	
At 1954	12° 04'	82° 41'	98	36.62	
Ex 0023	12° 00'	81° 00'	100	36.78	
At 1533	12° 53'	76° 18'	100	36.69	
V 12 53	12° 08.5'	75° 01'	72	36.751	
V 12 57	12° 27'	74° 29'	91	36.81	
Cf 356	12° 26'	73° 45'	95	36.757	
At 5734	12° 40'	71° 42'	100	36.717	
At 5234	12° 10'	68° 35'	98	36.721	
At 5694	12° 33'	68° 30'	89	36.787	
At 5695	12° 10'	68° 29'	95	36.718	
At 5693	12° 17'	67° 16'	100	36.682	
At 2797	12° 07'	67° 10'	56	36.79	
S F B 13	12° 32'	64° 50'	98	36.726	
At 2791	12° 13'	64° 40'	47	36.74	
Ch II 1786	12° 22'	64° 35'	100	36.80	
At 1502	12° 38'	64° 34'	50	36.71?	
At 1503	12° 12'	64° 34'	50	36.78	

SHIP AND STATION NUMBER	LAT. N	LONG. W	DEPTH OF SAL. MAX.	SAL. MAX.	NOTE
At 5663	12° 29'	62° 49'	100	36.703	
At 2755	12° 00'	62° 23'	100	36.77	
At 2756	12° 24'	61° 48'	93	36.78	
At 1958	13° 27'	81° 50'	135	36.68	
Ex 24	13° 37'	81° 37'	148	36.68	
At 1959	13° 17'	81° 30'	141	36.65	
At 1960	13° 19'	81° 12'	145	36.67	
At 1961	13° 28'	80° 54'	145	36.74	
At 1962	13° 34'	80° 30'	146	36.74	
At 1963	13° 35'	80° 08'	150	36.71	
At 1964	13° 42'	80° 00'	150	36.73	
At 1535	13° 47'	77° 48'	100	36.74	
At 1534	13° 20'	77° 03'	97	36.83	
At 1527	13° 15'	73° 58'	150	36.87	
Alb III 128	13° 40'	71° 28'	123	36.81	
Da II 3546	13° 11'	70° 26'	100	36.72	
V 12 52	13° 38'	68° 45'	130	36.964	
At 1509	13° 58'	68° 36'	145	36.83	
At 1508	13° 30'	68° 34'	49	36.83	
At 2799	13° 09'	67° 16'	83	36.82	
At 2789	13° 12'	64° 36'	147	36.83	
At 1500	13° 48'	64° 35'	123	37.00?	
At 2788	13° 42'	64° 35'	88	36.99	
At 2758	13° 25'	61° 12'	105	36.92	
At 2759	13° 35'	61° 09'	83	36.91	
At 1965	14° 09'	79° 40'	143	36.78	
At 1537	14° 36'	79° 14'	148	(36.67)	2)
S Pa 6	14° 05'	78° 00'	97	36.78	
At 1941	14° 46'	76° 47'	130	36.76	
S Pa 26	14° 54'	73° 47'	159	36.87	
S Pa 5	14° 19'	73° 44'	143	36.74	
Re 63-4	14° 13'	72° 19'	128	36.74	
S Pa 4	14° 25'	70° 52'	150	36.73	
Re 63-3	14° 26'	69° 21'	100	36.89	
At 1510	14° 54'	68° 33'	150	36.71	
S Pa 62-3	14° 37'	68° 03'	112	36.96	
At 2802	14° 46'	67° 13'	144	36.74	
At 2801	14° 10'	67° 13'	100	36.83	
At 2786	14° 43'	64° 33'	140	36.95	
At 2787	14° 15'	64° 30'	109	37.01	
At 5273	14° 14'	63° 24.8'	146	36.94	
Ch II 1794	14° 11'	63° 02'	100	36.97	
At 5283	14° 13'	62° 55'	146	36.98	
T T 197	14° 53'	62° 43'	100	37.16	
T T 199	14° 42'	62° 00'	100	37.00	
At 2765	14° 58'	61° 20'	127	37.07	
At 2764	14° 50'	61° 18'	125	37.07	
T T 159	14° 48'	61° 15.5'	100	37.07	
T T 204	14° 18'	61° 11'	100	36.92	
At 2763	14° 22'	61° 04'	109	36.98	
Ch II 1758	14° 20'	60° 52'	100	36.91	
At 1539	15° 35'	80° 38'	191	36.65	
At 1538	15° 12'	79° 54'	193	36.71	
At 1967	15° 08'	79° 16'	200	36.72	
Cf 391	15° 11'	79° 13'	170	36.727	
Ha 193	15° 00'	79° 00'	141	36.74	
At 1968	15° 27'	78° 55'	184	36.77	

SHIP AND STATION NUMBER	LAT. N	LONG. W	DEPTH OF SAL. MAX.	SAL. MAX.	NOTE
At 1940	15° 20'	76° 40'	150	36.75	
At 1525	15° 11'	74° 01'	145	36.78	
Cf 361	15° 38'	73° 56'	160	36.871	
At 1511	15° 47'	68° 30'	150	36.87	
At 2803	15° 18'	67° 11'	99	36.79	
At 3297E	15° 36'	66° 21'	121	36.85	
Re 59-15	15° 15'	65° 31'	103	36.96	
At 2784	15° 48'	64° 42'	109	37.07	
At 2785	15° 09'	64° 30'	108	37.05	
T T 196	15° 11'	63° 33'	100	37.05	
T T 193	15° 18.5'	62° 40'	100	37.00	
T T 192	15° 04'	62° 00'	100	37.13	
At 2769	15° 54'	61° 45'	86	37.10	
At 2768	15° 38'	61° 36'	94	37.12	
T T 164	15° 37'	61° 35'	100	37.07	
At 2767	15° 10'	61° 24'	98	37.06	
At 2766	15° 05'	61° 22'	115	37.11	
Ch II 1763	15° 04'	61° 16'	150	37.02	
At 1971	16° 28'	78° 25'	185	36.78	
At 1972	16° 41'	78° 14'	194	36.76	
Ha 146	16° 10'	76° 41'	170	36.80	
At 1939	16° 10'	76° 28'	181	36.76	
Cf 362	16° 26'	73° 57'	205	36.717	
At 1524	16° 09'	73° 55'	165	36.74	
At 5260	16° 14'	68° 38'	136	36.761	
At 1512	16° 42'	68° 36'	144	36.71	
S Pa 62-2	16° 18'	68° 04'	149	36.96	
At 2806	16° 58'	67° 20'	143	36.96	
At 2805	16° 28'	67° 11'	146	36.96	
At 2782	16° 44'	64° 34'	153	36.98	
At 1497	16° 17'	64° 33'	192	36.92	
At 2783	16° 14'	64° 30'	101	37.08	
At 2774	16° 52'	62° 25'	128	37.07	
At 2773	16° 36'	62° 10'	138	37.09	
At 2772	16° 31'	62° 06'	139	37.10	
At 2771	16° 23'	62° 00'	137	37.07	
At 2770	16° 17'	61° 55'	137	37.09	
At 1973	17° 12'	77° 49'	190	36.71	
At 1974	17° 23'	77° 39'	194	36.74	
At 1975	17° 33'	77° 36'	188	36.67	
At 1935	17° 45'	76° 40'	181	36.74	
At 1936	17° 28'	76° 40'	189	36.75	
At 1937	17° 12'	76° 33'	200	36.71	
At 1556	17° 55'	76° 05'	198	36.73	
Hd 58-4-26	17° 58.6'	76° 03.6'	161	36.73	
Ha 6	17° 43'	76° 00'	177	36.74	
At 1557	17° 59'	75° 54'	188	36.73	
S F B 14	17° 05'	74° 28'	175	36.786	
Cf 363	17° 04'	73° 55'	195	36.735	
At 1521	17° 56'	73° 54'	150	36.71	
Da II 1247	17° 57'	72° 51'	150	36.76	
At 1514	17° 43'	68° 36'	191	36.75	
At 5262	17° 45'	68° 35'	131	36.622	
At 5261	17° 05'	68° 35'	129	36.834	
At 1513	17° 27'	68° 33'	150	36.92	
At 1515	17° 57'	68° 28'	191	36.83	
Da II 1251	17° 48'	67° 22'	150	36.92	

Colombia and Venezuela Basins (continued)

SHIP AND STATION NUMBER	LAT. N	LONG. W	DEPTH OF SAL. MAX.	SAL. MAX.	NOTE
At 2808	17° 51'	67° 10'	123	36.95	
Pu 30	17° 26'	66° 08'	177	36.96	
Re 2	17° 36'	65° 58'	150	37.01	
Pu 24	17° 51'	65° 57'	149	36.96	
Pu 29	17° 38'	65° 57'	149	36.96	
At 5285	17° 54'	65° 51.5'	141	37.01	
Pu 28	17° 38'	65° 41'	134	37.03	
Pu 26	17° 51'	65° 26'	133	37.14	
Pu 27	17° 38'	65° 26'	150	37.05	
Pu 32	17° 26'	65° 26'	143	37.03	
At 5286	17° 54'	65° 20'	133	37.18	
Ch II 1813	17° 13'	65° 12'	150	36.97	
Da II 1269	17° 13'	64° 58'	150	36.96	
Da II 1290	17° 45'	64° 56'	150	37.00	
Ma 4	17° 43'	64° 56'	150	36.94	
Da II 1259	17° 43'	64° 56'	100	36.98	
Da II 1308	17° 43'	64° 55'	125	37.07	
Da II 1309	17° 43'	64° 55'	125	37.05	
Da II 1311	17° 43'	64° 55'	125	37.05	
Da II 1312	17° 43'	64° 55'	125	37.03	
Da II 1296	17° 43'	64° 55'	150	37.00	
Da II 1299	17° 43'	64° 55'	125	37.01	
Da II 1298	17° 43'	64° 55'	150	37.01	
Da II 1189	17° 58'	64° 41'	150	36.99	
Da II 1186	17° 58'	64° 41'	150	36.96	
At 2781	17° 10'	64° 33'	158	36.92	
At 1495	17° 40'	64° 30'	140	36.92	
At 5287	17° 54.5"	64° 16'	136	37.00	
At 2779	17° 43'	64° 14'	118	37.05	
At 2778	17° 45'	63° 57'	137	36.96	
At 2777	17° 48'	63° 41'	111	36.92	
At 2776	17° 45'	63° 25'	126	36.96	
At 2775	17° 30'	63° 07'	131	36.95	
Hd 58-4-27	18° 04.9'	75° 36.7'	169	36.81	
At 3298G	18° 10.5'	75° 06.5'	170	36.80	
Pu 21	18° 54'	75° 05'	150	36.89	
At 1561	18° 25'	74° 43'	150	36.71	
Hd 58-4-29	18° 15.1'	74° 37.2'	129	36.79	
Cf 366	18° 00'	73° 52'	150	36.735	
At 5263	18° 14'	68° 19'	121	36.749	
Pu 22	18° 03'	65° 26'	143	37.00	
Re 75-17	18° 00'	65° 24'	150	36.92	
At 1492	18° 09'	64° 44'	139	36.92	
At 1493	18° 01'	64° 36'	138	36.94	

Cayman and Yucatan Basins

SHIP AND STATION NUMBER	LAT. N	LONG. W	DEPTH OF SAL. MAX.	SAL. MAX.	NOTE
Cf 370	16° 08'	84° 23'	115	36.695	
At 1590	16° 32'	83° 54'	145	36.60	
At 1589	16° 16'	83° 52'	145	36.58	
Ex 26	16° 46'	83° 01'	149	36.67	
At 1586	16° 39'	81° 44'	150	36.55	
At 1585	16° 46'	81° 29'	145	36.56	
At 1542	16° 14'	81° 12'	142	36.58	
V 17 11	17° 51'	86° 57'	136	36.668	
V 17 14	17° 13'	84° 24'	179	36.694	
Ph 89	17° 14'	83° 50'	124	36.89	

SHIP AND STATION NUMBER	LAT. N	LONG. W	DEPTH OF SAL. MAX.	SAL. MAX.	NOTE
Ph 84	17° 39'	83° 12'	135	36.84	
V 17 17	17° 13'	82° 50'	135	36.798	
V 17 18	17° 48'	82° 49'	141	36.721	
At 1583	17° 50'	81° 28'	200	36.62	
Re 63-7	17° 13'	81° 05'	194	36.85	
At 1548	17° 08'	79° 30'	197	36.64	
Cf 388	17° 06'	79° 10'	135	36.657	
At 1551	17° 31'	78° 36'	198	36.67	
At 1552	17° 37'	78° 26'	197	36.65	
At 1553	17° 43'	78° 14'	191	36.67	
At 1554	17° 47'	78° 02'	197	36.64	
At 1555	17° 52'	77° 55'	199	36.71	
V 17 10	18° 22'	86° 21'	143	36.692	
V 17 12	18° 13'	85° 46'	154	36.690	
Cf 374	18° 27'	84° 31'	130	36.717	
V 17 15	18° 01'	84° 10'	150	36.768	
V 17 16	18° 22'	84° 00'	145	36.780	
S Pa 62-8	18° 31'	82° 57'	195	36.74	
Ph 79	18° 04'	82° 41'	145	36.76	
Ph 74	18° 34'	82° 04'	190	36.67	
At 1582	18° 21'	81° 25'	193	36.65	
Pu 35	18° 40'	80° 54'	183	36.76	
Pu 38	18° 42'	79° 52'	190	36.78	
Pu 40	18° 24'	79° 15'	188	36.76	
Da II 1217	18° 50'	79° 07'	150	36.74	
Pu 41	18° 56'	78° 49'	167	36.80	
Pu 42	18° 32'	78° 13'	195	36.76	
At 1568	18° 45'	77° 30'	199	36.76	
At 1569	18° 58'	77° 29'	180	36.71	
At 5070	18° 31'	76° 51'	197	36.78	
At 3298Y	18° 19'	75° 08'	192	36.80	
Pu 21	18° 54'	75° 05'	150	36.89	
Cn 231	18° 34'	73° 05'	194	36.80	
Cn 230	18° 34'	72° 56'	197	36.82	
At 1602	19° 44'	87° 21'	150	36.57	
At 1601	19° 37'	86° 55'	150	36.56	
At 1600	19° 33'	86° 24'	198	36.58	
Ex 28	19° 29'	85° 43'	150	36.72	
V 17 9	19° 06'	85° 41'	140	36.675	
At 1599	19° 18'	85° 40'	195	36.67	
V 17 8	19° 25'	85° 13'	198	36.755	
V 17 7	19° 40'	84° 53'	200	36.748	
At 1598	19° 07'	84° 47'	145	36.55	
Cf 376	19° 47'	84° 31'	190	36.668	
Cf 375	19° 06'	84° 30'	200	36.688	
At 1992	19° 32'	83° 50'	131	36.76	
At 1991	19° 05'	83° 50'	171	36.73	
Re 63-8	19° 30'	83° 10'	212	36.76	
At 1990	19° 03'	83° 00'	183	36.77	
Pu 33	19° 04'	81° 29'	175	36.78	
At 1986	19° 49'	81° 26'	159	36.71	
Ph 68	19° 11'	81° 26'	150	36.74	
At 1987	19° 30'	81° 23'	194	36.73	
At 1579	19° 24'	80° 52'	199	36.65	
At 1578	19° 30'	80° 31'	195	36.64	
At 1577	19° 36'	80° 11'	150	36.71	
At 1977	19° 49'	79° 46'	149	36.73	

SHIP AND STATION NUMBER	LAT. N	LONG. W	DEPTH OF SAL. MAX.	SAL. MAX.	NOTE
At 1576	19° 45'	79° 39'	150	36.67	
S Pa 74-18	19° 58'	79° 34'	227	36.76	
Pu 39	19° 20'	79° 25'	188	36.78	
Cf 384	19° 48'	79° 11'	185	36.826	
Cf 385	19° 16'	79° 11'	200	36.772	
At 1575	19° 48'	79° 00'	150	36.71	
At 1574	19° 49'	78° 25'	146	36.69	
At 1573	19° 45'	77° 44'	194	36.69	
At 3354	19° 38'	77° 42'	192	36.82	
At 1572	19° 38'	77° 42'	198	36.69	
At 1571	19° 27'	77° 35'	200	36.71	
At 1570	19° 16'	77° 28'	182	36.71	
At 5071	19° 05'	76° 38'	189	36.71	
At 5072	19° 31'	76° 26'	155	36.78	
At 5073	19° 51'	76° 21'	147	36.75	
Pu 20	19° 22'	75° 37'	150	36.78	
Ha 5	19° 12'	75° 12'	170	36.83	
Pu 19	19° 51'	75° 10'	150	36.85	
At 3299J	19° 41'	74° 08'	154	36.85	
At 1565	19° 57'	74° 05'	208	36.82	
At 1564	19° 55'	73° 52'	201	36.76	
V 17 2	19° 57'	73° 49'	148	36.789	
At 1563	19° 52'	73° 41'	168	36.80	
At 3301	19° 58'	73° 40'	167	36.87	
Hd 58-4-30	19° 52.5'	73° 28.2'	172	36.77	
At 3300A C	19° 31'	73° 26'	145	36.86	
At 3300G	19° 31'	73° 26'	169	36.87	
Ex 29	20° 48'	86° 21'	196	36.60	
Cf 377	20° 28'	84° 30'	200	36.772	
V 17 6	20° 01'	84° 21'	200	36.768	
S Pa 62-9	20° 42'	84° 16'	197	36.73	
V 17 5	20° 31'	84° 03'	210	36.755	
At 1993	20° 12'	83° 57'	194	36.76	
Ph 58	20° 49'	81° 43'	148	36.82	
Ph 62	20° 07'	81° 38'	150	36.83	
At 1984	20° 52'	81° 25'	191	36.75	
At 1985	20° 19'	81° 19'	200	36.73	
Pu 16	20° 54'	80° 56'	200	36.73	
Pu 17	20° 27'	80° 08'	150	36.80	
Pu 14	20° 58'	79° 58'	150	36.82	
At 1978	20° 02'	79° 37'	148	36.71	
At 1979	20° 18'	79° 27'	146	36.73	
At 1980	20° 35'	79° 19'	136	36.76	
At 1981	20° 53'	79° 11'	131	36.73	
Cf 383	20° 06'	79° 10'	190	36.764	
Cf 382	20° 35'	79° 10'	190	36.822	
Cf 381	20° 56'	79° 09'	160	36.850	
Pu 18	20° 00'	79° 09'	150	36.76	
At 1566	20° 03'	74° 12'	159	36.74	
Hd 58-4-32	20° 04.8'	73° 53.6'	149	36.74	
Alb III 130	20° 00'	73° 40'	186	36.74	
Cf 367	20° 04'	73° 39'	195	36.766	
Cf 378	21° 06'	84° 29'	195	36.773	
At 1996	21° 38'	84° 28'	150	36.69	
Cf 379	21° 36'	84° 28'	195	36.742	
At 1995	21° 27'	84° 22'	183	36.71	
Hd 58-4-16	21° 46.7'	83° 28.4'	196	36.73	

Cayman and Yucatan Basins (continued)

SHIP AND STATION NUMBER	LAT. N	LONG. W	DEPTH OF SAL. MAX.	SAL. MAX.	NOTE
Hd 58-4-15	21° 50.6'	83° 27.1'	194	36.66	
Hd 58-4-14	21° 52'	83° 24.9'	194	36.72	
V 17 3	21° 13'	83° 00'	187	36.735	
Hd 58-4-19	21° 26.3'	82° 49.6'	197	36.77	
Hd 58-4-18	21° 25.4'	82° 49.6'	147	36.77	
Hd 58-4-21	21° 31.3'	81° 56.4'	195	36.74	
Hd 58-4-20	21° 34.4'	81° 56.3'	200	36.78	
At 1982	21° 32'	81° 35'	132	36.69	
Hd 58-4-24	21° 43.9'	81° 02'	199	36.71	
Hd 58-4-23	21° 47.5'	80° 57.7'	173	36.79	
Hd 58-4-22	21° 45.8'	80° 54.3'	184	36.75	
Pu 15	21° 24'	80° 40'	192	36.73	
Cn 238	21° 29'	80° 20'	194	36.795	

Addendum of 1962

Ge 119	20° 23'	85° 19'	158	36.749	

Gulf of Mexico and Straits of Florida

At 2336	21° 41'	86° 22'	141	36.66	
Da II 1220	21° 34'	86° 19'	150	36.65	
Ja 55-3-10	21° 30'	86° 18'	90	36.65	
At 1605	21° 40'	86° 15'	146	36.60	
Ex 40	21° 37'	86° 14'	157	36.53	
Cn 245	21° 38'	86° 06'	160	36.666	
At 2000	21° 41'	86° 05'	145	36.70	
Ex 39	21° 45'	85° 57'	172	36.73	
At 2335	21° 42'	85° 57'	173	36.70	
Hd 58-4-10	21° 42'	85° 55'	150	36.70	
Ja 55-3- 8	21° 38'	85° 47.4'	191	36.77	
Cn 243	21° 45'	85° 46'	144	36.737	
M T 603	21° 47'	85° 42'	130	36.73	
Da II 1221	21° 49'	85° 41'	200	36.73	
Ex 38	21° 43'	85° 39'	191	36.75	
Cn 242	21° 48'	85° 35'	199	36.74	
Ja 55-3- 7	21° 43'	85° 32'	190	36.73	
Cn 240	21° 47'	85° 14'	193	36.755	
Al 360-18	21° 52'	85° 03'	200	36.74	
Da II 1222	21° 53'	85° 02'	200	36.69	
Hd 58-4-12	21° 51.5'	85° 01.3'	232	36.69	
Cn 239	21° 51'	85° 01'	167	36.763	
At 1997	21° 51'	85° 00'	150	36.69	
At 1610	21° 51'	85° 00'	183	36.64	
Al 1-15	22° 30'	85° 25'	142	36.71	
Al 362-17	22° 32'	84° 57'	149	36.80	
Ex 35	22° 33'	84° 56'	190	36.75	
Al 360-19	22° 16'	84° 54'	187	36.82	
Al 360-20	22° 53'	84° 42'	141	36.74	
Al 362-16	22° 33'	84° 28'	195	36.77	
Ph 23	22° 56'	84° 15'	180	36.78	
Ph 20	22° 48'	84° 02'	205	36.67	
Ge 511-12	22° 45'	78° 50'	200	36.78	
Ge 511-13	22° 50'	78° 47'	200	36.90	
Ge 511-14	22° 55'	78° 43'	150	36.97	
Pu 4	22° 20'	73° 30'	100	36.89	
Pu 5	22° 20'	73° 18'	150	36.82	
At 2339	23° 57'	86° 58'	138	36.73	

SHIP AND STATION NUMBER	LAT. N	LONG. W	DEPTH OF SAL. MAX.	SAL. MAX.	NOTE
Al 360-35	23° 30'	85° 59'	152	36.74	
Al 360-34	23° 28'	85° 17'	198	36.80	
Al 362-15/18	23° 00'	84° 57'	183	36.80	3)
Ph 25	23° 09'	84° 34'	188	36.83	
Al 360-21/33	23° 32'	84° 32'	198	36.75	
Ja 54-10-30	23° 55'	84° 15.4'	160	36.78	
Ph 29	23° 40'	84° 09'	178	36.78	
Ja 54-10-10	23° 33.5'	84° 05'	117	36.76	
Al 360-32	23° 24'	83° 55'	148	36.69	
Re 63-9	23° 35'	83° 54'	131	36.72	
Da II 1224	23° 25'	83° 43'	200	36.69	
Hd 58-4-86	23° 40'	82° 52'	192	36.70	
Ja 55-3-4	23° 15'	82° 52'	176	36.71	
At 2436	23° 55'	82° 42'	97	36.38	
At 2437	23° 34'	82° 36'	98	36.74	
Ph 12	23° 41'	82° 32'	147	36.67	
Ph 10	23° 49'	82° 31'	157	36.67	
At 2438	23° 12'	82° 31'	170	36.65	
At 2343	23° 15'	82° 30'	188	36.67	
Hd 58-4-85	23° 15.7'	82° 29.5'	171	36.67	
Ph 16	23° 18'	82° 29'	182	36.76	
At 2004	23° 30.5'	82° 20'	148	36.67	
At 3006	23° 14'	82° 19'	188	36.74	
At 2005	23° 47.5'	82° 17'	143	36.67	
Da II 1228	23° 35'	81° 54'	200	36.69	
Ge 392	23° 42'	81° 42'	145	36.66	
Ge 5827-4	23° 52.5'	81° 40.0'	147	36.75	
Ge 5810-12	23° 49.8'	81° 39'	197	36.74	
Ge 453	23° 26'	81° 39'	191	36.713	
Ge 80	23° 13'	81° 36'	193	36.70	
Ge 5827-6	23° 35.0'	81° 35.5'	143	36.78	
M T 302	23° 39'	80° 51'	150	36.73	
Ge 455	23° 23'	80° 48'	191	36.799	
M T 301	23° 45'	80° 40'	150	36.72	
At 3453	23° 24'	80° 30'	186	36.78	
Ge 511-9	23° 31'	80° 23'	150	36.74	
Ge 511-11	23° 15'	80° 20'	178	36.89	
Ge 511-17	23° 30'	79° 10'	100	36.90	
Gi 477-1	23° 46'	76° 57'	142	36.94	4)
Cn 257	23° 41'	76° 52'	148	36.937	4)
Cn 258	23° 39'	76° 38'	150	36.91	4)
At 2425	24° 31'	88° 05'	118	36.44	
At 2340	24° 11'	86° 25'	199	36.71	
Ja 54-10-37	24° 57'	85° 52'	198	36.75	
Al 1-31	24° 22'	85° 31'	200	36.74	
Al 362-21	24° 56'	85° 09'	178	36.58	
At 2351	24° 20'	84° 57'	202	36.69	
At 2342	24° 15'	84° 55'	209	36.65	
Ja 54-10-29	24° 37'	84° 43.6'	120	36.62	
Al 443-22	24° 37'	84° 32'	189	36.69	
Ex 32	24° 40'	84° 31'	148	36.70	
At 2350	24° 26'	84° 06'	123	36.36	
Al 360-23	24° 38'	83° 51'	137	36.44	
Da II 1226	24° 16'	82° 47'	125	36.53	
At 2346	24° 11'	82° 43'	80	36.37	
At 2006	24° 05'	82° 14'	141	36.49	
At 3010	24° 01.5'	82° 12'	100	(36.36)	

SHIP AND STATION NUMBER	LAT. N	LONG. W	DEPTH OF SAL. MAX.	SAL. MAX.	NOTE
At 2008	24° 24'	82° 10.5'	75	36.23	
S Pa 13	24° 19'	82° 04'	105	36.36	5)
At 3011	24° 12.5'	82° 03.5'	50	36.36	
Ge 6019-450	24° 08'	81° 48'	71	36.642	
Ge 5827- 2	24° 16'.9'	81° 43.5'	74	36.58	
Ge 5827- 3	24° 02.5'	81° 42.4'	97	36.68	
S Pa 12	24° 19'	81° 32'	110	36.53	5)
Ex 42	24° 14'	80° 57'	74	36.48	
Ge 511-4	24° 12'	80° 46'	145	36.49	
Gi 67	24° 42'	80° 42'	60	36.39	
Ge 5827-11	24° 22'	80° 36'	145	36.60	
Ge 511-6	24° 01'	80° 35'	176	36.60	
Ge 5827-10	24° 12'	80° 31'	190	36.74	
Ge 5827- 9	24° 01'	80° 29.9'	198	36.67	
Ge 5806- 7	24° 40.0'	80° 25.6'	150	36.42	
Ge 5812- 3	24° 29'	80° 15.7'	190	36.55	
Ge 5812- 4	24° 22.4'	80° 07.4'	199	36.67	
Da II 1231	24° 30'	80° 00'	200	36.69	
Ge 448	24° 05'	79° 46'	181	36.654	
M T 203	24° 09'	79° 44'	233	36.75	
M T 202	24° 13'	79° 32'	200	36.76	
Ge 447	24° 12'	79° 30'	189	36.836	
Ge 446	24° 12'	79° 20'	193	36.833	
Ge 5810-2	24° 21'	79° 17.4'	199	36.55	
Ge 5810-1	24° 56.3'	79° 17'	197	36.56	
Ge 5810-3	24° 11.4'	79° 16'	198	36.60	
Ge 5806-2	24° 11.4'	79° 14.9'	173	36.64	
Cn 251	24° 50'	77° 40'	150	36.907	
Gi 2	24° 28'	77° 28'	149	36.85	4)
Cn 253	24° 25'	77° 28'	190	36.878	4)
Cn 254	24° 11'	77° 22'	149	36.899	4)
Gi 1	24° 32'	77° 18'	150	36.87	4)
Gi 6	24° 02'	77° 18'	150	36.83	4)
Al 443-28	25° 14'	88° 04'	139	36.67	
At 2352	25° 00'	85° 17'	193	36.71	
Ja 54-10-7	25° 19'	85° 04'	136	36.68	
Ex 31	25° 22'	84° 23'	75	36.54	
Ge 532-2	25° 24'	79° 58'	108	36.37	
Ge 532-3	25° 26'	79° 51'	157	36.51	
Ge 581-11	25° 17'	79° 36'	187	36.64	
Ge 10	25° 16'	79° 28'	198	36.76	
Ge 532-5/6	25° 27'	79° 24'	155	36.75	3)
Ge 581-9	25° 15'	79° 20'	200	36.79	
Ge 581-8	25° 14'	79° 12'	150	36.71	
Cn 250	25° 06'	77° 45'	150	36.855	
At 5331	25° 27'	77° 09'	155	36.649	

SOURCES OF DATA

SHIP AND YEAR	ABBREVIATION	REFERENCES
Albatross III	Alb III	Reduced data cards received directly from Woods Hole Oceanographic Institution, Woods Hole, Massachusetts
Alaska 1951, 1952, 1953	Al	Conseil Permanent International Pour l'Exploration de la Mer. Bulletin Hydrographique pour l'année 1952

SHIP AND YEAR	ABBREVIATION	REFERENCES
Atlantis	At	Reduced data cards received directly from Woods Hole Oceanographic Institution, Woods Hole, Massachusetts
1932, 1933, 1934		
1935, 1937, 1938		Woods Hole Oceanographic Institution Atlas Series, Vol. I, 1960 F. C. Fuglister, The Atlantic Ocean Atlas of Temperature and Salinity Profiles and Data from International Geophysical year of 1957-58, Woods Hole Oceanographic Institution, Woods Hole, Massachusetts
1939, 1941, 1947		
1949, 1952, 1954		
1955, 1957, 1958		
1961		Conseil Permanent International pour l'Exploration de la Mer; Bulletin Hydrographique pour les années, 1931-55
		Data received from National Oceanographic Data Center, Washington 25 D. C.
Challenger II	Ch II	Conseil Permanent International pour l'Exploration de la Mer; Bulletin Hydrographique pour les années 1933, 1938-39
1938, 1936, 1935		
Crawford	Cf	Reduced data cards received directly from Woods Hole Oceanographic Institution, Woods Hole, Massachusetts
1956, 1957, 1958		
Caryn	Cn	Reduced data cards received directly from Woods Hole Oceanographic Institution,
1954, 1956		
		Data received from National Oceanographic Data Center, Washington 25, D. C.
Dana II	Da II	The Danish DANA Expeditions 1920-22 Oceanographic Report No. 1-8 Copenhagen, 1929
1921, 1922, 1928		
		Data received from National Oceanographic Data Center, Washington 25, D. C.
Discovery II	Di II	The Woods Hole Oceanographic Institution Atlas Series, Vol. I, 1960 F. C. Fuglister, The Atlantic Ocean Atlas of Temperature & Salinity Profiles and Data from International Geophysical Year 1957-58, Woods Hole Oceanographic Institution, Woods Hole, Massachusetts
1957		
Explorer	Ex	Data received from National Oceanographic Data Center, Washington 25, D. C.
1960		
Gerda	Ge	Data received from National Oceanographic Data Center, Washington 25, D. C.
1955, 1958, 1960,		
1962		

SHIP AND YEAR	ABBREVIATION	REFERENCES
Gill 1952	Gi	Data received from National Oceanographic Data Center, Washington 25, D. C.
Hannibal 1936, 1934	Ha	Data received from National Oceanographic Data Center, Washington 25, D. C.
Hidalgo 1958	Hd	Data received from National Oceanographic Data Center, Washington 25, D. C.
Jakkula 1954	Ja	The A and M College of Texas, Dept. of Oceanography and Meteorology, Oceanographic Survey of the Gulf of Mexico, Ref. No. 57-15A Data received from National Oceanographic Data Center, Washington 25, D. C.
Mable Taylor 1932	M T	Data received from National Oceanographic Data Center, Washington 25, D. C.
Margrethe 1914	Ma	Data received from National Oceanographic Data Center, Washington 25, D. C.
Pursuit 1953	Pu	Data received from National Oceanographic Data Center, Washington 25, D. C.
Physalia 1954	Ph	University of Miami, Marine Laboratory, Ref. 55-1
Rehobeth 1950	Re	Data received from National Oceanographic Data Center, Washington 25, D. C.
San Pablo 1950, 1953	S Pa	Data received from National Oceanographic Data Center, Washington 25, D. C.
Sheldrake 1953	Sh	Data received from National Oceanographic Data Center, Washington 25, D. C.
Spencer F. Baird 1960	S F B	Preliminary Data List (Cr B-6001) Scripps Institution of Oceanography, University of California, La Jolla, California
Theodore Tissler 1951	T T	Conseil Permanent International Pour l'Exploration de la Mer. Bulletin Hydrographique pour l'année 1951
Vema 1957, 1961	V	Manuscript Data, Lamont Geological Observatory, Palisades, New York

Notes

1) Bonaire Basin
2) Salinity probably too low
3) Average of two serial measurements

4) Tongue of the ocean
5) Average of six repetitions
6) Station is < 200 m; used as auxiliary value

TABLE III a

OBSERVATIONS IN THE CORE OF THE MAIN OXYGEN MINIMUM

1932 - 1937

I. Basins Outside the Antillean Arc

SHIP AND STATION NUMBER		LAT. N	LONG. W	DEPTH OF O₂ MIN	O₂ MIN	S o/oo	TEMP °C	NOTE
At	1203	8° 41'	57° 30'	852	3.21	34.60	5.17	3)
At	1202	8° 41'	56° 30'	418	2.93	35.12	8.70	
At	1201	8° 18'	55° 34'	260	2.90	35.41	10.41	
At	2749	11° 41'	60° 31'	505	2.90	34.85	8.06	1)
At	2747	12° 41'	60° 31'	374	2.85	35.01	9.38	
At	2748	12° 04'	60° 29'	403	3.09	34.88?	10.97?	2)
At	2746	13° 11'	60° 31'	380	2.84	34.96	(9.03)	2)
At	2744	13° 47'	60° 28'	346	2.81	35.16	10.10	
At	2745	13° 30'	60° 28'	434	2.83	34.98	9.31	
At	2741	14° 55'	60° 31'	449	2.82	35.06	9.46	
At	2743	14° 07'	60° 29'	433	2.88	35.08	9.33	
At	2742	14° 28'	60° 28'	435	2.87	35.08	9.70	
At	2737	16° 50'	61° 00'	557	3.00	35.04	8.80	
At	2777	17° 48'	63° 41'	433	3.07	35.52	12.02	
At	1492	18° 09'	64° 44'	742	3.06	34.90	7.22	
At	1493	18° 01'	64° 36'	745	3.05	34.85	6.92	
At	1491	18° 35'	64° 05'	698	2.96	35.01	8.06	
At	1490	18° 30'	63° 57'	677	2.94	34.97	7.68	
At	1489	18° 24'	63° 45'	580	2.99	35.14	9.40	
At	1488	18° 20'	63° 34'	493	2.95	35.15	9.08	
At	2733	18° 59'	62° 37'	657	3.19	35.15	9.02	
At	2735	18° 15'	61° 52'	541	2.96	35.07	9.82	
At	1486	19° 07'	63° 00'	711	2.84	35.11	7.79	
At	2732	19° 40'	62° 12'	550	3.19	35.25	10.34	
At	1208	20° 38'	68° 36'	795	3.20	35.07	8.06	
At	1485	20° 00'	62° 31'	655	2.79	35.23	9.35	
At	1484	20° 55'	62° 08'	782	2.97	35.10	7.65	
At	2731	20° 24'	61° 45'	817	3.30	35.10	7.17	
At	1209	21° 19'	68° 13'	754	3.17	35.09	8.59	
At	1483	21° 46'	62° 48'	840	3.23	35.25	9.55	
At	2730	21° 11'	61° 11'	702	3.36	35.34	9.73	
At	2729	21° 50'	60° 33'	807	3.24	35.09	8.15	
At	1210	22° 14'	67° 50'	800	3.18	35.05	7.91	
At	2728	22° 32'	60° 03'	861	3.33	35.00	7.51	
At	1211	23° 10'	67° 34'	872	3.38	35.07	7.88	
At	1212	23° 46'	67° 24'	798	3.36	35.30	9.94	
At	1482	23° 28'	62° 40'	895	3.32	35.08	7.35	
At	2727	23° 17'	59° 31'	872	3.48	35.03	7.30	
At	1213	24° 45'	67° 05'	969	3.59	34.98	6.60	
At	2726	24° 00'	59° 03'	788	3.51	35.23	9.05	
At	1481	25° 19'	66° 53'	790	3.51	--	10.23	

2. Colombia, Venezuela, Grenada and Bonaire Basins

At	1949	9° 48'	80° 04'	496	2.75	34.96	8.39	
At	1948	9° 39'	79° 54'	380	2.81	35.30	10.52	
				480	2.81	34.94	8.37	

SHIP AND STATION NUMBER		LAT. N	LONG. W	DEPTH OF O$_2$ MIN	O$_2$ MIN	S o/oo	TEMP °C	NOTE
At	1947	9° 49'	79° 32'	397	2.81	35.13	9.83	
At	1951	10° 44'	81° 15'	446	2.75	34.97	8.59	
At	1950	10° 15'	80° 28'	483	2.76	34.97	8.77	
At	1946	10° 19'	79° 17'	560	2.87	34.84	7.32	
At	1945	10° 55'	79° 04'	541	2.69	34.87	7.59	
At	1953	11° 48'	82° 28'	483	2.76	35.06	9.39	
At	1952	11° 15'	81° 50'	499	2.82	34.99	8.88	
At	1944	11° 38'	78° 30'	429	2.70	35.11	9.60	
At	1531	11° 55'	74° 52'	400	2.87	35.19	10.42	
At	1529	11° 52'	74° 19'	394	2.72	35.19	10.36	
At	1505	11° 49'	68° 32'	294	3.03	35.34	11.78	
At	2796	11° 42'	67° 11'	305	2.87	35.20	10.65	
At	2795	11° 21'	67° 08'	390	2.87	34.97	9.15	
At	2794	11° 00'	67° 05'	416	2.88	34.92	8.50	
At	2792	11° 56'	64° 43'	353	2.88	35.05	9.57	
				444	2.88	34.89	8.36	
At	2754	11° 44'	62° 13'	371	2.90	35.07	9.73	
At	1954	12° 04'	82° 41'	492	2.75	34.96	8.61	
At	1943	12° 39'	77° 41'	447	2.82	35.09	9.77	
At	1533	12° 53'	76° 18'	499	2.79	34.97	8.58	
At	1532	12° 21'	75° 29'	395	2.74	35.23	10.72	
				494	2.74	35.17?	8.43	2)
At	1528	12° 18'	74° 14'	400	2.65	35.05	9.73	
At	1506	12° 28'	68° 34'	291	2.87	35.37	11.70	
At	2798	12° 29'	67° 14'	298	2.81	35.30	11.24	
				396	2.81	35.06	9.36	
At	2797	12° 07'	67° 10'	334	2.88	35.18	10.47	
				446	2.88	34.88	--	
At	2791	12° 13'	64° 40'	390	2.88	34.95	8.76	
At	2790	12° 45'	64° 38'	409	2.89	35.01	9.48	
At	1504	12° 03'	64° 35'	493	2.45	34.89	8.34	3)
				589	2.45	34.79	7.45	3)
At	1502	12° 38'	64° 34'	499	2.87	34.83	7.69	
At	1503	12° 12'	64° 34'	398	3.01	34.97	9.03	
At	2755	12° 00'	62° 23'	456	2.81	34.96	8.87	
At	2756	12° 24'	61° 48'	344	2.92	35.19	10.71	
				483	2.92	34.87	8.19	
At	1958	13° 27'	81° 50'	426	2.75	35.18	10.37	
At	1959	13° 17'	81° 30'	558	2.76	34.93	8.39	
At	1960	13° 19'	81° 12'	580	2.81	34.92	8.35	
At	1961	13° 28'	80° 54'	578	2.83	34.97	8.74	
At	1962	13° 34'	80° 30'	484	2.75	35.03	9.34	
At	1963	13° 35'	80° 08'	599	2.85	35.07	10.42	
At	1964	13° 42'	80° 00'	500	2.75	35.05	9.38	
At	1535	13° 47'	77° 48'	400	2.81	35.12	10.17	
At	1942	13° 33'	77° 03'	489	2.91	35.02	8.86	
At	1534	13° 20'	77° 03'	481	2.85	34.93	8.49	
At	1527	13° 15'	73° 58'	500	2.75	34.92	8.10	
At	1509	13° 58'	68° 36'	579	2.87	34.85	7.87	
At	1508	13° 30'	68° 34'	460	2.66	34.88	8.27	
At	2800	13° 37'	67° 20'	445	2.78	34.90	8.68	
At	2799	13° 09'	67° 15'	395	2.72	35.02	9.35	
At	2789	13° 12'	64° 36'	441	2.68	34.93	8.74	
At	2788	13° 42'	64° 35'	494	2.90	34.90	8.40	
At	1500	13° 48'	64° 35'	478	2.93	34.90	8.50	
				590	2.93	34.76	7.09	

SHIP AND STATION NUMBER		LAT. N	LONG. W	DEPTH OF O_2 MIN	O_2 MIN	S o/oo	TEMP °C	NOTE
At	1501	13° 13'	64° 33'	289	2.94	35.35	11.76	
At	2757	13° 05'	61° 25'	474	2.86	34.88	8.51	
At	2758	13° 25'	61° 12'	518	2.96	34.80	7.52	
At	2760	13° 44'	61° 09'	447	2.80	34.87	8.32	
At	2759	13° 35'	61° 09'	448	2.90	34.95	8.71	
At	1965	14° 09'	79° 40'	458	3.01	35.11	9.81	3)
At	1966	14° 42'	79° 18'	553	2.84	34.97	8.67	
At	1537	14° 36'	79° 14'	492	2.87	35.07	9.60	
At	1536	14° 12'	78° 46'	481	2.78	34.94	8.69	
At	1941	14° 46'	76° 42'	528	2.97	35.07	8.91	
At	1526	14° 15'	74° 01'	500	3.01	34.95	8.68	
At	1510	14° 54'	68° 33'	600	2.71	34.85	7.66	
At	2802	14° 46'	67° 13'	462	2.82	34.97	9.09	
At	2801	14° 10'	67° 13'	538	2.92	34.72	6.95	
At	2786	14° 43'	64° 33'	593	2.83	34.76	7.06	
At	1499	14° 38'	64° 30'	547	2.88	34.76	7.31	
At	2787	14° 15'	64° 30'	522	2.80	34.84	7.89	
At	2765	14° 58'	61° 20'	443	2.92	35.08	9.26	
At	2764	14° 50'	61° 18'	498	2.92	34.97	8.71	
At	2763	14° 22'	61° 04'	444	2.79	35.10	7.68	
At	2761	14° 07'	61° 03'	298	2.92	35.10	9.91	
At	2762	14° 17'	61° 02'	351	2.85	35.28	11.00	
At	1539	15° 35'	80° 38'	377	2.86	35.41	11.73	
At	1538	15° 12'	79° 54'	580	2.82	34.88	8.34	
At	1967	15° 08'	79° 16'	499	2.84	35.22	10.31	
At	1968	15° 27'	78° 55'	557	2.82	35.11	9.44	
At	1969	15° 57'	78° 41'	589	2.83	35.03	--	
At	1940	15° 20'	76° 40'	580	2.93	35.05	8.82	
At	1525	15° 11'	74° 01'	479	2.97	35.16	9.89	
At	1511	15° 47'	68° 30'	499	2.85	35.05	9.52	
At	2803	15° 18'	67° 11'	414	2.81	35.15	10.37	
At	2784	15° 48'	64° 42'	597	2.87	34.89	--	
At	2785	15° 09'	64° 30'	452	2.81	35.03	9.18	
At	1498	15° 24'	64° 29'	550	2.96	34.88	8.19	
At	2769	15° 54'	61° 45'	419	2.98	35.26	10.59	
At	2768	15° 38'	61° 36'	433	2.93	35.08	9.57	
At	2767	15° 10'	61° 24'	464	2.96	35.15	9.94	
At	1970	16° 12'	78° 36'	587	2.81	35.04	8.85	
At	1971	16° 28'	78° 25'	562	2.89	35.09	9.44	
At	1938	16° 56'	76° 29'	565	3.09	35.09	9.41	
At	1939	16° 10'	76° 28'	551	2.93	35.09	9.44	
At	1524	16° 09'	73° 55'	541	3.11	35.12	9.74	
At	1512	16° 42'	68° 36'	769	2.91	34.78	7.02	
At	2804	16° 02'	67° 17'	539	2.94	35.03	8.69	
At	2805	16° 28'	67° 11'	587	2.90	34.92	7.95	
At	2782	16° 44'	64° 34'	503	2.79	35.04	9.47	
At	1497	16° 17'	64° 33'	573	2.75	34.83	8.02	
At	2783	16° 14'	64° 30'	470	2.77	35.08	9.72	
At	2773	16° 36'	62° 10'	531	2.96	34.99	8.88	
At	2772	16° 31'	62° 06'	553	2.94	34.96	8.42	
At	2771	16° 23'	62° 00'	453	2.91	35.11	9.90	
At	2770	16° 17'	61° 55'	457	2.94	35.08	9.71	
At	1974	17° 23'	77° 39'	589	2.94	35.02	8.57	
At	1975	17° 33'	77° 36'	580	2.94	(35.45)	9.73	2)
At	1935	17° 45'	76° 40'	550	2.94	35.21	10.08	
At	1936	17° 28'	76° 40'	572	2.95	35.12	9.41	

SHIP AND STATION NUMBER		LAT. N	LONG. W	DEPTH OF O₂ MIN	O₂ MIN	S o/oo	TEMP °C	NOTE
At	1937	17° 12'	76° 33'	598	2.86	35.01	8.81	
At	1557	17° 59'	75° 54'	468	3.77	35.71	12.98	
At	1522	17° 34'	73° 55'	792	3.20	34.85	6.84	
At	1523	17° 04'	73° 55'	600	3.18	35.12	9.38	
At	1521	17° 56'	73° 54'	600	3.09	35.07	--	
At	1514	17° 43'	68° 36'	563	2.98	35.04	9.38	
				656	2.98	34.92	8.02	
At	1513	17° 27'	68° 33'	600	3.03	34.90?	8.31	
At	1515	17° 57'	68° 28'	564	3.13	35.25	10.45	
At	2807	17° 28'	67° 15'	513	2.88	35.06	9.47	
At	2781	17° 10'	64° 33'	544	2.87	35.12	9.46	
At	1494	17° 55'	64° 31'	734	2.97	34.79?	6.62	
At	1495	17° 40'	64° 30'	564	3.03	35.30	10.25	
At	1496	17° 06'	64° 29'	558	2.83	35.08	9.59	
At	2779	17° 43'	64° 14'	479	3.02	35.34	10.45	
				653	3.02	34.96	7.83	
At	1558	18° 05'	75° 31'	720	3.28	35.08	8.50	
At	1559	18° 13'	75° 08'	741	3.26	34.92	7.28	
At	1560	18° 22'	74° 49'	661	3.15	35.10	8.74	1)

3. Cayman and Yucatan Basins

		LAT. N	LONG. W	DEPTH OF O₂ MIN	O₂ MIN	S o/oo	TEMP °C	NOTE
At	1591	16° 59'	83° 57'	472	2.88	35.07	8.99	
At	1590	16° 32'	83° 54'	475	2.93	35.07	8.68	
At	1589	16° 16'	83° 52'	486	2.91	35.14	9.24	
At	1544	16° 30'	80° 56'	391	2.81	35.03	9.45	1)
At	1546	16° 43'	80° 14'	483	2.84	35.03	9.53	
At	1547	16° 54'	79° 51'	490	2.97	35.19	10.42	
At	1594	17° 54'	83° 58'	452	2.92	35.25	10.45	
At	1592	17° 23'	83° 58'	450	2.97	35.06	8.99	
At	1583	17° 50'	81° 28'	600	3.17	34.92	7.64	
At	1584	17° 16'	81° 25'	473	3.04	34.97	8.65	
At	1548	17° 08'	79° 30'	492	2.99	35.28	10.95	
				591	2.99	35.08	9.33	
At	1549	17° 16'	79° 08'	596	2.82	35.07	9.30	
At	1551	17° 31'	78° 36'	594	2.95	35.10	9.23	
At	1552	17° 37'	78° 26'	494	2.93	35.28	10.62	
At	1553	17° 43'	78° 14'	574	2.95	35.14	9.51	1)
At	1554	17° 47'	78° 02'	591	2.91	35.03	8.65	.1)
At	1597	18° 56'	84° 08'	600	2.89	35.14	9.59	
At	1595	18° 24'	83° 59'	487	2.97	35.39	11.33	
At	1596	18° 43'	83° 57'	600	2.99	35.14	9.45	
At	1582	18° 21'	81° 25'	484	2.96	35.26	10.81	
At	1581	18° 58'	81° 21'	600	3.09	35.17	9.88	
At	1567	18° 35'	77° 31'	800	3.31	34.90	6.60	
At	1568	18° 45'	77° 30'	697	3.19	35.05	8.44	
At	1569	18° 58'	77° 29'	694	3.28	34.94	7.36	
At	1601	19° 37'	86° 55'	400	3.08	35.17	9.98	
At	1600	19° 33'	86° 24'	489	3.10	35.25	10.34	
At	1599	19° 18'	85° 40'	592	3.05	35.07	9.26	
At	1598	19° 07'	84° 47'	483	2.83	35.32	11.07	
At	1992	19° 32'	83° 50'	543	2.94	35.16	9.96	
At	1991	19° 05'	83° 50'	518	2.91	35.06	8.83	
At	1990	19° 03'	83° 00'	733	3.04	34.85	7.30	3)
At	1989	19° 08'	82° 22'	596	2.94	35.17	10.02	
At	1988	19° 14'	81° 38'	589	2.88	35.24	10.48	
At	1986	19° 49'	81° 26'	613	2.99	35.29	10.50	

Cayman and Yucatan Basins (continued)

SHIP AND STATION NUMBER		LAT. N	LONG. W	DEPTH OF O₂ MIN	O₂ MIN	S o/oo	TEMP °C	NOTE
At	1987	19° 30'	81° 23'	782	2.95	34.94	7.47	
At	1580	19° 12'	81° 20'	598	3.06	35.16	9.85	
At	1579	19° 24'	80° 52'	594	3.10	35.23	9.94	
At	1578	19° 30'	80° 31'	584	3.21	35.28	10.55	
At	1577	19° 36'	80° 11'	700	3.15	35.01	8.44	
At	1977	19° 49'	79° 46'	596	3.31	35.35	10.70	
At	1576	19° 45'	79° 39'	800	3.24	34.90	6.85	
At	1575	19° 48'	79° 00'	800	3.44	34.85	6.91	
At	1574	19° 49'	78° 25'	778	3.09	34.97	7.69	1)
At	1573	19° 45'	77° 44'	800	3.21	34.94	7.38	
At	1571	19° 27'	77° 35'	798	3.19	34.90	7.02	
At	1570	19° 16'	77° 28'	712	3.19	35.05	8.57	
At	1565	19° 57'	74° 05'	710	3.23	35.23	9.41	
At	1564	19° 55'	73° 52'	585	3.30	35.46	11.07	
At	1563	19° 52'	73° 41'	728	3.33	35.37	9.16	
At	1562	19° 48'	73° 32'	728	3.45	35.05	7.86	
At	1994	20° 41'	84° 00'	657	2.82	35.04	8.65	
At	1993	20° 12'	83° 57'	480	2.66	35.60	12.93	3)
At	1984	20° 52'	81° 25'	563	3.05	35.34	10.92	
				758	3.05	34.91	7.57	
At	1985	20° 19'	81° 19'	597	3.05	35.33	10.78	
At	1978	20° 02'	79° 37'	796	3.19	34.94	7.30	
At	1979	20° 18'	79° 27'	588	3.29	35.32	10.53	
				788	3.29	34.95	7.21	
At	1980	20° 35'	79° 19'	729	3.24	35.05	8.11	
At	1981	20° 53'	79° 11'	757	3.09	34.98	7.98	
At	1995	21° 27'	84° 22'	545	3.44	35.42	11.46	
At	1982	21° 32'	81° 35'	571	3.10	35.39	11.33	
At	1983	21° 16'	81° 33'	622	2.88	35.15	9.62	3)

4. Gulf of Mexico Basin and Straits of Florida

SHIP AND STATION NUMBER		LAT. N	LONG. W	DEPTH OF O₂ MIN	O₂ MIN	S o/oo	TEMP °C	NOTE
At	1605	21° 40'	86° 15'	449	2.89	35.26	10.48	
At	2000	21° 41'	86° 05'	479	2.85	35.23	10.30	
At	2335	21° 42'	85° 57'	426	2.88	35.45	11.85	
At	1606	21° 51'	85° 53'	563	2.94	35.17	9.91	
At	1607	21° 55'	85° 44'	467	3.07	35.60	12.33	
				565	3.07	35.25	10.29	
At	1999	21° 43'	85° 38'	649	2.91	35.00	--	
At	2334	21° 43'	85° 29'	740	2.88	34.97	8.23	
At	1608	21° 53'	85° 26'	600	2.98	35.21	10.25	
At	1998	21° 48'	85° 20'	761	2.95	35.17	--	
At	1609	21° 51'	85° 10'	788	3.07	35.01	8.19	
At	2333	21° 51'	85° 05'	689	2.93	35.01	8.48	
At	1996	21° 38'	84° 28'	794	3.19	34.88	7.25	
At	2436	23° 55'	82° 42'	290	3.04	35.32	10.81	
At	2437	23° 34'	82° 36'	471	2.75	35.08	9.35	
At	2345	23° 52'	82° 34'	354	2.82	35.14	9.54	
At	2438	23° 12'	82° 31'	525	2.81	35.18	9.93	
At	2344	23° 33'	82° 30'	432	2.82	35.01	8.60	
At	2343	23° 15'	82° 30'	581	2.84	35.11	9.35	
At	2005	23° 47.5'	82° 17'	471	2.58	35.17	9.90	3)
At	2003	23° 15'	82° 16'	497	2.88	35.67	13.12	
At	2340	24° 11'	86° 25'	595	2.83	35.25	10.41	
At	2341	24° 15'	85° 44'	766	2.77	35.03	8.54	
At	2342	24° 15'	84° 55'	657	2.73	35.02	8.45	
At	2350	24° 26'	84° 06'	325	2.71	35.10	9.42	

SHIP AND STATION NUMBER	LAT. N	LONG. W	DEPTH OF O$_2$ MIN	O$_2$ MIN	S o/oo	TEMP °C	NOTE
At 2346	24° 11'	82° 43'	222	2.78	35.41	11.46	
At 2435	24° 11'	82° 42'	356	2.92	35.05	8.91	
At 2006	24° 05'	82° 14'	375	2.91	35.26	10.60	
At 2352	25° 00'	85° 17'	771	2.89	34.94	7.72	

SOURCES OF DATA 1932 - 1937

SHIP	ABBREVIATION	REFERENCE
Atlantis	At	Reduced data cards received directly from Woods Hole Oceanographic Institution Woods Hole, Massachusetts
		The Woods Hole Oceanographic Institution Atlas Series; Vol. I, 1960, F.C. Fuglister, The Atlantic Ocean Atlas of Temperature and Salinity Profiles and Data from International Geophysical Year of 1957-58 Woods Hole Oceanographic Institution, Woods Hole, Massachusetts
		Data received from National Oceanographic Data Center, Washington 25, D. C.
		Conseil Permanent International Pour l'Exploration de la Mer, Bulletin Hydrographique pour l'années, 1932-37

Notes

1) Deepest water bottle
2) Brackets and question marks are from original data sheets
3) Depth and (or) oxygen value questionable

TABLE III b

OBSERVATIONS IN THE CORE OF THE MAIN OXYGEN MINIMUM

1954 - 1958   **

1. Basins Outside the Antillean Arc

SHIP AND STATION NUMBER		LAT. N	LONG. W	DEPTH OF O₂ MIN	O2 MIN	S o/oo	TEMP °C	NOTE
Cf	184	8° 16'	57° 42'	470	2.77	34.784	8.00	
Cf	183	8° 19'	56° 52'	500	2.87	34.776	7.73	
Cf	182	8° 26'	55° 57'	380	2.87	34.730	7.86	
Cf	181	8° 25'	55° 10'	545	2.80	34.681	7.31	
At	5280	11° 29'	60° 46'	148	3.01	36.27	17.41	1)
At	5228	11° 53'	60° 37'	481	2.77	34.812	7.91	
At	5227	12° 17'	60° 21'	492	2.81	34.898	8.56	
At	5226	12° 45'	60° 07'	425	2.68	35.083	9.54	
At	5279	12° 41'	59° 40'	369	2.76	35.09	9.85	
				464	2.76	34.87	8.22	
At	5278	12° 36'	58° 34'	496	2.82	34.81	7.70	
At	5225	13° 07'	59° 52'	461	2.83	34.87	8.38	
At	5275	13° 54'	59° 47'	495	2.56	34.95	8.29	
At	5224	13° 40'	59° 25'	467	2.68	35.38	--	
At	5276	13° 25'	58° 19'	394	2.92	34.90	8.90	
At	5277	13° 50'	56° 53'	385	2.58	--	10.96	
At	5274	14° 08'	60° 42'	388	2.62	35.28	10.94	
At	5223	14° 30'	58° 54'	490	2.74	35.227?	--	
At	5222	15° 20'	58° 19'	419	2.70	35.338	--	
				506	2.70	35.085	9.44	
Cf	309	16° 15'	60° 28'	435	2.55	35.345	11.60	
Cf	308	16° 14'	59° 42'	405	2.62	35.302	11.38	
Cf	307	16° 16'	58° 54'	585	2.73	34.866	7.98	
At	5221	16° 12'	57° 49'	572	2.62	35.032	8.89	
Cf	306	16° 13'	57° 31'	550	2.72	35.130	8.99	
Cf	305	16° 14'	56° 08'	490	2.66	35.257	10.27	
At	5285	17° 54'	65° 51.5'	660	2.68	34.92	7.82	
At	5286	17° 53'	65° 18'	626	2.81	35.01	8.47	
Cf	332	17° 53'	64° 18'	480	2.74	35.262	10.59	
At	5287	17° 54.5'	64° 16'	660	2.87	34.90	7.76	
At	5220	17° 30'	56° 47'	562	2.74	35.239	9.88	
Cf	327	18° 55'	68° 14'	695	2.94	35.170	9.16	
At	5264	18° 50'	68° 10'	477	3.08	35.53	--	
Cf	330	18° 20'	64° 17'	795	2.95	34.826	6.60	
Cf	331	18° 07'	64° 16'	675	2.77	34.887	7.61	
At	5288	18° 52'	63° 05'	626	3.01	35.16	9.18	
At	5219	18° 50'	55° 49'	581	2.85	35.331	10.47	
				669	2.85	35.070	8.51	
Cf	326	19° 06'	68° 12'	695	2.92	35.171	9.16	
Cf	325	19° 36'	68° 04'	595	2.37	35.110	--	1)
At	5291	19° 52'	66° 35'	625	2.78	35.33	10.50	
At	5168	19° 21'	66° 18'	706	2.92	35.09	8.39	
At	5166	19° 55'	64° 51'	490	2.96	35.55	12.30	
At	5165	19° 25'	64° 40'	730	2.97	34.98	8.42	

** Suspicious (too low) oxygen values because of analytic difficulties

[156]

SHIP AND STATION NUMBER	LAT. N	LONG. W	DEPTH OF O$_2$ MIN	O$_2$ MIN	S o/oo	TEMP °C	NOTE
At 5290	19° 54'	64° 32'	673	2.80	34.99	8.60	
At 5289	19° 56'	62° 50.2'	739	2.91	35.18	8.51	
Cf 368	20° 23'	73° 34'	755	2.99	--	9.46	
Cn 218	20° 45'	68° 28'	722	3.04	35.21	9.52	
Cf 324	20° 34'	67° 52'	695	2.91	35.246	9.84	
At 5167	20° 25'	64° 53'	784	2.96	34.98	7.61	
At 5218	20° 01'	55° 02'	740	2.86	34.971	7.83	
Cn 216	20° 02'	55° 00'	488	3.02	35.68	12.68	
Hd 58-4-34	21° 15.4'	74° 29.9'	738	3.25	35.33	10.20	
Cf 369	21° 54'	73° 15'	690	2.99	35.349	10.50	
Cn 219	21° 43'	68° 11'	770	3.17	35.18	9.04	
Cf 323	21° 33'	67° 36'	775	2.91	35.168	9.19	
Cn 215	21° 04'	55° 41'	744	3.09	35.08	7.92	
Cn 220	22° 43'	67° 47'	784	3.13	35.16	8.82	
Cf 322	22° 34'	67° 18'	780	2.94	35.159	9.17	
Cn 214	22° 25'	56° 15'	771	3.12	35.18	8.38	
Cn 257	23° 41'	76° 52'	640	3.15	35.532	11.56	
Cn 221	23° 40'	67° 38'	717	3.33	35.36	10.02	
Cf 321	23° 30'	67° 05'	795	2.97	35.198	9.31	
Cn 212	23° 57'	57° 39'	780	3.35	35.39	9.52	
			877	3.35	35.20	7.80	
Di II 3624	24° 31'	75° 28'	700	3.17	35.33	10.27	
Di II 3623	24° 32'	74° 56'	794	3.15	35.15	8.57	
Di II 3622	24° 30'	73° 47'	778	3.13	35.17	8.83	
Di II 3621	24° 33'	71° 53'	887	3.21	35.19	8.88	
Di II 3620	24° 29'	70° 10'	895	3.08	35.18	9.06	
Di II 3619	24° 28'	68° 20'	782	3.17	35.26	9.63	
Cn 222	24° 36'	67° 22'	933	3.35	35.11	7.63	
Cf 320	24° 29'	66° 50'	790	3.04	35.249	9.62	
Di II 3618	24° 32'	66° 28'	789	3.12	35.23	9.42	
Di II 3617	24° 30'	64° 47'	797	3.22	35.20	8.82	
Di II 3616	24° 27'	62° 57'	875	2.99	35.02	7.77	
Di II 3615	24° 31'	61° 08'	791	3.11	35.23	9.18	
Di II 3614	24° 29'	59° 18'	896	3.22	35.07	7.56	
Cn 211	24° 48'	58° 20'	894	3.29	35.18	--	
Di II 3613	24° 32'	57° 30'	796	3.03	35.17	8.84	
Di II 3612	24° 31'	55° 41'	796	3.31	35.29	9.34	
At 5163	25° 29'	76° 06'	765	3.15	35.21	--	
Hd 58-4-37	25° 10.3'	74° 58'	732	3.35	35.23	9.80	
Cf 319	25° 27'	66° 30'	650	3.09	35.697	13.16	

2. Colombia, Venezuela, Grenada and Bonaire Basins

SHIP AND STATION NUMBER	LAT. N	LONG. W	DEPTH OF O$_2$ MIN	O$_2$ MIN	S o/oo	TEMP °C	NOTE
Cf 399	9° 51'	79° 17'	390	2.67	35.209	10.35	
			490	2.67	34.939	8.37	
Cf 398	10° 22'	79° 18'	450	2.64	35.020	8.98	
At 5746	10° 10'	76° 40'	429	2.61	34.811?	9.30	
			446	2.61	35.074	9.45	
At 5689	10° 46'	67° 16'	495	2.62	34.902	8.34	
At 5597	10° 59'	66° 05'	193	3.35	36.391	--	1)
Cf 396	11° 52'	79° 22'	435	2.62	35.098	9.66	
			525	2.62	34.967	8.55	
Cf 397	11° 03'	79° 18'	380	2.64	35.174	10.24	
At 5745	11° 04'	75° 29'	372	2.58	35.237	10.55	
At 5744	11° 00'	75° 26'	368	2.59	35.156	10.05	2)
At 5740	11° 51'	74° 54'	428	2.60	34.987	8.86	
At 5739	11° 31'	74° 47'	360	2.57	35.218	10.70	

SHIP AND STATION NUMBER		LAT. N	LONG. W	DEPTH OF O₂ MIN	O₂ MIN	S o/oo	TEMP °C	NOTE
At	5737	11° 38'	74° 07'	598	2.55	34.771	6.84	
Cf	355	11° 51'	73° 46'	465	2.60	34.965	8.78	
At	5233	11° 47'	68° 36'	464	2.76	34.933	8.59	
At	5696	11° 47'	68° 30'	391	2.80	35.185	10.46	
At	5692	11° 55'	67° 18'	675	2.35	34.774	6.26	
At	5690	11° 01'	67° 16'	400	2.61	35.104	--	
At	5691	11° 28'	67° 13'	387	2.55	35.070	9.68	
At	5688	11° 16'	65° 41'	400	2.67	34.999	9.28	
At	5266	11° 18'	65° 39'	389	2.79	35.10	9.94	
At	5603	11° 15'	65° 07'	498	2.60	34.87	--	
At	5665	11° 44'	64° 36'	440	2.61	34.929	8.80	
At	5666	11° 30'	64° 36'	494	2.64	34.874	8.37	
Cf	345	11° 34'	64° 31'	335	2.64	35.139	10.36	
				420	2.64	34.877	8.30	
At	5664	11° 58'	64° 28'	348	2.67	34.973?	10.27	
				398	2.67	34.963	9.19	
				448	2.67	34.907	8.65	
				498	2.67	34.876	8.33	
At	5662	11° 52'	62° 44'	393	2.72	34.876	8.69	
				491	2.72	34.819	7.95	
At	5661	11° 36'	62° 43'	190	3.03	36.328	17.24	1)
Cf	395	12° 26'	79° 18'	555	2.65	34.940	8.28	
V	12 53	12° 08.5'	75° 01'	434	2.66	35.100	9.64	1)
At	5738	12° 00'	74° 06'	297	2.58	35.504	12.43	
Cf	356	12° 26'	73° 45'	470	2.67	34.974	8.84	
At	5734	12° 40'	71° 42'	399	2.65	34.993	9.13	
At	5235	12° 35'	68° 35'	461	2.82	35.045	9.26	
				558	2.82	34.854	7.64	
At	5234	12° 10'	68° 35'	394	2.78	35.077	9.83	
At	5694	12° 33'	68° 30'	463	2.61	35.008	9.18	
At	5695	12° 10'	68° 29'	394	2.68	35.161	10.34	
At	5693	12° 17'	67° 16'	600	2.52	34.780	7.12	
Cf	341	12° 30'	64° 32'	440	2.61	34.955	9.06	
Cf	342	12° 06'	64° 32'	435	2.59	34.887	8.30	
At	5663	12° 29'	62° 49'	398	2.64	35.128	10.24	
Cf	394	13° 00'	79° 15'	565	2.63	34.951	8.63	
Cf	393	13° 45'	79° 12'	480	2.65	35.155	10.08	
				575	2.65	34.925	8.36	
Cf	358	13° 44'	73° 56'	510	2.64	34.966	8.76	
Cf	357	13° 06'	73° 55'	465	2.64	34.991	9.02	
At	5733	13° 02'	71° 42'	381	2.63	35.229	10.71	
At	5257	13° 07'	68° 37'	556	2.79	34.852	7.86	
At	5272	13° 30'	65° 24'	398	2.21	--	9.51	1)
Cf	340	13° 05'	64° 32'	390	2.48	35.076	10.01	
Cf	339	13° 47'	64° 28'	790	2.44	34.745	5.90	3)
At	5282	13° 09'	62° 15'	385	2.76	35.01	9.62	
				482	2.76	34.78	8.02	
Cf	392	14° 38'	79° 06'	550	2.59	35.074	9.40	
V	12 58	14° 22'	74° 56.5'	520	2.49	35.00	9.10	1)
Cf	360	14° 59'	73° 58'	575	2.74	35.056	8.92	
Cf	359	14° 20'	73° 58'	530	2.62	--	9.09	
At	5258	14° 04'	68° 48'	718	2.81	34.809	7.56	
Cf	338	14° 32'	64° 41'	500	2.66	34.944	8.81	
At	5273	14° 14'	63° 24.8'	518	2.75	34.85	7.60	1)
At	5283	14° 13'	62° 55'	390	2.66	35.44	12.09	
Cf	391	15° 11'	79° 13'	520	2.60	35.131	9.75	

SHIP AND STATION NUMBER	LAT. N	LONG. W	DEPTH OF O₂ MIN	O₂ MIN	S o/oo	°C	NOTE
Cf 390	15° 46'	79° 11'	515	2.60	35.234	10.47	
Cf 361	15° 38'	73° 56'	555	2.70	35.106	9.35	
At 5259	15° 11'	68° 44'	618	2.81	34.828	7.62	
Cf 337	15° 08'	64° 34'	485	2.66	34.988	9.00	
Cf 336	15° 48'	64° 26'	490	2.64	35.004	9.22	
V 12 60	16° 58.5'	74° 22'	687	2.49	34.95	8.12	1)
Cf 362	16° 26'	73° 57'	665	2.71	35.013	8.57	
At 5260	16° 14'	68° 38'	561	2.85	35.069	9.31	
At 5284	16° 03'	66° 02'	444	2.74	35.28	10.96	
Cf 335	16° 25'	64° 28'	560	2.67	34.954	8.56	
Cf 363	17° 04'	73° 55'	590	2.74	35.152	9.76	
Cf 364	17° 45'	73° 49'	600	2.69	35.147	9.67	
Cf 365	17° 57'	73° 52'	670	2.80	34.946	7.94	
At 5262	17° 45'	68° 35'	525	2.82	35.155	10.26	
At 5261	17° 05'	68° 35'	525	2.87	35.103	9.37	
Cn 217	17° 25'	66° 08'	563	2.88	35.08	9.41	
Cf 334	17° 05'	64° 32'	395	2.74	35.435	11.97	
Cf 333	17° 30'	64° 25'	565	2.69	34.956	8.60	
Hd 58-4-28	18° 11.8'	75° 04.5'	734	3.40	34.88	7.56	
Hd 58-4-29	18° 15.1'	74° 37.2'	672	3.31	34.96	8.12	
At 5263	18° 14'	68° 19'	607	3.11	35.243	10.00	

3. Cayman and Yucatan Basins

Cf 371	16° 26'	84° 24'	460	2.68	34.989	8.54	
Cf 389	16° 26'	79° 10'	620	2.61	34.932	8.18	
Cf 373	17° 46'	84° 29'	455	2.67	34.975	8.35	
Cf 372	17° 07'	84° 28'	390	2.62	35.062	9.14	
Cf 388	17° 06'	79° 10'	610	2.60	35.002	8.80	
Cf 387	17° 47'	79° 09'	590	2.65	35.090	9.44	
Cf 374	18° 27'	84° 31'	565	2.68	35.101	9.39	
Cf 386	18° 30'	79° 13'	580	2.65	35.206	10.09	
Cn 237	18° 43'	73° 23'	600	3.00	35.29	10.11	
Cn 231	18° 34'	73° 05'	683	2.98	35.10	8.71	
Cn 230	18° 34'	72° 56'	787	3.02	35.01	7.43	
Cf 376	19° 47'	84° 31'	565	2.67	35.055	9.08	
Cf 375	19° 06'	84° 30'	600	2.61	35.096	9.69	
Cf 384	19° 48'	79° 11'	675	2.74	35.073	9.04	2)
Cf 385	19° 16'	79° 11'	695	2.77	35.021	8.48	
Hd 58-4-30	19° 52.5'	73° 28.2'	648	3.19	35.23	9.08	
Cf 377	20° 28'	84° 30'	695	2.70	34.981	8.47	
Cf 382	20° 35'	79° 10'	680	2.66	35.162	9.71	
Cf 383	20° 06'	79° 10'	670	2.66	35.114	9.36	
Hd 58-4-32	20° 04.8'	73° 53.6'	746	3.07	34.90	7.72	
Hd 58-4-31	20° 01.2'	73° 39.2'	638	3.55	35.36	10.18	
Cf 367	20° 04'	73° 39'	685	2.91	35.133	8.86	
Ja 55-3-10	21° 30'	86° 18'	276	2.65	35.47	13.94	
Ja 55-3-9	21° 34'	86° 02.8'	411	2.84	35.63	12.97	
Ja 55-3-7	21° 43'	85° 32'	476	2.71	36.43	12.59	
Ja 55-3-6	21° 47'	85° 16'	694	2.71	35.04	8.41	
Ja 55-3-5	21° 53'	85° 02'	698	2.69	35.04	9.03	
Cf 378	21° 06'	84° 29'	790	2.57	34.823	6.73	
Cf 379	21° 36'	84° 28'	585	2.68	35.323	11.00	
			680	2.68	35.021	8.80	
Hd 58-4-16	21° 46.7'	83° 28.4'	737	2.97	34.97	8.06	
Hd 58-4-15	21° 50.6'	83° 27.1'	731	2.96	34.99	8.53	
Hd 58-4-22	21° 45.8'	80° 54.3'	690	2.83	35.04	8.98	

Cayman and Yucatan Basins (continued)

SHIP AND STATION NUMBER	LAT. N	LONG. W	DEPTH OF O₂ MIN	O₂ MIN	S o/oo	TEMP °C	NOTE
Cn 238	21° 29'	80° 20'	679	2.69	--	9.35	
Ja 55-3-11	22° 46'	85° 16'	591	2.65	35.25	10.30	
Ja 54-10-12	22° 50'	84° 18.5'	695	2.56	36.03	8.29	
Ja 54-10-35	23° 45.2'	85° 05.5'	836	2.68	35.17	9.84	
Ja 54-10-14	23° 59'	85° 00'	595	2.64	35.29	10.86	
Ja 54-10-30	23° 55'	84° 15.4'	800	2.70	35.44	13.04	
Ja 54-10-32	23° 00'	83° 39.6'	600	2.72	35.24	10.48	
			700	2.72	34.85	8.26	
Ja 55-3-4	23° 15'	82° 52'	443	2.75	35.69	13.46	
Ge 5716-3	23° 49.3'	82° 06.6'	467	2.62	35.04	8.38	
Ge 5827-4	23° 52.5'	81° 40'	495	2.56	35.18	9.62	
Ge 5810-12	23° 49.8'	81° 39'	491	2.39	35.39	12.14	
Ge 5827-5	23° 42.6'	81° 37.6'	490	2.54	35.41	11.44	
Ge 5810-11	23° 33.7'	81° 35.3'	500	2.72	35.46	12.67	
Ge 5827-7	23° 24'	81° 33.5'	792	2.81	34.94	7.21	
Ge 5806-4	23° 32.7'	81° 17.2'	463	2.64	35.60	12.98	
Ge 5810-9	23° 23'	80° 47.6'	483	2.94	35.66	13.46	
Ge 5810-8	23° 30'	80° 40'	587	2.84	35.21	10.51	
Ge 5810-7	23. 38.3'	80° 31.2'	500	2.66	35.46	12.50	

4. Gulf of Mexico Basin and Straits of Florida

SHIP AND STATION NUMBER	LAT. N	LONG. W	DEPTH OF O₂ MIN	O₂ MIN	S o/oo	TEMP °C	NOTE
Cn 247	21° 34'	86° 12'	480	2.71	35.092	8.75	
Cn 246	21° 36'	86° 09'	516	2.79	35.131	9.43	
Cn 244	21° 48'	85° 56'	555	2.71	35.023	8.80	
Hd 58-4-10	21° 42'	85° 55'	595	2.74	35.14	9.33	
Ja 55-3-8	21° 38'	85° 47.4'	670	2.51	34.92	8.06	
Cn 243	21° 45'	85° 46'	578	2.70	35.105	9.45	
Cn 242	21° 48'	85° 35'	596	2.70	35.05	9.11	
Cn 241	21° 48'	85° 25'	650	2.72	34.969	8.16	
Cn 240	21° 47'	85° 14'	678	2.66	35.053	8.96	
Hd 58-4-35	22° 43.7'	74° 31'	693	3.40	35.35	10.85	
Hd 58-4-86	23° 40'	82° 52'	548	2.88	35.26	10.06	
Hd 58-4-85	23° 15.7'	82° 29.5'	484	2.77	35.60	12.88	
At 2004	23° 30.5'	82° 20'	580	2.82	35.13	9.46	
Cn 255	23° 57'	77° 17'	701	3.19	35.949	9.95	
Cn 256	23° 44'	77° 09'	672	3.14	35.416	10.61	
Cn 258	23° 39'	76° 38'	600	3.14	35.52	11.48	
Ja 54-10-36	24° 19.1'	85° 21.5'	436	2.67	34.96	8.57	
Ja 54-10-15	24° 34.5'	85° 16'	628	2.62	35.14	9.74	
Ja 54-10-8	24° 47'	84° 48'	555	2.44	35.08	8.45	
Ja 54-10-29	24° 37'	84° 43.6'	482	2.72	34.99	8.87	
			624	2.72	34.87	7.96	
Ja 54-10-9	24° 13'	84° 26'	480	2.43	35.05	9.44	
Hd 58-4-87	24° 19'	83° 34'	412	2.99	35.24	11.32	
Ge 5827-2	24° 16.9'	81° 43.5'	297	2.66	35.34	9.61	
Ge 5810-13	24° 07.1'	81° 43'	493	2.41	35.25	10.28	
Ge 5827-3	24° 02.5'	81° 42.4'	485	2.11	35.19	8.90	
Ge 5806-5	24° 10.1'	81° 26.4'	325	2.40	35.39	11.75	
Ge 511-3	24° 19'	80° 52'	357	2.70	35.46	11.27	
Ge 511-4	24° 12'	80° 46'	525	2.66	35.21	9.54	
Ge 511-6	24° 01'	80° 35'	577	2.65	35.33	10.34	
Ge 5827-10	24° 12'	80° 31'	475	2.30	35.26	10.62	
Ge 5827-9	24° 01'	80° 29.9'	495	2.69	35.36	10.94	
Ge 581-2	24° 46'	79° 57'	194	2.74	35.19	9.92	1)
Ge 5812-5	24° 14'	79° 56.7'	295	2.81	36.44	18.40	1)
Cn 251	24° 50'	77° 40'	700	3.13	35.315	9.93	

SHIP AND STATION NUMBER	LAT. N	LONG. W	DEPTH OF O2 MIN	O2 MIN	S o/oo	TEMP °C	NOTE
Cn 252	24° 39'	77° 30'	700	3.14	35.31	9.91	
Cn 253	24° 25'	77° 28'	673	3.16	35.409	10.58	
Ja 55-3-12	25° 00'	86° 00'	676	2.44	34.94	7.22	
Ja 55-8-4	25° 00'	86° 00'	237	3.07	35.38	11.45	1)
Ja 54-10-16	25° 09'	85° 44'	275	2.63	35.25	10.51	
Ja 55-3-3	25° 14'	85° 17'	471	2.53	35.68	13.59	
Ge 532-2	25° 24'	79° 58'	275	2.79	35.25	9.87	
Ge 532-3	25° 26'	79° 51'	228	1.97	35.93	14.98	
Ge 581-12	25° 18'	79° 44'	378	2.72	35.40	11.45	
			464	2.72	34.99	8.54	
Ge 532-4	25° 26'	79° 42'	337	1.85	35.76	13.70	
Ge 581-11	25° 17'	79° 36'	470	2.67	35.26	10.92	
Hd 58-4-80	25° 22.4'	79° 35.1'	533	2.77	35.16	10.10	
Ge 532-6	25° 27'	79° 24'	560	2.76	35.30	10.75	
Ge 581-9	25° 15'	79° 20'	650	2.72	35.12	9.91	
Cn 250	25° 06'	77° 45'	690	3.14	35.371	9.92	
At 5332	25° 20'	77° 19'	772	3.25	35.206	8.87	
At 5331	25° 27'	77° 09'	582	3.27	--	11.34	

SOURCES OF DATA 1954 - 1958

SHIP	ABBREVIATION	REFERENCE
Atlantis	At	Data received from National Oceanographic Data Center, Washington 25, D. C.
		Reduced data cards received directly from Woods Hole Oceanographic Institution Woods Hole, Massachusetts
		Conseil Permanent International Pour l'Exploration de la Mer, Bulletin Hydrographique pour l'années 1954 and 1955
Caryn	Cn	Data received from National Oceanographic Data Center, Washington 25, D. C.
		Reduced data cards received directly from Woods Hole Oceanographic Institution Woods Hole, Massachusetts
Crawford	Cf	Reduced data cards received directly from Woods Hole Oceanographic Institution Woods Hole, Massachusetts
		The Woods Hole Oceanographic Institution Atlas Series; Vol I, 1960, F. C. Fuglister, The Atlantic Ocean Atlas of Temperature and Salinity Profiles and data from International Geophysical Year of 1957-58 Woods Hole Oceanographic Institution, Woods Hole, Massachusetts
Discovery II	Di II	The Woods Hole Oceanographic Institution Atlas Series; Vol I, 1960, F. C. Fuglister,

SHIP	ABBREVIATION	REFERENCE
		The Atlantic Ocean Atlas of Temperature and Salinity Profiles and data from International Geophysical Year of 1957-58 Woods Hole Oceanographic Institution Woods Hole, Massachusetts
Gerda	Ge	Data received from National Oceanographic Data Center, Washington 25, D. C.
Hidalgo	Hd	Data received from National Oceanographic Data Center, Washington 25, D. C.
Jakkula	Ja	The A & M College of Texas, Dept. of Oceanology & Meteorology, Ref. 57-15A
		Data received from National Oceanographic Data Center, Washington 25, D. C.
Vema	V	Manuscript Data, Lamont Geological Observatory, Palisades, New York

Notes

1) Depth and (or) O_2 questionable
2) Deepest water bottle
3) Depth of O_2 Min probably too great

TABLE IV

OBSERVATIONS IN THE CORE OF THE SUBANTARCTIC INTERMEDIATE WATER

(Intermediate Salinity Minimum)

I. Basins Outside the Antillean Arc

SHIP AND STATION NUMBER		LAT. N	LONG. W	DEPTH OF SAL. MIN.	SAL. MIN.	TEMP °C	% SIW	NOTE
At	5060	8° 47'	58° 28'	643	34.60	5.87	30	1)
At	1203	8° 41'	57° 30'	677	(34.52)	6.09		1),4),2)
Cf	183	8° 19'	56° 52'	750	34.619	5.63	28	
Cf	182	8° 26'	55° 57'	680	34.578	5.84		
Cf	181	8° 25'	55° 10'	720	34.602	6.05	30	1)
At	5059	9° 08'	58° 20'	607	34.61	6.10	29	1)
At	5058	9° 42'	58° 01'	743	34.57	5.35	32	1)
Alb III 127		10° 19'	57° 46'	653	34.61	6.13	29	1)
At	5057	10° 13'	57° 45'	701	34.61	5.65	29	1),3)
At	5056	10° 31'	57° 20'	767	34.62	5.34	28	
At	5228	11° 53'	60° 37'	751	34.659	5.42	25	
Ch II 1790		11° 44'	58° 35'	750	34.67	5.87	24	
Alb III 126		11° 01'	56° 48'	775	34.61	5.56	29	
At	2747	12° 41'	60° 31'	764	34.60	5.30	30	
At	5227	12° 17'	60° 21'	788	34.654	5.67	26	
At	5226	12° 45'	60° 07'	696	34.669	5.96	27	1)
At	5279	12° 41'	59° 40'	843	34.64	5.30	27	
At	5278	12° 36'	58° 34'	695	34.69	6.01	22	1)
At	3283	12° 07'	58° 17'	778	34.65	5.44	26	5)
At	3282	12° 10'	56° 43'	750	34.63	5.56	27	
At	2746	13° 11'	60° 31'	783	34.69	5.86	22	
At	2744	13° 47'	60° 28'	736	34.61	5.31	29	1)
At	2745	13° 30'	60° 28'	724	34.62	5.46	28	1)
Ch II 1796		13° 40'	60° 26'	750	34.67	6.03	24	
At	5225	13° 07'	59° 52'	647	34.68	6.19	23	1)
Da II 1182		13° 03'	59° 50'	800	34.70	6.04	21	
Ch II 1781		13° 58'	59° 30'	750	34.67	5.83	24	
At	5224	13° 40'	59° 25'	758	34.68	5.49	23	
At	5000	13° 03'	58° 43.5'	736	34.62	5.63	28	1)
At	3285	13° 56'	58° 35'	788	34.70	6.30	21	
At	5276	13° 25'	58° 19'	690	34.61	5.37	29	1)
At	4999	13° 07'	57° 59'	716	34.57	5.77	32	1)
Da II 1181		13° 07'	57° 20'	800	34.63	5.54	27	
At	3280	13° 49'	56° 49'	767	34.63	5.84	27	
At	3281	13° 01'	56° 40'	687	34.61	5.96	29	1)
At	4997	13° 15'	56° 23'	711	34.61	6.11	29	1)
At	4996	13° 19'	55° 35'	764	34.69	6.18	22	
At	3265	13° 02'	55° 05'	783	34.62	5.61	28	
At	5274	14° 08'	60° 42'	687	34.71	6.18	20	1)
At	2741	14° 55'	60° 31'	851	34.69	6.14	22	
At	2743	14° 07'	60° 29'	700	34.64	5.75	27	1)
At	2742	14° 28'	60° 28'	750	34.70	5.96	21	7)
At	3296A	14° 56'	60° 16'	788	34.70	5.53	21	
At	5223	14° 30'	58° 54'	784	34.701	5.85	21	7)
At	3286	14° 40'	58° 40'	783	34.69	5.81	22	

Basins Outside the Antillean Arc (continued)

SHIP AND STATION NUMBER		LAT. N	LONG. W	DEPTH OF SAL. MIN.	SAL. MIN.	TEMP °C	% SIW	NOTE
At	3279	14° 39'	56° 46'	710	34.65	5.96	26	1)
At	3267	14° 42'	55° 08'	756	34.66	5.58	25	
Ch II	1762	15° 12'	61° 04'	750	34.74	5.86	17	
At	2739	15° 55'	60° 48'	700	34.79	6.26	12	1)
At	2740	15° 29'	60° 37'	782	34.73	5.97	9	
At	3295	15° 28'	60° 08'	805	34.67	5.45	24	
At	3287	15° 30'	58° 45'	717	34.67	6.08	24	1)
At	5222	15° 20'	58° 19'	776	34.703	5.88	21	3)
At	2737	16° 50'	61° 00'	839	34.83	5.89	7	
At	5061	16° 28.5'	60° 46'	717	34.82	6.87	9	1)
Cf	309	16° 15'	60° 28'	735	34.686	5.89	22	1)
Ch II	1806	16° 07'	60° 20'	750	34.73	6.37	18	
At	3294	16° 18'	60° 05'	785	34.67	5.86	24	
Cf	307	16° 16'	58° 54'	675	34.701	6.66	21	1)
At	5221	16° 12'	57° 49'	865	34.691			
At	5849	16° 15'	57° 31'	665	34.717	7.28	19	1)
Cf	306	16° 13'	57° 31'	830	34.723	5.70	19	
At	3277	16° 23'	56° 50'	795	34.70	5.89	21	
Cf	305	16° 14'	56° 08'	780	34.786	6.11	12	
At	3269	16° 29'	55° 19'	783	34.79	5.92	12	
Ch II	1808	17° 33'	61° 10'	875	34.83	5.85	7	1), 3)
At	3293	17° 08'	60° 10'	861	34.65	5.74	26	1)
At	5063	17° 30'	59° 54'	966	34.71	5.85	20	1)
At	5064	17° 59'	59° 20'	886	34.66	6.02	25	1)
At	3289	17° 09'	59° 00'	882	34.66	5.75	25	1)
At	3276	17° 13'	56° 48'	798	34.78	6.41	13	
At	5220	17° 30'	56° 47'	843	34.74	5.78	17	
Ch II	1327	17° 04'	56° 00'	750	34.80	6.66	11	
Ch II	1668	17° 10'	56° 00'	750	34.74	5.97	11	
At	3270	17° 23'	55° 19'	839	34.80	(5.63)	11	6)
At	1491	18° 35'	64° 05'	817	34.87	6.59	3	
At	2735	18° 15'	61° 52'	792	34.76	6.63	15	
At	3291	18° 47'	60° 25'	879	34.79	5.88	12	1)
At	5065	18° 27'	58° 51'	988	34.69	5.43	22	1)
At	5066	18° 53'	58° 22'	886	34.78	5.80	13	1)
At	3275	18° 11'	56° 46'	878	34.72	5.76	19	1)
Da II	3544	18° 25'	56° 03'	1000	34.71	5.34	20	1)
At	5219	18° 50'	55° 49'	846	34.78	6.10	13	
At	3271	18° 17'	55° 19'	789	34.78	6.09	13	
At	5165	19° 26'	64° 40'	921	34.81	5.94	10	1)
At	5290	19° 54'	64° 32'	866	34.90	6.72	1	1)
At	3274	19° 02'	56° 42'	849	34.74	5.79	17	
At	3272	19° 19'	55° 17'	873	34.78	5.79	13	3)
At	5218	20° 01'	55° 02'	837	34.845	6.57		

2. Colombia and Venezuela Basins

Ha	234	9° 40'	81° 44'	585	34.79	7.07	12	1)
Ha	235	9° 57'	81° 36'	727	34.79	6.11	12	1)
Ha	241	9° 19'	81° 22'	576	34.78	7.04	13	1)
Ha	209	9° 13'	80° 55'	566	34.78	6.98	13	1)
Ha	211	9° 42'	80° 54'	736	34.78	6.05	13	1)
Ha	203	9° 46'	80° 05'	709	34.76	(6.33)	(15)	1)
Da II	1202	9° 40'	79° 56'	800	34.79	5.80	12	
At	1948	9° 39'	79° 54'	680	34.79	6.49	12	1)
At	1947	9° 49'	79° 32'	760	34.80	6.06	11	
Cf	399	9° 51'	79° 17'	685	34.777	6.38	13	1)
Ha	222	10° 03'	82° 25'	682	34.78	(3.74)	(13)	1)

Colombia and Venezuela Basins (continued)

SHIP AND STATION NUMBER		LAT. N	LONG. W	DEPTH OF SAL. MIN.	SAL. MIN.	TEMP °C	% SIW	NOTE
Ha	223	10° 20'	82° 16'	588	34.79	6.77	12	1)
Ha	224	10° 38'	82° 05'	556	34.76	6.70	15	1)
At	1951	10° 44'	81° 15'	649	34.80	6.65	11	1)
Ha	237	10° 12'	81° 02'	556	34.76	5.61	15	1)
Ha	212	10° 02'	80° 53'	742	34.78	6.21	13	1)
Ha	201	10° 01'	80° 38'	599	34.76		15	1)
At	1950	10° 15'	80° 28'	782	34.80	6.04	11	
Ha	205	10° 32'	80° 24'	773	34.76	6.00	15	
Ha	204	10° 14'	80° 16'	725	34.79	6.25	12	1)
Cf	398	10° 22'	79° 18'	635	34.774	6.47	14	1)
At	1945	10° 55'	79° 04'	731	34.81	5.99	10	1)
At	5689	10° 46'	67° 16'	694	34.755	6.07	15	1)
At	1953	11° 48'	82° 28'	731	34.78	6.36	13	1)
At	1952	11° 15'	81° 50'	797	34.80	5.89	11	
Cf	396	11° 52'	79° 22'	705	34.796	6.84	11	1)
Cf	397	11° 03'	79° 18'	665	34.793	6.62	12	1)
At	1944	11° 38'	78° 30'	626	34.82	7.01	9	1)
Da II	3547	11° 00'	77° 40'	600	34.79	7.05	12	1)
At	5745	11° 04'	75° 29'	657	34.793	6.70	12	1)
At	1531	11° 55'	74° 52'	800	34.79	5.84	12	
At	5739	11° 31'	74° 47'	731	34.768	6.13	14	1)
At	1529	11° 52'	74° 19'	790	34.81	5.92	10	
At	5737	11° 38'	74° 07'	598	34.771	6.84	14	1)
Cf	355	11° 51'	73° 46'	745	34.793	5.88	12	1)
At	5233	11° 47'	68° 36'	643	34.727	6.35	18	1)
At	1505	11° 49'	68° 32'	686	34.72	6.02	19	1), 7)
At	5696	11° 47'	68° 30'	782	34.768	5.67	14	
At	5692	11° 55'	67° 18'	771	34.774	5.82	14	
At	5690	11° 01'	67° 16'	700	34.745	6.15	16	1)
At	5691	11° 28'	67° 13'	727	34.755	6.13	14	1)
At	2796	11° 42'	67° 11'	634	34.71	6.21	20	1)
At	2795	11° 21'	67° 08'	597	34.73	6.77	18	1)
At	2792	11° 56'	64° 43'	729	34.70	6.03	21	1)
At	5665	11° 44'	64° 36'	686	34.745	6.21	16	1)
At	5666	11° 30'	64° 36'	694	34.742	6.36	17	1)
Cf	345	11° 34'	64° 31'	680	34.738	6.13	17	1)
At	5664	11° 58'	64° 28'	696	34.748	6.54	16	1)
Ch II	1784	11° 55'	62° 44'	750	34.70	6.03	21	
At	5662	11° 52'	62° 44'	590	34.738	6.75	17	1)
At	2754	11° 44'	62° 13'	735	34.65	5.78	26	1)
At	1954	12° 04'	82° 41'	783	34.79	6.26	12	
Cf	395	12° 26'	79° 18'	835	34.793	5.97	12	
Cf	1943	12° 39'	79° 41'	729	34.78	6.18	13	1)
At	1533	12° 53'	76° 18'	782	34.82	5.90	9	
At	1532	12° 21'	75° 29'	790	34.79	5.88	12	
V 12	53	12° 08'	75° 01'	(740)	(34.778)	(6.65)	(13)	
At	1528	12° 18'	74° 14'	800	34.76	5.80	19	
At	5738	12° 00'	74° 06'	584	34.774	6.98	14	1)
Cf	356	12° 26'	73° 45'	655	34.764	6.56	15	1)
At	5234	12° 10'	68° 35'	592	34.759	7.00	15	1)
At	5235	12° 35'	68° 35'	655	34.727	6.28	18	1)
At	1506	12° 28'	68° 34'	582	34.72	6.58	19	1)
At	1507	12° 53'	68° 32'	764	34.78	5.76	13	
At	5694	12° 33'	68° 30'	751	34.766	6.14	14	
At	5695	12° 10'	68° 29'	788	34.763	5.99	14	
At	5693	12° 17'	67° 16'	694	34.745	6.41	16	1
At	2798	12° 29'	67° 14'	591	34.71	6.41	20	1

SHIP AND STATION NUMBER		LAT. N	LONG. W	DEPTH OF SAL. MIN.	SAL. MIN.	TEMP °C	% SIW	NOTE
At	2797	12° 07'	67° 10'	668	3 4.70	5.96	21	
At	2791	12° 13'	64° 40'	764	3 4.78	5.64	13	
At	2790	12° 45'	64° 38'	668	3 4.69	5.77	22	
Ch II	1786	12° 22'	64° 35'	750	3 4.72	5.78	19	
At	1504	12° 03'	64° 35'	778	3 4.76	5.94	15	
At	1502	12° 38'	64° 34'	598	3 4.76	6.80	15	1)
At	1503	12° 12'	64° 34'	797	34.77	5.75	14	
Cf	341	12° 30'	64° 32'	715	34.733	6.17	18	1)
Cf	342	12° 06'	64° 32'	700	34.737	6.10	17	1)
Ch II	1787	12° 40'	63° 15'	750	34.68	6.05	23	
Re	59-16	12° 54'	63° 02'	853	34.71	5.49	20	1)
At	5663	12° 29'	62° 49'	798	34.720	5.92	19	
At	2755	12° 00'	62° 23'	691	34.65	6.15	26	1)
Ch II	1788	12° 39'	62° 02'	750	34.67	5.74	24	
At	2756	12° 24'	61° 48'	636	34.65	6.09	26	1)
At	1959	13° 17'	81° 30'	746	34.78	6.36	13	1)
At	1960	13° 19'	81° 12'	775	34.79	5.86	12	
At	1962	13° 34'	80° 30'	776	34.79	5.98	12	
At	1964	13° 42'	80° 00'	798	34.79	6.07	12	
Cf	394	13° 00'	79° 15'	755	34.794	6.69	12	
Cf	393	13° 45'	79° 12'	765	34.796	6.73	11	
At	1535	13° 47'	77° 48'	600	34.79	7.25	11	1)
At	1942	13° 33'	77° 03'	685	34.83	6.49	7	1), 3)
At	1534	13° 20'	77° 03'	769	34.80	5.94	11	
At	1527	13° 15'	73° 58'	800	34.80	5.84	11	
Cf	358	13° 44'	73° 56'	770	34.776	6.15	13	
Cf	357	13° 06'	73° 55'	745	34.741	6.20	17	1)
At	5733	13° 02'	71° 42'	660	34.755	6.52	15	1)
Da II	3546	13° 11'	70° 26'	800	34.74	5.89	17	
At	5257	13° 07'	68° 37'	751	34.701	6.15	21	
At	1509	13° 58'	68° 36'	773	34.74	6.22	17	
At	1508	13° 30'	68° 34'	546	34.76	7.10	15	1)
At	2800	13° 37'	67° 20'	770	3 4.74	5.66	17	
At	2799	13° 09'	67° 15'	770	3 4.74	5.80	17	
At	5272	13° 30'	65° 24'	695	3 4.70	5.98	21	1)
At	2788	13° 42'	64° 35'	800	3 4.70	5.62	21	
At	1500	13° 48'	64° 35'	701	34.70	6.17	21	1)
At	1501	13° 13'	64° 33'	575	3 4.70	6.59	21	1)
Cf	340	13° 05'	64° 32'	780	34.729	6.25	18	
Cf	339	13° 47'	64° 28'	690	34.737	6.47	17	1)
Ch II	1791	13° 25'	62° 37'	750	34.72	6.03	19	
At	5282	13° 09'	62° 15'	674	(34.68)	6.28	(23)	2)
Da II	1183	13° 47'	61° 26'	700	3 4.69	6.12	18	3)
At	2757	13° 05'	61° 25'	782	3 4.70	5.67	22	
At	2758	13° 25'	61° 12'	621	34.67	6.12	24	1)
At	2759	13° 35'	61° 09'	755	34.71	5.52	20	
At	2760	13° 44'	61° 09'	744	34.70	5.85	21	1)
At	1965	14° 09'	79° 40'	666	3 4.81	6.18	10	1)
At	1966	14° 42'	79° 18'	747	34.77	6.36	14	
At	1537	14° 36'	79° 14'	787	34.76	6.06	15	
Cf	392	14° 38'	79° 06'	835	3 4.790	6.21	12	
At	1536	14° 12'	78° 46'	768	34. 76	6.21	15	
Da II	1214	14° 21'	76° 50'	800	3 4.74	5.82	17	
At	1941	14° 46'	76° 47'	746	34.82	5.88	9	1)
V 12	58	14° 22'	74° 56'	745	34.77	6.19	14	1)
At	1526	14° 15'	74° 01'	944	34.81	5.74	10	1)
Cf	360	14° 59'	73° 58'	765	3 4.808	6.20	9	

SHIP AND STATION NUMBER		LAT. N	LONG. W	DEPTH OF SAL. MIN.	SAL. MIN.	TEMP °C	% SIW	NOTE
S Pa	62-4	14° 25'	70° 52'	677	34.70	6.64	21	1)
At	5258	14° 04'	68° 48'	854	34.721	6.38	19	
At	1510	14° 54'	68° 33'	800	34.76	5.94	15	
S Pa	62-3	14° 37'	68° 03'	814	34.76	5.95	15	
At	2802	14° 46'	67° 13'	717	34.69	5.93	22	1)
At	2801	14° 10'	67° 13'	646	34.67	6.11	24	1)
Cf	338	14° 32'	64° 41'	700	34.740	6.34	17	1)
At	2786	14° 43'	64° 33'	800	34.70	5.77	21	
Ch II	1793	14° 01'	64° 31'	750	34.70	5.90	21	
At	1499	14° 38'	64° 30'	744	34.69	5.99	22	
Ca	31	14° 46'	63° 26'	625	34.69	6.64	22	1)
Ch II	1794	14° 11'	63° 02'	750	34.72	6.03	19	
At	5283	14° 13'	62° 55'	781	34.73	(5.37)	18	6)
Ch II	1801	14° 56'	62° 05'	750	34.68	6.21	23	
At	2765	14° 58'	61° 20'	703	34.71	6.04	20	1)
At	2764	14° 50'	61° 18'	674	34.75	6.77	16	1)
Da II	1285	14° 38'	61° 16'	600	34.74	6.82	17	1)
At	2763	14° 22'	61° 04'	653	34.70	6.42	21	1)
At	2761	14° 07'	61° 03'	714	34.70	5.91	21	1)
At	2762	14° 17'	61° 02'	698	34.70	6.10	21	
Ch II	1758	14° 20'	60° 52'	850	34.71	6.19	20	1)
At	1539	15° 35'	80° 38'	746	34.78	6.00	13	1)
At	1538	15° 12'	79° 54'	772	34.76	6.31	15	
At	1967	15° 08'	79° 16'	790	34.79	6.19	12	
Cf	391	15° 11'	79° 13'	800	34.777	6.22	13	
Cf	390	15° 46'	79° 11'	800	34.83	6.41	7	3)
Ha	193	15° 00'	79° 00'	706	34.83	6.80	7	1)
At	1968	15° 27'	78° 55'	748	34.81	6.68	10	1)
At	1940	15° 20'	76° 40'	797	34.83	5.92	7	
At	1525	15° 11'	74° 01'	765	34.79	6.12	12	
Cf	361	15° 38'	73° 56'	795	34.798	5.95	11	
At	5259	15° 11'	68° 44'	814	34.731	6.15	18	
At	1511	15° 47'	68° 30'	798	34.74	6.10	17	
Ca	32	15° 18'	68° 11'	772	34.71	5.84	20	
At	2803	15° 18'	67° 11'	813	34.75	5.67	16	
At	3297Y	15° 37'	66° 21'	779	34.76	6.24	15	
At	3297E	15° 36'	66° 21'	780	34.78	5.92	13	
At	2784	15° 48'	64° 42'	720	34.74	6.40	17	1)
Cf	337	15° 08'	64° 34'	780	34.732	6.25	18	
At	2785	15° 09'	64° 30'	767	34.70	5.91	21	
At	1498	15° 24'	64° 29'	733	34.72	6.01	19	1)
Cf	336	15° 48'	64° 26'	785	34.726	6.09	18	
Ch II	1803	15° 33'	64° 11'	750	34.79	6.50	12	
Ch II	1804	15° 42'	63° 04'	750	34.73	6.34	18	
Ch II	1805	15° 37'	61° 48'	750	34.73	6.17	18	
At	2769	15° 54'	61° 45'	795	34.75	5.83	16	
At	2768	15° 38'	61° 36'	692	34.73	6.43	18	1)
At	2767	15° 10'	61° 24'	666	34.69	5.71	22	1)
At	2766	15° 05'	61° 22'	774	34.74	5.72	17	
Ch II	1763	15° 04'	61° 16'	724	34.78	6.19	13	1)
At	1970	16° 12'	78° 36'	783	34.84	6.67	6	
At	1971	16° 28'	78° 25'	762	34.86	6.68	4	
At	1972	16° 41'	78° 14'	784	34.81	6.45	10	
At	1938	16° 56'	76° 29'	862	34.83	6.21	7	1)
At	1939	16° 10'	76° 28'	842	34.81	6.15	10	
Cf	362	16° 26'	73° 57'	835	34.809	6.21	10	
At	5260	16° 14'	68° 38'	656	34.786	6.84	12	1)

SHIP AND STATION NUMBER		LAT. N	LONG. W	DEPTH OF SAL. MIN.	SAL. MIN.	TEMP °C	% SIW	NOTE
At	1512	16° 42'	68° 36'	820	34.78	6.18	13	
At	2806	16° 58'	67° 20'	789	34.83	6.49	7	
At	2805	16° 28'	67° 11'	787	34.78	5.86	13	
At	5284	16° 03'	66° 02'	806	34.75	6.00	16	
At	2782	16° 44'	64° 34'	802	34.72	6.14	19	
At	2783	16° 14'	64° 30'	750	34.74	6.36	17	
Cf	335	16° 25'	64° 28'	755	34.725	6.21	18	
Ch II	1811	16° 17'	63° 55'	750	34.78	6.50	13	
Ch II	1810	16° 17'	63° 55'	750	34.79	6.11	12	
At	2773	16° 36'	62° 10'	721	34.74	6.33	17	1)
At	2772	16° 31'	62° 06'	764	34.73	6.08	18	
At	2771	16° 23'	62° 00'	744	34.72	5.99	19	1)
At	2770	16° 17'	61° 55'	734	34.76	5.99	15	1)
At	1974	17° 23'	77° 39'	789	34.80	6.58	11	
At	1975	17° 33'	77° 36'	777	34.87	6.66	3	
At	1936	17° 28'	76° 40'	769	34.84	6.80	6	
At	1937	17° 12'	76° 33'	795	34.83	6.57	3	
Cf	363	17° 04'	73° 55'	885	34.843	5.87	5	1)
At	1522	17° 34'	73° 55'	792	34.855	6.84	4	
At	1523	17° 04'	73° 55'	800	34.88	6.98	2	
At	1521	17° 56'	73° 54'	800	34.87	6.78	3	
Cf	365	17° 57'	73° 52'	870	34.843	6.07	6	1)
Cf	364	17° 45'	73° 49'	800	34.834	6.64	7	
Da II	1247	17° 57'	72° 51'	800	34.83	6.85	7	
At	1514	17° 43'	68° 36'	776	34.80	6.89	11	
At	5261	17° 05'	68° 35'	710	34.803	6.68	11	1)
At	5262	17° 45'	68° 35'	812	34.890	6.58	1	3)
At	1515	17° 57'	68° 28'	755	34.89	6.91	1	
Da II	1251	17° 48'	67° 22'	800	34.85	6.97	5	
At	2807	17° 28'	67° 15'	818	34.78	6.21	13	
Pu	30	17° 26'	66° 08'	710	34.83	7.37	7	1)
Cn	217	17° 25'	66° 08'	858	34.83	6.11	7	1)
At	5285	17o 54'	65° 51.5'	849	34.84	6.06	6	
At	5286	17° 53'	65° 20'	817	34.81	6.30	10	
Da II	1269	17° 13'	64° 58'	800	34.74	6.11	17	
Da II	1290	17° 45'	64° 56'	800	34.85	6.85	5	
Da II	1277	17° 45'	64° 56'	800	34.83	6.88	7	
Da II	1266A	17° 45'	64° 56'	800	34.83	6.66	7	
Da II	1266B	17° 45'	64° 56'	800	34.83	6.60	7	
Da II	1259	17° 43'	64° 56'	800	34.85	6.85	5	
Da II	1189	17° 58'	64° 41'	800	34.82	6.53	9	
Da II	1186	17° 58'	64° 41'	800	34.86	6.88	4	
At	2781	17° 10'	64° 33'	735	34.79	6.71	12	1)
Cf	334	17° 05'	64° 32'	790	34.763	6.20	15	
At	1495	17° 40'	64° 30'	756	34.81	6.60	10	
At	1496	17° 06'	64° 29'	747	34.77	6.38	14	
Cf	333	17° 30'	64° 25'	855	34.781	5.98	13	
Ch II	1811	17° 30'	64° 21'	750	34.81	6.54	10	
Cf	332	17° 53'	64° 18'	770	34.78	6.62	13	
At	5287	17° 54'	64° 16'	854	34.84	6.09	6	1)
At	2777	17° 48'	63° 41'	812	34.87	6.32	3	
At	1493	18° 01'	64° 36'	822	34.84	6.47	6	3)
Cf	330	18° 20'	64° 17'	795	34.826	6.60	8	
Cf	331	18° 07'	64° 16'	770	34.833	6.76	7	

3. Cayman and Yucatan Basins

Cf	371	16° 26'	84° 24'	645	34.843	6.51	6	1)
At	1591	16° 59'	83° 57'	695	34.87	7.07	3	1)

SHIP AND STATION NUMBER	LAT. N	LONG. W	DEPTH OF SAL. MIN.	SAL. MIN.	TEMP °C	% SIW	NOTE
At 1590	16° 32'	83° 54'	747	34.85	6.06	5	1)
Cf 389	16° 26'	79° 10'	815	3 4.804	6.23	11	
V 17 11	17° 51'	86° 57'	743	(34.852)		(5)	2)
V 17 13	17° 01'	84° 44'	744	34.843		6	
Cf 373	17° 46'	84° 29'	640	34.831	6.78	7	1)
Cf 372	17° 07'	84° 28'	585	34.832	6.58	7	1)
At 1593	17° 28'	83° 59'	800	34.85	5.78	5	
At 1594	17° 54'	83° 58'	718	34.85	6.43	5	1)
Ph 84	17° 39'	83° 12'	709	34.83	5.95	7	1)
V 17 17	17° 13'	82° 50'	745	(34.842)	6.06	(6)	1)
At 1584	17° 16'	81° 25'	754	34.83	6.02	7	
At 1548	17° 08'	79° 30'	788	34.79	6.22	12	
Cf 388	17° 06'	79° 10'	810	34.804	6.43	11	
Cf 387	17° 47'	79° 09'	790	34.840	6.44	6	
At 1549	17° 16'	79° 08'	794	34.85	6.74	5	
Cf 374	18° 27'	84° 31'	810	34.836	6.23	6	
At 1597	18° 56'	84° 08'	800	34.85	6.59	5	
V 17 16	18° 22'	84° 00'	808	(34.845)	5.96	(5)	
At 1595	18° 24'	83° 59'	778	34.83	6.22	7	
At 1596	18° 43'	83° 57'	800	34.85	6.40	5	
V 17 22	18° 31'	81° 30'	790	34.822	6.10	8	
At 1582	18° 21'	81° 25'	778	34.83	6.59	7	
At 1581	18° 58'	81° 21'	800	34.87	6.93	3	
Cf 386	18° 30'	79° 13'	775	34.814	6.74	10	
Da II 1217	18° 50'	79° 07'	800	34.78	6.23	13	
At 1567	18° 35'	77° 31'	800	34.90	6.60	1	
At 1601	19° 37'	86° 55'	800	(34.84)	(5.70)	(6)	2)
At 1600	19° 33'	86° 24'	842	(34.83)	5.91	(7)	2)
V 17 9	19° 06'	85° 41'	746	(34.757)	6.52	(15)	2)
At 1599	19° 18'	85° 40'	792	34.83	6.45	9	
V 17 8	19° 25'	85° 13'	840	(34.830)		(7)	2)
V 17 7	19° 40'	84° 53'	787	34.835	6.58	7	
At 1598	19° 07'	84° 47'	766	34.88	6.92	2	
Cf 376	19° 47'	84° 31'	750	34.825	6.70	8	
Cf 375	19° 06'	84° 30'	800	34.818	6.39	9	
At 1992	19° 32'	83° 50'	843	(34.85)	5.92	(5)	2)
At 1991	19° 05'	83° 50'	701	34.88	6.80	2	1)
At 1988	19° 14'	81° 38'	786	34.86	6.91	4	
At 1986	19° 49'	81° 26'	904	34.90	6.26	1	1)
At 1580	19° 72'	81° 20'	800	34.88	6.89	2	
At 1579	19° 24'	80° 52'	800	34.81	6.70	10	
At 1577	19° 36'	80° 11'	900	34.85	5.62	5	1)
At 1977	19° 49'	79° 46'	790	34.89	7.01	1	
At 1576	19° 45'	79° 39'	800	34.90	6.85	1	
Pu 39	19° 20'	79° 25'	756	34.85	6.44	5	
At 1575	19° 48'	79° 00'	800	34.85	6.91	5	
At 1572	19° 38'	77° 42'	889	34.90	6.23	1	1), 3)
At 3301	19° 58'	73° 40'	840	34.90	6.64	1	
Cf 377	20° 28'	84° 30'	795	34.850	7.02	5	
V 17 6	20° 01'	84° 21'	800	34.871	6.11	3	
V 17 5	20° 31'	84° 03'	777	34.881	6.63	2	
At 1994	20° 41'	84° 00'	841	34.86	6.29	4	
At 1980	20° 35'	79° 19'	847	34.86	6.33	4	
At 1981	20° 53'	79° 11'	834	34.88	6.47	2	
Cf 382	20° 35'	79° 10'	875	(34.894)	(6.36)	(1)	2)
Cf 383	20° 06'	79° 10'	865	34.834	6.33	8	1)
Cf 367	20° 04'	73° 39'	780	34.880	6.64	2	

SHIP AND STATION NUMBER	LAT. N	LONG. W	DEPTH OF SAL. MIN.	SAL. MIN.	TEMP °C	% SIW	NOTE
Da II 1220	21° 34'	86° 19'	800	(34.81)	5.63	(10)	2)
Cn 245	21° 38'	86° 06'	702	34.84	5.97	6	1)
At 2335	21° 42'	85° 57'	774	34.83	6.40	7	
Cn 243	21° 45'	85° 46'	768	34.844	6.76	6	
Da II 1221	21° 49'	85° 41'	800	34.83	6.66	7	
Cf 378	21° 06'	84° 29'	790	34.823	6.73	9	
Cf 379	21° 36'	84° 28'	880	34.845	6.07	6	1)
At 1995	21° 27'	84° 22'	894	(34.88)	5.82	(2)	7)
Cn 238	21° 29'	80° 20'	873	34.860	6.19	4	1)

SOURCES OF DATA

SHIP AND YEAR	ABBREVIATION	REFERENCES
Albatross III 1952	Alb III	Reduced data cards received directly from Woods Hole Oceanographic Institution, Woods Hole, Massachusetts Conseil Permanent International pour l'Exploration de la Mer; Bulletin Hydrographique pour l'année 1952
Atlantis 1932, 1933, 1934, 1937, 1939, 1952, 1954, 1955, 1957, 1958, 1961	At	Reduced data cards received directly from Woods Hole Oceanographic Institution, Woods Hole, Massachusetts The Woods Hole Oceanographic Institution Atlas Series, Vol I, 1960, F. C. Fuglister, The Atlantic Ocean Atlas of Temperature and Salinity Profiles and data from International Geophysical Year of 1957-58, Woods Hole Oceanographic Institution, Woods Hole, Massachusetts Conseil Permanent International pour l'Exploration de la Mer; Bulletin Hydrographique pour les années, 1932-55 Data received from National Oceanographic Data Center, Washington 25, D. C.
Carnegie 1928	Ca	Data received from National Oceanographic Data Center, Washington 25, D. C. Deutsche Atlantische Expedition METEOR Band VI, Erster Teil, Berlin, 1936
Caryn 1954	Cn	Reduced data cards received directly from Woods Hole Oceanographic Institution, Woods Hole, Massachusetts Data received from National Oceanographic Data Center, Washington 25, D. C.

SHIP AND YEAR	ABBREVIATION	REFERENCES
Challenger II 1933, 1935, 1936, 1938	Ch II	Conseil Permanent International pour l'Exploration de la Mer; Bulletin Hydrographique pour l'années 1933, 1935, 1936, 1938
Crawford 1957, 1958	Cf	Reduced data cards received from Woods Hole Oceanographic Institution, Woods Hole, Massachusetts
Dana II 1921, 1922, 1928	Da II	The Danish DANA Expeditions, 1920-22 Oceanographic Report No. 1-8, Copenhagen, 1929 Data received from National Oceanographic Data Center, Washington 25, D. C.
Hannibal 1936	Ha	Data received from National Oceanographic Data Center, Washington 25, D. C.
Physalia 1954	Ph	University of Miami, Marine Laboratory, Ref. 55-1
Pursuit 1953	Pu	Data received from National Oceanographic Data Center, Washington 25, D. C.
Rehoboth 1950	Re	Data received from National Oceanographic Data Center, Washington 25, D. C. H. O. Publication #617c, 1952
San Pablo 1950	S Pa	Data received from National Oceanographic Data Center, Washington 25, D. C. H. O. Publication #617D, 1953
Vema 1957, 1961	V	Manuscript Data, Lamont Geological Observatory, Palisades, New York

Notes

1) These values have not been used for the construction of the T/S relationship because of widely-spaced observation points. They lie too far from the center of the core layer which is between 750 and 850 meters.
The relatively steep gradient of temperature distorts that relationship.
They have, however, been utilized for the construction of isohalines in the

       core map because contrary to the temperature, the vertical gradient of salinity in the core layers is very small.

2) Doubtful values.
3) Average of two observations
4) Salinity probably too low
5) Secondary salinity minimum
6) Temperature too low
7) Observations too widely spaced

TABLE V

OBSERVATIONS IN THE CORE OF THE NORTH ATLANTIC DEEP WATER

(Intermediate Oxygen Maximum)

1.Observations Within the Tongue of the Main Spreading of the NADW (upper O_2 Maximum) Along the Outside of the Antillean Arc in the North America Basin

1a   DANA   1921-22

STATION	LAT. N	LONG. W	DEPTH m	O_2 m/l	S o/oo	TEMP °C	NOTE
1181	13° 07'	57° 20'	2500	5.67	34.97	3.05	
1185	17° 41'	60° 58'	2500	(5.41)	(34.94)	(3.22)	8b)
1261	19° 04'	65° 43'	2000	6.02	34.97	3.43	8a)
1242	24° 05'	74° 36'	1500	5.97	34.96	3.93	
			(2000)	(5.88)	(34.96)	(3.48)	
1241	25° 18'	74° 00'	(2500)	(5.82)	(34.94)	(3.12)	1)
Tobago B.							
1182	13° 03'	59° 50'	(1500)	(5.58)	(34.99)	(4.10)	1)
Average of 7 observations			21 hm	5.76	34.96	3.48	**
Standard Deviation			± 4 hm	±0.22	± 0.02	±0.40	

** These averages are not representative for the concerned area and year (because of the small number of observations and their uneven distribution.

1b   ATLANTIS   1932-33

STATION	LAT. N	LONG. W	DEPTH m	O_2 m/l	S o/oo	TEMP °C	NOTE
1208	20° 38'	68° 36'	1600	6.22	34.99	3.69	
1209	21° 19'	68° 13'	1629	6.07	34.96	3.60	
			2021	6.07	34.96	3.39	
1483	21° 46'	62° 48'	1880	6.06	34.98	3.51	
1210	22° 14'	67° 50'	2500	6.04	34.98	(3.00)	3)
1212	23° 46'	67° 24'	1569	6.14	(35.02)	4.11	2)
Average of 6 observations			19 hm	6.10	34.98	3.55	**
Standard Deviation			± 3 hm	±0.12	± 0.01	±0.30	

** These averages have to be combined with those of the period, 1937, in order to have representative ATLANTIS averages for the period, 1932-37.

OBSERVATIONS WITHIN THE BRANCHES TO THE EAST:

STATION	LAT. N	LONG. W	DEPTH m	O_2 m/l	S o/oo	TEMP °C	NOTE
1202	8° 41'	56° 30'	(1835)	(5.94)	(34.97)	(3.29)	1)
1486	19° 07'	63° 00'	(1910)	(5.84)	(34.98)	(3.65)	1)
1485	20° 00'	62° 31'	1920	5.82	34.98	3.64	
1484	20° 55'	62° 08'	1949	6.04	34.98	3.57	
1482	23° 28'	62° 40'	2441	5.86	34.95	3.06	
1481	25° 19'	66° 53'	1595	5.90	34.95	3.95	5)
			2490	6.03	34.98	3.12	5)

1c ATLANTIS 1937

STATION	LAT. N	LONG. W	DEPTH m	O$_2$ m/l	S o/oo	TEMP °C	NOTE
2742	14° 28'	60° 28'	(1599)	(6.13)	(34.97)	(3.82)	1)
2740	15° 29'	60° 37'	1698	6.29	34.96	3.68	
2737	16° 50'	61° 00'	1906	6.19	34.98	3.50	
2736	17° 32'	61° 10'	(2007)	(6.20)	(34.97)	(3.38)	1)
2733	18° 59'	62° 37'	(2225)	(6.29)	(34.97)	(3.25)	1)
2735	18° 15'	61° 52'	2178	6.43	34.96	3.30	9), 1)
2732	19° 40'	62° 12'	(2371)	(6.29)	(34.97)	(3.17)	1)
Tobago B. 2747	12° 41'	60° 31'	(1681)	(6.12)	(34.98)	(3.67)	1)
Tobago B. 2748	12° 04'	60° 29'	(1460)	(6.09)	(34.97)	(3.82)	1)
Tobago B. 2746	13° 11'	60° 31'	(1997)	(6.12)	(34.96)	(3.62)	1)
Tobago B. 2745	13° 30'	60° 28'	(1539)	(6.05)	(34.96)	(3.74)	1)
Average of 10 observations			18 hm	6.18	34.97	3.57	} **
Standard Deviation			± 3 hm	±0.09	± 0.01	±0.23	

** See footnote under 1b

OBSERVATIONS WITHIN THE BRANCHES TO THE EAST IN 20° - 24° N:

STATION	LAT. N	LONG. W	DEPTH m	O$_2$ m/l	S o/oo	TEMP °C	NOTE
2731	20° 24'	61° 45'	1730	6.10	35.00	3.76	
2730	21° 21'	61° 11'	1820	5.98	35.02	3.84	
2729	21° 50'	60° 33'	2128	6.17	34.97	3.43	
2728	22° 32'	60° 03'	1835	6.20	34.99	3.62	
2726	24° 00'	59° 03'	1564	5.84	35.03	4.35	

1e ATLANTIS 1937

STATION	LAT. N	LONG. W	DEPTH m	O$_2$ m/l	S o/oo	TEMP °C	NOTE
5059	9° 08'	58° 20'	(1966)	(6.13)	(34.96)	(3.18)	1)
5058	9° 41'	58° 00'	(1718)	(6.15)	(34.96)	3.68	
5057	10° 13'	57° 45'	2086	6.06	34.94	3.28	
5056	10° 31'	57° 20'	1844	6.13	35.00	3.68	
5063	17° 30'	59° 54'	1933	6.00	34.97	3.56	
			(2419)	(6.00)	(34.95)	(3.08)	1)
5064	17° 59'	59° 20'	1815	5.98	34.98	3.71	
			(2288)	(5.98)	(34.96)	(3.25)	1)
5065	18° 27'	58° 51'	1965	6.05	34.95	3.56	
5066	18° 53'	58° 22'	1831	6.00	34.97	3.74	
			2312	6.00	34.96	3.23	
5067	20° 46'	59° 10'	1830	5.83	34.98	3.84	
Average of 12 observations			20 hm	6.03	34.97	3.48	
Standard Deviation			± 2 hm	±0.09	± 0.02	±0.26	

ALBATROSS 1952

STATION	LAT. N	LONG. W	DEPTH m	O$_2$ m/l	S o/oo	TEMP °C	NOTE
126	11° 01'	56° 48'	1923	(5.59)	(34.99)	(3.61)	1)

1d ATLANTIS 1939

STATION	LAT. N	LONG. W	DEPTH m	O$_2$ m/l	S o/oo	TEMP °C	NOTE
3285	13° 56'	58° 35'	1670	5.77	35.00	3.71	
3280	13° 49'	56° 49'	(1738)	(5.84)	(35.00)	(3.79)	1)

[174]

STATION	LAT. N	LONG. W	DEPTH m	O$_2$ m/l	S o/oo	TEMP °C	NOTE
3281	13° 01'	56° 40'	(1711)	(5.68)	(35.00)	(3.95)	1)
3279	14° 39'	56° 46'	(1878)	(5.74)	(34.99)	3.62	1)
3295	15° 28'	60° 08'	2032	5.88	34.97	3.48	
			2227	5.88	34.97	3.33	
3268	15° 39'	55° 13'	1823	5.66	34.98	3.57	
3293	17° 08'	60° 10'	2046	5.86	34.99	3.49	
			2052	5.94	34.98	3.44	
3289	17° 09'	59° 00'	1837	5.94	34.97	3.60	
3291	18° 47'	60° 25'	2218	5.90	34.99	3.35	
3275	18° 11'	56° 46'	1922	5.80	34.99	3.58	
3273	19° 52'	56° 51'	1895	5.70	35.00	3.64	
Average of 13 observations			19 hm	5.81	34.99	3.58	**
Standard Deviation			± 2 hm	±0.10	± 0.01	±0.17	

** These averages are not representative for the entire concerned area because the observations cover only the southern part (10°-20°N) of the tongue of the main spreading of the NADW.

1f   ATLANTIS AND CARYN   1954 - 55

STATION	LAT. N	LONG. W	DEPTH m	O$_2$ m/l	S o/oo	TEMP °C	NOTE
At 5278	12° 36'	58° 34'	(1744)	(5.72)	(35.03)	(3.85)	1)
At 5276	13° 25'	58° 19'	1858	5.84	35.02	3.63	
At 5277	13° 50'	56° 53'	2008	5.69	34.99	3.51	
			2387	5.69	34.97	3.17	
At 5223	14° 30'	58° 54'	2070	5.81	34.97	3.38	
At 5222	15° 20'	58° 19'	2561	5.67	34.95	3.03	
At 5220	17° 30'	56° 47'	2426	5.57	34.961	3.12	
At 5288	18° 52'	63° 05'	2400	5.78	35.02	3.21	
At 5291	19° 52'	66° 35'	1964	5.46	34.98	3.42	
At 5168	19° 21'	66° 18'	2197	5.78	35.00	3.32	
At 5166	19° 55'	64° 51'	2092	5.70	35.01	3.46	
At 5165	19° 25'	64° 40'	1838	5.71	34.99	3.69	
At 5290	19° 54'	64° 32'	2395	5.47	34.96	3.10	
At 5289	19° 56'	62° 50'	1948	5.47	(35.02)	3.56	2)
At 5167	20° 25'	64° 53'	1652	5.75	35.03	3.91	
Cn 219	21° 43'	68° 11'	1929	5.92	35.02	3.57	
			2219	5.92	35.01	3.29	
Cn 220	22° 43'	67° 47'	1958	5.92	35.00	3.53	
			2250	5.92	34.98	3.20	
At 5164	23° 54'	73° 46'	2560	5.71	34.99	3.19	
Cn 221	23° 40'	67° 38'	1664	5.81	(35.04)	3.91	2)
Cn 222	24° 36'	67° 22'	1835	5.70	34.98	3.92	5)
			2118	5.70	34.98	3.48	
At 5163	25° 30'	76° 06'	2013	5.75	34.98	(3.50)	3)
Tobago B. At 5228	11° 53'	60° 37'	(1499)	(5.65)	(34.987)	(3.92)	1)
Tobago B. At 5227	12° 17'	60° 21'	1800	5.75	34.972	3.69	
Tobago B. At 5226	12° 45'	60° 07'	1656	5.77	34.98	3.75	
Tobago B. At 5225	13° 07'	59° 52'	(1407)	(5.59)	(34.99)	(3.90)	1)
Average of 28 observations			20 hm	5.72	34.99	3.51	**
Standard Deviation			± 3 hm	±0.13	± 0.01	±0.28	

** Suspicious (too low) oxygen averages because of analytic difficulties

OBSERVATIONS WITHIN THE BRANCH TO THE EAST IN 20° - 24° N.

STATION	LAT. N	LONG. W	DEPTH m	O₂ m/l	S o/oo	TEMP °C	NOTE
At 5218	20° 01'	55° 02'	2475	5.45	34.964	3.06	
Cn 216	20° 02'	55° 00'	1741	5.58	35.00	3.95	
Cn 215	21° 04'	55° 41'	1671	5.67	35.00	4.03	
Cn 214	22° 25'	56° 15'	1696	5.64	35.03	3.96	
Cn 212	23° 57'	57° 39'	1751	5.67	35.09	3.97	
Cn 213	23° 10'	57° 00'	1707	5.67	35.05	4.01	

OBSERVATIONS WITHIN THE TONGUE OF OCEAN:

STATION	LAT. N	LONG. W	DEPTH m	O₂ m/l	S o/oo	TEMP °C	NOTE
Cn 225	23° 57'	77° 17'	(1250)	(5.16)	(35.016)	(4.53)	1)
Cn 256	23° 44'	77° 09'	(1365)	(5.32)	(35.006)	(4.20)	1)
Cn 257	23° 41'	76° 52'	1231	5.18	35.018	4.58	
Cn 251	24° 50'	77° 40'	(1700)	(5.64)	(34.982)	(3.71)	1)
Cn 252	24° 39'	77° 30'	(1500)	(5.58)	(34.996)	(3.94)	1)
Cn 253	24° 25'	77° 28'	(1554)	(5.53)	(34.99)	(3.91)	1)
Cn 254	24° 11'	77° 22'	(1454)	(5.49)	(35.002)	(4.05)	1)
Cn 250	25° 06'	77° 45'	2270	5.67	34.960	3.25	

1g CRAWFORD AND DISCOVERY 1957 - 58

STATION	LAT. N	LONG. W	DEPTH m	O₂ m/l	S o/oo	TEMP °C	NOTE
Cf 183	8° 19'	56° 52'	1840	5.97	34.974	3.46	
Cf 182	8° 26'	55° 57'	1925	5.84	34.967	3.33	
Cf 181	8° 25'	55° 10'	1850	5.90	34.980	3.51	
Cf 309	16° 15'	60° 28'	2045	5.73	34.978	3.45	
Cf 307	16° 16'	58° 54'	(2180)	(5.64)	(34.974)	(3.27)	1)
Cf 306	16° 13'	57° 31'	1905	5.66	34.974	3.60	
Cf 305	16° 14'	56° 08'	1940	5.64	34.984	3.59	
Cf 326	19° 06'	68° 12'	1670	5.81	34.988	3.79	
Cf 325	19° 36'	68° 04'	1845	5.61	34.989	3.79	
Cf 324	20° 34'	67° 52'	1590	5.63	34.99	4.00	
Cf 323	21° 33'	67° 36'	1750	5.64	34.984	3.76	
Cf 322	22° 34'	67° 18'	1820	5.74	34.987	3.78	
Cf 321	23° 30'	67° 05'	2250	5.55	34.981	3.27	
Di 3623	24° 32'	74° 56'	1867	5.76	34.99	3.67	
			2166	5.76	34.98	3.39	
Di 3622	24° 30'	73° 47'	2213	5.80	34.98	3.46	
Di 3621	24° 33'	71° 53'	2307	5.75	34.97	3.25	
Di 3620	24° 29'	70° 10'	2338	5.74	34.97	3.32	
Average of 18 observations			20 hm	5.73	34.98	3.54	**⎫ **
Standard Deviation			± 2 hm	±0.11	± 0.01	±0.22	** ⎬ **

** Suspicious (too low) oxygen averages because of analytic difficulties

OBSERVATIONS WITHIN THE BRANCH TO THE EAST IN 24° - 25° N

STATION	LAT. N	LONG. W	DEPTH m	O₂ m/l	S o/oo	TEMP °C	NOTE
Di 3619	24° 28'	68° 20'	2285	5.59	34.97	3.17	⎫
Di 3618	24° 32'	66° 28'	1815	5.64	34.99	3.67	
Di 3617	24° 30'	64° 47'	1630	5.49	35.01	3.87	
Di 3616	24° 27'	62° 57'	2389	5.57	34.97	3.17	
Di 3615	24° 31'	61° 08'	2388	5.45	34.97	3.12	⎬ **
Di 3614	24° 29'	59° 18'	2393	5.54	34.97	3.16	
Di 3613	24° 32'	57° 30'	2794	5.40	34.95	2.89	
Cf 319	25° 27'	66° 30'	2115	5.52	34.996	3.49	⎭

** Suspicious (too low) oxygen averages because of analytic difficulties

1g HIDALGO 1958

STATION	LAT. N	LONG. W	DEPTH m	O$_2$ m/1	S o/oo	TEMP °C	NOTE
58-4-35	22° 43.7'	74° 31'	(1385)	(6.18)	(34.94)	(4.14)	4)

1h ATLANTIS 1961

STATION	LAT. N	LONG. W	DEPTH m	O$_2$ m/1	S o/oo	TEMP °C	NOTE
6180	18° 56'	66° 09'	1805	6.09	34.983	3.75	
			2095	6.09	34.980	3.47	
6165	18° 51'	66° 08'	1581	6.22	34.986	3.86	
6182	19° 52'	66° 09'	2223	6.19	34.970	3.40	
6166	19° 18'	66° 09'	1764	6.16	34.986	3.78	
6167	19° 44'	66° 07'	2102	6.11	34.968	3.41	
6181	19° 16'	66° 06'	1772	(6.28)	34.981	3.65	7)
6168	20° 09'	66° 09'	1698	6.18	34.981	3.76	
6170	20° 58'	66° 08'	1872	6.18	34.993	3.70	
6184	20° 47'	66° 07'	2152	6.09	34.972	3.42	
6169	20° 31'	66° 06'	1808	6.11	34.980	3.74	
6164	21° 25'	66° 09'	1906	6.19	34.984	3.70	
6183	21° 16'	66° 07'	1726	6.15	34.986	3.79	
6186	21° 47'	66° 06'	1744	6.15	34.981	3.75	
6185	21° 17'	66° 05'	1778	6.17	34.987	3.74	
6163	21° 52'	66° 04'	1826	6.12	34.982	3.76	16)
6188	22° 47'	66° 09'	1958	6.10	34.978	3.54	
6187	22° 17'	66° 06'	1780	6.02	(35.000)	3.81	
6162	22° 14'	66° 06'	1780	6.16	34.993	3.83	
6161	22° 41'	66° 04'	1773	5.99	(35.000)	3.84	
Average of 19 observations			19 hm	6.13	34.98	3.88	
Standard Deviation			± 2 hm	± 0.06	± 0.01	± 0.08	

2. Observations in the Core of the Middle North Atlantic Deep Water (upper O$_2$ Maximum)

Within the Cayman Basin

2a DANA 1922

STATION	LAT. N	LONG. W	DEPTH m	O$_2$ m/1	S o/oo	TEMP °C	NOTE
1217	18° 50'	79° 07'	2000	5.50	34.99	4.11	
1245	19° 35'	73° 27'	(1950)	(5.58)	(35.01)	(4.10)	1)

2b ATLANTIS 1933 - 34

STATION	LAT. N	LONG. W	DEPTH m	O$_2$ m/1	S o/oo	TEMP °C	NOTE
1591	16° 59'	83° 57'	(1591')	(5.11)	(34.97)	(4.20)	2)
1594	17° 54'	83° 58'	2436	5.73	34.99	4.06	
1583	17° 50'	81° 28'	2405	6.12	34.99	4.04	
1582	18° 21'	81° 25'	1898	6.00	34.99	4.12	
			2373	6.00	34.99	4.08	
1581	18° 58'	81° 21'	2489	5.97	34.97	4.05	
1569	18° 58'	77° 29'	2487	5.63	34.99	4.08	
1987	19° 30'	81° 23'	1347	6.05	35.00	4.31	
1580	19° 12'	81° 20'	(1600)	(5.60)	(34.99)	(4.14)	1)
1579	19° 24'	80° 52'	1500	(5.31)	34.94	4.19	10)
1578	19° 30'	80° 31'	1570	5.83	34.97	4.16	
1573	19° 45'	77° 44'	(1200)	(5.75)	(34.96)	(4.35)	11)
1572	19° 38'	77° 42'	(2986)	(5.74)	(35.01)	(4.08)	1)
1571	19° 27'	77° 35'	2440	5.99	34.97	4.09	
1570	19° 16'	77° 28'	2463	5.80	34.97	4.10	
1565	19° 57'	74° 05'	(1599)	(6.18)	(34.97)	(4.15)	1)

STATION	LAT. N	LONG. W	DEPTH m	O$_2$ m/l	S o/oo	TEMP °C	NOTE
1564	19° 55'	73° 52'	(2274)	(5.75)	(34.99)	(4.05)	1)
1563	19° 52'	73o 41'	(2012)	(5.83)	(34.97)	(4.07)	1)
Average of 16 observations			21 hm	5.87	34.98	4.12	
Standard Deviation			± 5 hm	±0.17	± 0.01	±0.09	

2c ATLANTIS 1939

3301	19° 58'	73° 40'	(2304)	(5.44)	(34.99)	(4.10)	1)

2d CARYN 1956, VEMA 1957 and CRAWFORD 1958

Cf 373	17° 46'	84° 29'	2740	5.24	34.991	4.10	
Cf 372	17° 07'	84° 28'	(2160)	(5.19)	(34.976)	(4.06)	1)
Cf 386	18° 30'	79° 13'	2870	5.25	34.982	4.11	
Cn 237	18° 43'	73° 23'	1603	5.02'	(34.98)	4.18	5)
Cn 231	18° 34'	73° 05'	(1278)	(4.56)	(34.99)	(4.53)	1)
Cn 233	18° 34'	73° 02'	(1178)	(4.76)	(34.97)	(4.68)	
Cf 385	19° 16'	79° 11'	(3080)	(5.21)	(34.990)	(4.13)	6)
V 12 61	19° 55'	75° 08.5'	1700	4.98	34.99	4.18	
Cf 367	20° 04'	73° 39'	1620	5.20	34.996	4.24	
Average of 9 observations			20 hm	4.95	34.99	4.25	} **
Standard Deviation			± 7 hm	±0.24	± 0.01	±0.21	

** Suspicious (too low) oxygen averages because of analytic difficulties

2e HIDALGO 1958

58-4-32	20° 05'	73° 54'	1987	(5.60)	39.95	4.07	7)
58-4-31	20° 01'	73° 39'	1779	(6.48)	35.05	4.16	7)

2f VEMA 1961

17-13	17° 01'	84° 44'	(2448)	(5.48)	(34.982)	(4.05)	1)
17-14	17° 13'	84° 24'	2529	5.38	34.975	--	
17-15	18° 01'	84° 10'	2513	5.56	34.987	4.07	
17-21	18° 39'	81° 58'	(1750)	(5.39)	(34.994)	(4.14)	1)
17-22	18° 31'	81° 30'	(3725)	(5.59)	(34.984)	(4.19)	6)
Average of 4 observations			23 hm	5.45	34.99	4.08	} **
Standard Deviation			± 3 hm	±0.08	± 0.01	±0.05	

** These averages are not representative for the concerned area and year (because
of the small number of observations and their uneven distribution)

3. Observations in the Core of the Middle North Atlantic Deep Water (upper O$_2$ Maximum) Within the Yucatan Basin

3a DANA 1922

1221	21° 49'	85° 41'	(2000)	(5.27)	(35.01)	(4.12)	1)

3b   ATLANTIS 1933 - 34

STATION	LAT. N	LONG. W	DEPTH m	O_2 m/1	S o/oo	TEMP °C	NOTE
1597	18° 56'	84° 08'	1990	5.78	34.97	4.07	
1600	19° 33'	86° 24'	2470	5.94	34.98	4.04	
1599	19° 18'	85° 40'	1956	5.82	34.97	4.08	
1598	19° 07'	84° 47'	2482	6.01	34.97	4.08	
1992	19° 32'	83° 50'	(2212)	(5.61)	(34.99)	(4.05)	1)
1977	19° 49'	79° 46'	1380	5.75	34.98	4.24	
1978	20° 02'	79° 37'	1467	5.86	34.98	4.18	
1979	20° 18'	79° 27'	1717	5.73	34.98	4.14	
1980	20° 35'	79° 19'	2248	5.81	(35.02)	4.09	2)
1981	20° 53'	79° 11'	(1715)	(5.35)	(34.96)	(4.14)	1)
2000	21° 41'	86° 05'	(1624)	(4.99)	(34.97)	(4.19)	1)
1606	21° 51'	85° 53'	(1732)	(5.03)	(34.98)	(4.19)	1)
1607	21° 55'	85° 44'	(1661)	(5.11)	(34.97)	(4.17)	1)
1999	21° 43'	85° 38'	(1985)	(5.89)	(34.97)	(4.07)	1)
1608	21° 53'	85° 26'	(1945)	(5.43'	(35.00)	(4.11)	1)
1998	21° 48'	85° 20'	(1538)	(5.40)	(34.96)	(4.18)	1)
1609	21° 51'	85° 10'	(1600)	(5.58)	(34.99)	(4.06)	3)
1995	21° 27'	84° 22'	2320	6.03	34.99	4.12	
1983	21° 16'	81° 33'	1705	5.99	34.99	4.13	
Average of 19 observations			19 hm	5.64	34.98	4.13	
Standard Deviation			± 3 hm	±0.33	± 0.01	±0.06	

3c   CARYN 1956 AND CRAWFORD 1958

STATION	LAT. N	LONG. W	DEPTH m	O_2 m/1	S o/oo	TEMP °C	NOTE
Cf 374	18° 27'	84° 31'	(1685)	(4.98)	(34.982)	(4.16)	1)
Cf 376	19° 47'	84° 31'	(3830)	(5.24)	(35.068)	(4.22)	6)
Cf 375	19° 06'	84° 30'	2495	5.24	34.986	4.07	
Cf 377	20° 28'	84° 30'	(3035)	(5.25)	(35.006	(4.12)	6)
Cf 383	20° 06'	79° 10'	(1895)	(5.18)	(34.988)	(4.11)	1)
Cf 382	20° 35'	79° 10'	2070	5.23	34.987	4.13	
Cn 242	21° 48'	85° 35'	1948	5.11	34.988	4.10	1)
Cn 241	21° 48'	85° 25'	(1602)	(4.74)	(34.973)	(4:22)	1)
Cn 240	21° 47'	85° 14'	(1777)	(4.86)	(34.978)	(4.11)	1)
Cf 378	21° 06'	84° 29'	2760	5.23	34.983	4.10	
Cf 379	21° 36'	84° 28'	2520	5.29	34.992	4.10	
Cn 238	21° 29'	80° 20'	2860	5.03	34.990	4.11	
Average of 10 observations			22 hm	5.09	34.99	4.12	} **
Standard Deviation			± 5 hm	±0.18	± 0.01	±0.04	

** Suspicious (too low) oxygen averages because of analytic difficulties

3d   HIDALGO   1958

STATION	LAT. N	LONG. W	DEPTH m	O_2 m/1	S o/oo	TEMP °C	NOTE
58-4-11	21° 52'	85o 23'	(1807)	(4.73)	(34.88)	(4.20)	4)
58-4-16	21° 46.7'	83° 28.4'	(1868)	(5.37)	(34.95)	(4.18)	4)

3e   VEMA   1961

STATION	LAT. N	LONG. W	DEPTH m	O_2 m/1	S o/oo	TEMP °C	NOTE
17-11	17° 51'	86° 57'	1919	5.43	(34.99)	4.04	2), 5)
17-10	18° 22'	86° 21'	2513	5.48	34.978	4.05	
17-20	18° 22'	82° 23'	(2015)	(5.40)	(34.996)	(4.10)	1)

STATION	LAT. N	LONG. W	DEPTH m	O$_2$ m/l	S o/oo	TEMP °C	NOTE
17- 9	19° 06'	85° 41'	2314	5.38	34.982	4.09	
17- 6	20° 01'	84° 21'	2000	5.44	34.985	4.11	
17- 5	20° 31'	84° 03'	2585	5.35	34.992	4.09	15)
17- 3	21° 13'	83° 00'	(2630)	(5.58)	(34.972)	(4.09)	4)
Average of 6 observations			22 hm	5.41	34.99	4.08	} **
Standard Deviation			± 3 hm	±0.05	± 0.01	±0.03	

**   These averages are not representative for the concerned area and year (because of the small number of observations and their uneven distribution)

4. Observations Within the Core Layer of the North Atlantic Deep Water Within the Venezuela Basin.

4a   DANA   1922

STATION	LAT. N	LONG. W	DEPTH m	O$_2$ m/l	S o/oo	TEMP °C	NOTE
II 1251	17° 48'	67° 22'	2000	5.08	34.96	4.07	
II 1269	17° 13'	64° 58'	1800	4.87	34.96	4.06	
Average of 2 observations			19 hm	4.98	34.96	4.07	

4b   ATLANTIS   1933

STATION	LAT. N	LONG. W	DEPTH m	O$_2$ m/l	S o/oo	TEMP °C	NOTE
1506	12° 28'	68° 34'	(2309)	(5.48)	(34.99)	(4.05)	1)
1507	12° 53'	68° 32'	(2000)	(5.08)	(34.97)	(4.03)	1)
1502	12° 38'	64° 34'	1982	5.22	34.96	4.05	
1509	13° 58'	68° 36'	1400	5.19	34.96	4.26	
1508	13° 30'	68° 34'	2485	(6.33)	34.97	4.04	7)
1500	13° 48'	64° 35'	1505	5.42	34.97	4.16	
1501	13° 13'	64° 33'	1988	5.26	34.97	4.05	
1510	14° 54'	68° 33'	2495	5.24	34.97	4.06	
1499	14° 38'	64° 30'	1588	5.36	34.96	4.11	
			2544	5.16	34.97	4.09	
1511	15° 47'	68° 30'	1975	4.99	34.97	4.06	
1498	15° 24'	64° 29'	2336	4.94	34.97	4.08	
1512	16° 42'	68° 36'	1310	5.16	34.97	4.24	
1514	17° 43'	68° 36'	(1952)	(5.08)	(34.99)	(4.05)	1)
1513	17° 27'	68° 33'	2000	5.04	34.97	4.08	
1496	17° 06'	64° 29'	2552	4.92	34.97	4.09	
Average of 15 observations			20 hm	5.17	34.97	4.10	
Standard Deviation			± 4 hm	±0.17	± 0.01	±0.07	

4c   ATLANTIS   1937

STATION	LAT. N	LONG. W	DEPTH m	O$_2$ m/l	S o/oo	TEMP °C	NOTE
2797	12° 07'	67° 10'	(2314)	(5.44)	(34.95)	(4.01)	1)
2791	12° 13'	64° 40'	(2444)	(5.08)	(34.99)	(4.08)	1)
2790	12° 45'	64° 38'	2292	5.04	34.98	4.05	
2800	13° 37'	67° 20'	2241	5.02	(34.97	4.05	12)
2799	13° 06'	67° 13'	2606	5.03	34.97	4.06	
2789	13° 12'	64° 36'	(2723)	(5.04)	(34.99)	(4.11)	1)
2788	13° 42'	64° 35'	2613	5.03	34.98	4.10	2)
2802	14° 46'	67° 13'	2296	5.04	34.95	4.06	2)
2801	14° 10'	67° 13'	2158	5.00	34.97	4.08	2)
2786	14° 43'	64° 33'	2233	4.95	34.97	4.05	2)

STATION	LAT. N	LONG. W	DEPTH m	O$_2$ m/l	S o/oo	TEMP °C	NOTE
2803	15° 18'	67° 11'	2075	5.01	34.97	4.08	2)
2784	15° 48'	64° 42'	2428	4.99	34.97	4.06	
2785	15° 09'	64° 30'	(2659)	(5.00)	(34.97)	(4.10)	1), 2)
2806	16° 58'	67° 20'	2476	5.07	34.97	4.06	
2804	16° 02'	67° 17'	2155	5.04	34.99	4.08	2)
2805	16° 28'	67° 11'	1958	5.06	34.97	4.07	2)
2782	16° 44'	64° 34'	(2374)	(5.00)	(34.98)	(4.08)	1)
2783	16° 14'	64° 30'	2392	4.98	(34.97)	(4.08)	1)
2807	17° 28'	67° 15'	2083	5.03	34.97	4.08	2)
2781	17° 10'	64° 33'	2641	5.02	34.97	4.10	2)
Average of 19 observations			24 hm	5.04	34.97	4.07	
Standard Deviation			± 2 hm	±0.10	± 0.01	±0.02	

4d ATLANTIS AND CARYN 1954 - 55

STATION	LAT. N	LONG. W	DEPTH m	O$_2$ m/l	S o/oo	TEMP °C	NOTE
At 5234	12° 10'	68° 35'	(1486)	(4.62)	(34.975)	(4.13)	1)
At 5235	12° 35'	68° 35'	1971	4.79	34.984	4.05	
At 5257	13° 07'	68° 37'	2120	4.77	34.977	4.05	
At 5272	13° 30'	65° 24'	2572	4.83	34.97	4.09	2)
At 5258	14° 04'	68° 48'	2951	4.80	34.970	4.11	
At 5259	15° 11'	68° 44'	2920	4.85	34.983	4.11	
At 5260	16° 14'	68° 38'	2675	4.92	34.973	4.09	
At 5261	17° 05'	68° 35'	2714	4.80	34.979	4.11	
Cn 217	17° 25'	66° 08'	2553	4.87	34.99	4.08	
Average of 9 observations			24 hm	4.81	34.98	4.09	} **
Standard Deviation			± 5 hm	±0.08	± 0.01	±0.03	

** Suspicious (too low) oxygen averages because of analytic difficulties

4e ATLANTIS AND CRAWFORD 1958

STATION	LAT. N	LONG. W	DEPTH m	O$_2$ m/l	S o/oo	TEMP °C	NOTE
At 5694	12° 33'	68° 30'	1774	5.11	34.972	3.96	
			2275	4.97	34.974	4.03	
At 5693	12° 17'	67° 16'	1554	4.51	34.970	(4.00)	3)
Cf 341	12° 30'	64° 32'	2405	4.65	34.981	4.07	
Cf 342	12° 06'	64° 32'	(1630)	(4.57)	(34.976)	(4.08)	1)
Cf 340	13° 05'	64° 32'	2365	4.66	34.977	4.06	
Cf 339	13° 47'	64° 28'	2395	4.66	34.981	4.07	
Cf 338	14° 32'	64° 41'	2330	4.76	34.976	4.07	
Cf 337	15° 08'	64° 34'	2265	4.80	34.979	4.07	
Cf 336	15° 48'	64° 26'	2485	4.70	34.976	4.07	
Cf 335	16° 25'	64° 28'	2220	4.72	34.977	4.06	
Cf 334	17° 05'	64° 32'	2400	4.72	34.979	4.08	
Cf 333	17° 30'	64° 25'	2270	4.71	34.978	4.05	
			2485	4.71	34.980	4.08	
Average of 14 observations			22 hm	4.73	34.98	4.05	} **
Standard Deviation			± 3 hm	±0.15	± 0.00	±0.00	

** Suspicious (too low) oxygen averages because of analytic difficulties

4f SPENCER F. BAIRD 1960

STATION	LAT. N	LONG. W	DEPTH m	O$_2$ m/l	S o/oo	TEMP °C	NOTE
13	12° 32'	64° 50'	2409	4.60	(35.009)	4.08	2)
10	13° 55'	64° 52'	2238	4.97	34.976	4.04	

STATION	LAT. N	LONG. W	DEPTH m	O_2 m/l	S o/oo	TEMP °C	NOTE
8	14° 55'	64° 53'	2321	4.46)	(35.011)	4.04	13), 15)
1	15° 24'	67° 08'	2776	4.74	(35.059)	4.08	13)
6	16° 05'	64° 51'	2443	4.55	(35.051)	4.05	13), 15)
14	17° 05'	74° 28'	2326	4.71	34.987)	3.95	
4	17° 17'	64° 50'	2499	4.64	(35.062)	4.05	13)
Average of 7 observations			(24 hm)	(4.69)	(35.01)	(4.04)	14)
Standard Deviation			(± 3 hm)	(±0.17)	--	(±0.04)	

5. Observations in the Core Layer of the North Atlantic Deep Water (Upper O_2 Maximum)

Within the Grenada Basin

5a DANA 1921 - 22

1183	13° 47'	61° 26'	1800	4.66	34.93	4.10	
1285	14° 38'	61° 16'	(1500)	(4.60)	(34.96)	(4.16)	1)
Average of 2 observations			17 hm	4.63	34.945	4.130	

5b ATLANTIS 1937

2755	12° 00'	62° 23'	(1874)	(4.78)	(34.97)	(4.10)	1)
2756	12° 24'	61° 48'	(2147)	(4.82)	(34.97)	(4.12)	1)
2757	13° 05'	61° 25'	(1973)	(4.81)	(34.99)	(4.10)	1)
2758	13° 25'	61° 12'	1250	4.63	34.96	4.27	
2759	13° 35'	61° 09'	(2014)	(4.81)	(34.97)	(4.11)	1)
2765	14° 58'	61° 20'	(1849)	(4.78)	(34.99)	(4.11)	1)
2763	14° 22'	61° 04'	(1809)	(4.79)	(34.97)	(4.10)	1)
2767	15° 10'	61° 24'	(1956)	(4.82)	(34.97)	(4.10)	1)
2766	15° 05'	61° 22'	(1721)	(4.83)	(34.96)	(4.12)	1)
Average of 9 observations			18 hm	4.79	34.97	4.13	
Standard Deviation			± 3 hm	±0.06	± 0.01	±0.05	

5c ATLANTIS 1958

5662	11° 52'	62° 44'	(1495)	(4.41)	(34.964)	(4.18)	1), 4)
5663	12° 29'	62° 49'	2465	4.63	34.974	4.14	
5282	13° 09'	62° 15'	1961	4.60	34.97	4.11	
Average of 2 observations			22 hm	4.61	34.97	4.13	**

** Suspicious (too low) oxygen averages because of analytic difficulties

6. Observations in the Core Layer of North Atlantic Deep Water Within the Colombia Basin
(upper O_2 Maximum)

6a DANA 1922

1214	14° 21'	76° 50'	2000	4.63	34.96	4.06	
1247	17° 57'	72° 51'	(2000)	(5.03)	(34.97)	(4.07)	1)
Average of 2 observations			20 hm	4.83	34.965	4.065	

[182]

6 b ATLANTIS 1933 - 34

STATION	LAT. N	LONG. W	DEPTH m	O₂ m/1	S o/oo	TEMP °C	NOTE
1951	10° 44'	81° 15'	2325	5.05	34.97	4.04	
1950	10° 15'	80° 28'	1533	5.16	34.97	4.11	
1946	10° 19'	79° 17'	1344	5.52	34.96	4.25	
			(2418)	(5.08)	(35.00)	(4.06)	1)
1945	10° 55'	79° 04'	1379	4.55	34.97	4.21	
			2577	4.93	34.97	4.09	
1952	11° 15'	81° 50'	1976	4.94	34.98	4.05	2)
1944	11° 38'	78° 30'	1966	5.02	35.00	4.05	
1531	11° 55'	74° 52'	1584	4.70	34.96?	4.17	
			2477	4.91	34.97	4.08	
1529	11° 52'	74° 19'	(1800)	(4.94)	(34.99)	(4.05)	1)
1943	12° 39'	77° 41'	2193	4.95	34.98	4.06	2)
1533	12° 53'	76° 18'	2499	5.34	34.99	4.08	
1532	12° 21'	75° 29'	2478	5.03	34.96	4.07	
1528	12° 18'	74° 14'	2000	5.17	34.97	4.04	
1959	13° 17'	81° 30'	1310	4.99	34.94	4.30	
1535	13° 47'	77° 48'	2460	5.55	34.99	4.06	
1942	13° 33'	77° 03'	1541	4.83	34.965	4.14	
			(2423)	(4.99)	(34.965)	(4.07)	1)
1534	13° 20'	77° 03'	1496	5.40	(35.05)	4.19	2)
1527	13° 15'	73° 58'	2485	4.91	34.98	4.06	
1965	14° 09'	79° 40'	1330	4.87	34.95	4.34	
			(1930)	(5.10)	(34.99)	(4.05)	1)
1966	14° 42'	79° 18'	1494	4.82	34.95	4.25	
1537	14° 36'	79° 14'	(2382)	(4.99)	(34.97)	(4.06)	1)
1536	14° 12'	78° 46'	(1636)	(4.94)	(34.97)	(4.07)	1)
1941	14° 48'	76° 54'	2410	(5.14)	(34.97)	(4.06)	1)
1526	14° 15'	74° 01'	2347	(5.15)	(34.97)	(4.06)	1) 2)
1538	15° 12'	79° 54'	(1773)	(5.68)	(34.99)	(4.08)	1)
1967	15° 08'	79° 16'	1579	4.99	34.97	4.11	
1968	15° 27'	78° 55'	(1777)	(4.92)	(34.99)	(4.07)	1)
1940	15° 20'	76° 40'	(1704)	(4.98)	(34.98)	(4.05)	1)
1525	15° 11'	74° 01'	2462	5.17	34.97	4.06	
1970	16° 12'	78° 36'	(1359)	(4.85)	(34.98)	(4.29)	1)
1971	16° 28'	78° 25'	1147	5.16	34.97	4.62	
1972	16° 41'	78° 14'	1169	4.99	34.96	4.59	
1938	16° 56'	76° 29'	1413	5.31	34.98	4.32	
1939	16° 10'	76° 28'	(1642)	(4.99)	(34.97)	(4.07)	1)
1524	16° 09'	73° 55'	2000	5.05)	(35.02)	4.08	2)
1936	17° 38'	76° 40'	(1539)	(4.99)	(34.97)	(4.12)	1)
1937	17° 12'	76° 33'	1789	4.99	34.98	4.08	1)
1522	17° 34'	73° 55'	1354	5.08	34.97	4.36	
			2445	4.95	34.97	4.06	
1523	17° 04'	73° 55'	1495	5.14	34.96	4.20	
			2493	5.31	34.97	4.06	
1521	17° 56'	73° 54'	1400	5.12	34.99	4.28	
1558	18° 05'	75o 31'	1581	5.40	34.94	4.15	
Average of 47 observations			19 hm	5.06	34.98	4.14	
Standard Deviation			± 4 hm	±0.21	± 0.02	±0.13	

6c CRAWFORD AND ATLANTIS 1958

STATION	LAT. N	LONG. W	DEPTH m	O₂ m/1	S o/oo	TEMP °C	NOTE
Cf 399	9o 51'	79° 17'	1290	4.50	34.953	4.37	
			(1490)	(4.50)	(34.975)	(4.19)	1)
Cf 398	10° 22'	79° 18'	1755	4.64	34.978	4.04	

[183]

STATION	LAT. N	LONG. W	DEPTH m	O$_2$ m/l	S o/oo	TEMP °C	NOTE
			2340	4.79	34.977	4.06	
At 5746	10° 10'	76° 40'	(1860)	(4.72)	(34.972)	(4.03)	1)
Cf 396	11° 52'	79° 22'	2440	4.74	34.983	4.06	
Cf 397	11° 03'	79° 18'	2140	4.67	34.982	4.06	
Cf 355	11° 51'	73° 46'	(1720)	(4.57)	(34.978)	(4.09)	1)
Cf 395	12° 26'	79° 18'	2540	4.75	34.986	4.08	
Cf 356	12° 26'	73° 45'	1690	4.69	34.978	4.05	
			2280	4.87	34.978	4.06	
Cf 394	13° 00'	79° 15'	2295	4.64	34.979	4.07	
Cf 393	13° 45'	79° 12'	2415	4.65	34.982	4.07	
Cf 358	13° 44'	73° 56'	2435	4.64	34.986	4.06	
Cf 357	13° 06'	73° 55'	2325	4.69	34.981	4.06	
Cf 392	14° 38'	79° 06'	1905	4.71	34.980	4.08	
			(2205)	(4.72)	(34.968)	(4.06)	1)
Cf 360	14° 59'	73° 58'	2685	4.66	34.979	4.08	
Cf 359	14° 20'	73° 58'	1885	4.60	(34.98)	4.07	5)
Cf 391	15° 11'	79° 13'	1805	4.58	34.972	4.06	
			(2205)	(4.62)	(34.977)	(4.06)	1)
Cf 361	15° 38'	73° 56'	2380	4.76	34.980	4.06	
Cf 362	16° 26'	73° 57'	2410	4.68	34.982	4.07	
Cf 363	17° 04'	73° 55'	2460	4.75	34.983	4.06	
Cf 364	17° 45'	73° 49'	1940	4.75	34.984	4.04	

		DEPTH	O$_2$	S o/oo	TEMP °C	
Average of 25 observations		21 hm	4.68	34.98	4.08	} **
Standard Deviation		± 4 hm	±0.09	± 0.01	±0.07	

** Suspicious (too low) oxygen averages because of analytic difficulties

7. Observations in the Core Layer of North Atlantic Deep Water Within the Virgin Islands Basin

7a   DANA 1921

1186	17° 58'	64° 41'	2500	5.59	34.95	3.72	
1189	17° 58'	64° 41'	2500	5.59	34.97	3.72	
Average of 2 observations			25 hm	5.59	34.96	3.72	

7b   ATLANTIS 1933

1493	18° 01'	64° 36'	2293	6.14	34.99	3.68	
			2646	6.28	34.97	3.71	1)
Average of 2 observations			24 hm	6.21	34.98	3.70	

7c   PURSUIT 1953

31	17° 26'	65° 42'	2429	(5.28)	(34.97)	(4.11)	1), 5), 7)
26	17° 51'	65° 26'	2154	6.08	34.96	--	
			2610	6.05	(35.03)	3.76	13)
Average of 3 observations			24 hm	6.06	(34.97)	3.76	

7d ATLANTIS 1955

STATION	LAT. N	LONG. W	DEPTH m	O$_2$ m/l	S o/oo	TEMP °C	NOTE
5286	17° 53'	65° 18'	2116	5.71	34.97	3.75	15)
			2856	5.76	34.97	3.76	15)
Average of 2 observations			25 hm	5.74	34.97	3.76	

7e CRAWFORD 1958

330	18° 20'	64° 17'	2340	5.74	34.981	3.70	1)
331	18° 07'	64° 16'	2465	5.41	34.981	3.96	
Average of 2 observations			24 hm	5.57	34.98	3.83	

7f SPENCER F. BAIRD 1960

| 2 | 17° 54' | 64° 52' | 23.48 | 5.69 | (35.363) | 3.73 | 2) |

8. Observations in the Core Layer of North Atlantic Deep Water Within the Hispaniola Basin

8a DANA 1921

1244	20° 23'	73° 24'	2000	5.97	34.97	3.54	
1243	21° 04'	73° 48'	2000	5.93	34.96	3.44	1)
Average of 2 observations			20 hm	5.95	34.96	3.49	

8b CRAWFORD AND HIDALGO 1958

Hd 58-4-32	20° 05'	73° 54'	1987	5.60	34.95	4.07	1)
Cf 367	20° 04'	73° 39'	1620	5.29	34.996	4.24	
			2610	5.43	35.006	4.13	1)
Cf 368	20° 23'	73° 34'	1985	5.63	34.98	3.60	
			2580	5.65	34.97	3.20	5)
Cf 369	21° 54'	73° 15'	1530	5.64	35.002	4.00	
			2335	5.67	34.975	3.33	
Average of 7 observations			21 hm	5.56	34.98	3.79	
Standard Deviation			± 4 hm	±0.05	± 0.05	±0.42	

SOURCES OF DATA

SHIP	ABBREVIATION	REFERENCE
Atlantis	At	Reduced data cards received directly from Woods Hole Oceanographic Institution Woods Hole, Massachusetts
1933, 1934, 1937, 1939 1952, 1954, 1955, 1958		
1961		The Woods Hole Oceanographic Institution

SHIP	ABBREVIATION	REFERENCE
		Atlas Series, Vol I, 1960, F. C. Fuglister The Atlantic Ocean Atlas of Temperature and Salinity Profiles and Data from International Geophysical Year, 1957-58, Woods Hole Oceanographic Institution, Woods Hole, Massachusetts
		Conseil Permanent International Pour l'Exploration de la Mer. Bulletin Hydrographique (Pour l'années: 1938-39, 1940-46; 1947; 1948; 1949; 1952; 1953; 1954; 1955)
		Data received from National Oceanographic Data Center, Washington 25, D. C.
Caryn 1954, 1955, 1956	Cn	Reduced data cards received directly from Woods Hole Oceanographic Institution, Woods Hole, Massachusetts
		Conseil Permanent International Pour l'Exploration de la Mer; Bulletin Hydrographique (Pour l'année: 1954)
Crawford 1957, 1958	Cf	Reduced data cards received directly from Woods Hole Oceanographic Institution Woods Hole, Massachusetts
		The Woods Hole Oceanographic Institution Atlas Series; Vol I, 1960, F. C. Fuglister, The Atlantic Ocean Atlas of Temperature and Salinity Profiles and data from International Geophysical Year of 1957-58 Woods Hole Oceanographic Institution, Woods Hole, Massachusetts
Dana II 1921, 1922	Da I	The Danish "DANA" Expeditions, 1920-22 Oceanographic Report No. 1 - 8
		Data received from National Oceanographic Data Center, Washington 25, D. C.
Discovery II 1957, 1958	Di II	The Woods Hole Oceanographic Institution Atlas Series, Vol I, 1960, F. C. Fuglister, The Atlantic Ocean Atlas of Temperature and Salinity Profiles and data from International Geophysical Year of 1957-58, Woods Hole Oceanographic Institution, Woods Hole, Massachusetts
Hidalgo 1958	Hd	Data reports for two IGY Cruises; Ref. No. 59-15D, April, 1959 The Agricultural and Mechanical College of Texas, Dept. of Oceanography and Meteorology

SHIP	ABBREVIATION	REFERENCE
		Data received from National Oceanographic Data Center, Washington 25, D.C.
Pursuit 1953	Pu	Data received from National Oceanographic Data Center, Washington 25, D. C.
S. F. Baird 1960	S F B	Preliminary Data List (Cr. B-6001), Scripps Institution of Oceanography, University of California, La Jolla, California
Vema 1957, 1961, 1962	V	Manuscript Data, Lamont Geological Observatory, Palisades, New York

Notes

1) Deepest observation
2) Salinity probably too high
3) Temperature interpolated
4) Doubtful values
5) Salinity Interpolated
6) No upper O_2 maximum apparent
7) Doubtful oxygen
8a) Secondary O_2 maximum 6.09 in 3000 m
8b) Secondary O_2 maximum 5.53 in 3500 m
9) Oxygen probably too high
10) Oxygen probably too low
11) Depth probably too shallow
12) Salinity doubtful
13) Salinity systematically too high
14) Averages are only valid for the eastern margin of the basin
15) Not a pronounced oxygen maximum
16) Average of observations in 1586 and 2066 m

TABLE VI

LIST OF THE OBSERVATIONS IN THE CORE OF THE ANTARCTIC BOTTOM WATER

AND THE CARIBBEAN BOTTOM WATER

(Potential Temperature and Bottom Salinity)

North America Basin

SHIP AND STATION NUMBER		LAT. N	LONG. W	DEPTH OF OBS. m	DIST. FROM BOTTOM	TEMP °C	POT. TEMP °C	SAL. o/oo	σtp	NOTE
Cf	183	8° 19'	56° 52'	2015	235	3.29	3.13	34.969	27.87	
Cf	182	8° 26'	55° 57'	2405	400	2.95	2.76	34.950	27.89	
Cf	181	8° 25'	55° 10'	2775	135	2.81	2.58	34.936	27.89	
At	5059	9° 08'	58° 20'	1966	339	3.18	3.02	34.96	27.87	
At	5058	9° 42'	58° 01'	2700	175	2.64	2.42	34.91	27.89	
At	5057	10° 13'	57° 45'	2961	389	2.46	2.22	34.89	27.89	
At	5056	10° 31'	57° 20'	3322	428	2.37	2.09	(34.95)	(27.94)	1)
At	5278	12° 36'	58° 34'	1646	205	3.88	3.74	35.05	27.87	
				1744	107	3.85	3.70	35.03	27.86	
Ca	30	12° 54'	56° 15'	4703	0	2.17	1.73	(34.93)	(27.96)	2)
Ch II	178	13° 58'	59° 30'	2500	367	3.14	2.93	34.97	27.89	
V 18	9	13° 29'	58° 52'	2514	0	3.28	(3.01)	--	--	6)
At	5276	13° 25'	58° 19'	2750	130	2.78	2.55	(34.98)	(27.93)	1)
Da II	1181	13° 07'	57° 20'	4500	250	2.30	1.88	34.91	27.93	
At	5277	13° 50'	56° 53'	4203	609	2.29	1.81	34.89	27.92	
				4492	320	2.23	1.81	--	--	
V 18	10	13° 29'	55° 59'	4923	0	2.04	1.50	--	--	10)
				4923	0	2.11	1.65	--	--	6)
Ch II	1566	14° 00'	59° 30'	2500	367	3.24	3.03	34.97	27.88	
Ch II	32	14° 18'	58° 59'	3000	600	2.58	(2.33)	(34.98)	(27.95)	1)
At	5223	14° 30'	58° 54'	3351	49	2.40	2.12	34.921	27.92	
V 15	10	14° 14'	57° 06'	5002	--	1.87	1.40	--	--	6)
At	5222	15° 20'	58° 19'	4040	510	2.29	1.93	34.903	27.92	
Ch II	1807	16° 37'	61° 15'	(1800)	212	3.68	3.53	(35.02)	(27.87)	1)
Cf	309	16° 15'	60° 28'	4250	529	2.35	1.96	34.908	27.93	
Cf	308	16° 14'	59° 42'	5015	0	2.12	1.64	34.858	27.91	
Alb III	367	16° 51'	58° 21'	5511	144	1.90	1.36	(34.86)	(27.93)	2)
				5630	25	1.92	(1.37)	34.86	27.93	(11)
				5645	10	1.90	1.34	(34.87)	(27.94)	2)
				5651	4	1.92	1.36	34.84	27.91	
Cf	306	16° 13'	57° 31'	5015	0	2.05	1.58	34.856	27.91	
Cf	305	16° 14'	56° 08'	4940	160	2.07	1.61	34.862	27.91	
Ch II	1808	17° 33'	61° 10'	3000	695	2.94	2.68	34.94	27.88	
Da II	1185	17° 41'	60° 58'	4500	450	2.36	1.94	34.92	27.93	
At	5220	17° 30'	56° 47'	5290	210	1.96	1.45	34.841	27.91	
At	4476	18° 43'	67° 00'	1660	305	3.80	3.66	--	--	
V 15 Th 5		18° 46'	66° 31'	1895	201	3.71	3.55	34.985	27.84	4)
				2041	55	3.60	3.43	35.009	27.87	
				2059	37	3.61	3.43	34.989	27.85	
				2074	22	3.62	3.44	34.985	27.85	
At	6180	18° 56'	66° 09'	3167	149	2.57	2.31	34.930	27.91	
				3265	51	2.53	2.25	34.923	27.91	
At	6165	18° 51'	66° 08'	2791	0	3.11	2.87	34.950	27.88	
At	1491	18° 34'	64° 06'	1800	184	3.67	3.52	34.97	27.84	
At	5288	18° 52'	63° 05'	5352	528	2.06	(1.54)	(34.89)	(27.94)	1)

SHIP AND STATION NUMBER	LAT. N	LONG. W	DEPTH OF OBS. m	DIST. FROM BOTTOM	TEMP °C	POT. TEMP °C	SAL. o/oo	σtp	NOTE
			5557	323	1.99	1.44	34.86	27.92	
Ch I 22	18° 40'	62° 56'	2606	0	3.50	3.27	--	--	
Ch I 21	18° 54'	61° 28'	5532	0	1.94	1.40	(34.84)	(27.91)	2)
Ch I 20	18° 56'	59° 35'	5441	473	2.22	(1.68)	--	--	11)
At 5066	18° 53'	58° 22'	4924	376	2.10	1.64	34.87	27.92	
Ra	18° 06'	56° 52'	5495	0	2.00	1.46	(34.85)	(27.91)	2)
At 5219	18° 50'	55° 49'	5195	0	1.94	1.44	34.841	27.91	
Cf 326	19° 06'	68° 12'	4055	35	2.42	2.05	34.910	27.92	
Cf 325	19° 36'	68° 04'	6545	1475	2.10	1.41	34.837	27.91	
At 4755	19° 35'	68° 03'	6880	487	2.14	1.39	34.80	27.88	
Gu 16	19° 07'	67° 51'	3319	0	2.50	2.22	--	--	
Gu 15	19° 36'	67° 32'	8444	0	2.22	(1.21)	(34.82)	(27.91)	2)
Sh 7012	19° 05'	67° 05'	4000	575	2.32	(1.96)	34.92	(27.93)	11)
			4500	75	2.31	1.89	(34.96)	(27.97)	1)
V 15 Core 189	19° 22'	66° 31'	7965	--	2.30	(1.37)	(34.883)	(27.95)	1)
At 6182	19° 52'	66° 09'	7343	437	2.20	1.37	34.832	27.91	
At 6166	19° 18'	66° 09'	6896	1014	2.12	1.36	34.831	27.91	
At 6167	19° 44'	66° 07'	6891	569	2.11	1.36	34.832	27.91	
At 6181	19° 16'	66° 06'	7176	443	2.17	1.37	34.836	27.91	
At 5169	19° 02'	66° 05'	3474	406	2.465	2.17	34.92	27.92	
At 4750	19° 56'	66° 01'	6837	543	2.11	1.37	34.80	27.88	
V 15 19	19° 50'	65° 53'	8315	--	2.36	1.36	--	--	
V 15 Core 190	19° 49'	65° 53'	8341	0	2.36	1.36	34.844	27.91	
Da 1261	19° 04'	65° 43'	5000	340	2.55	2.06	34.94	27.94	
Gu 13	19° 44'	65° 24'	7452	0	2.28	(1.43)	(34.84)	(27.91)	2)
Gu 12	19° 03'	65° 05'	3610	0	2.50	2.19	--	--	
V 15 Th 6	19° 14'	65° 02'	4176	1822	2.34	1.96	34.945	27.96	4)
			4368	1630	2.31	1.91	34.908	27.93	
			4386	1612	2.31	1.90	34.905	27.93	
			4401	1597	2.32	1.91	34.913	27.93	
At 5166	19° 55'	64° 51'	6942	878	2.15	1.39	34.86	27.93	
At 5165	19° 26'	64° 40'	5005	300	2.20	1.72	34.89	27.92	
Ch I 19	19° 15'	57° 47'	5486	0	1.94	1.40	(34.84)	(27.91)	2)
Ch I 18	19° 41'	55° 13'	4846	0	2.22	1.76	(34.89)	(27.92)	2)
Cf 44	20° 48'	70° 17'	3534	161	2.41	2.11	34.92	27.92	
Cf 324	20° 34'	67° 52'	4920	0	2.29	1.82	34.887	27.92	
V 15 Core 186	20° 26'	67° 40'	5158	--	1.97	1.48	--	--	
V 15 Th 1	20° 25'	67° 40'	5121	51	2.00	1.51	34.863	27.92	4)
			5148	24	1.96	1.47	--	--	4)
			5172	--	1.97	1.48	--	--	4)
Gu 14	20° 11'	66° 44'	5914	0	2.00	(1.40)	(34.84)	(27.91)	2)
V 15 26	20° 50'	66° 27'	5055	356	2.21	1.72	(34.912)	(27.94)	3)
			5245	166	2.08	1.57	(34.923)	(27.96)	3)
			5280	131	2.10	1.59	34.864	27.91	
			5305	106	2.06	1.55	34.857	27.92	
			5355	56	2.03	1.51	(34.943)	(27.98)	3)
			5370	41	2.01	1.49	(34.936)	(27.98)	3)
V 15 Core 181	20° 49'	66° 25'	5411	0	2.03	1.50	--	--	
V 15 30	20° 22'	66° 25'	4000	1650	(2.22)	(1.87)	--	--	3)
V 15 13	20° 49'	66° 25'	5227	--	2.00	1.50	--	--	5)
V 15 Th 4	20° 21'	66° 24'	4527	1195	2.32	1.90	34.947	27.96	
			5668	54	2.01	1.44	34.896	27.95	
			5686	36	1.99	1.42	34.848	27.92	

SHIP AND STATION NUMBER		LAT. N	LONG. W	DEPTH OF OBS. m	DIST. FROM BOTTOM	TEMP °C	POT. TEMP °C	SAL. o/oo	σtp	NOTE
				5701	21	1.98	1.41	34.840	27.91	
At	6172	20° 59'	66° 19'	5358	117	2.12	1.60	34.861	27.91	
				5457	18	2.06	1.53	34.853	27.91	
At	6178	20° 09'	66° 15'	5849	--	2.02	1.43	34.842	27.91	
At	6171	20° 50'	66° 13'	5004	139	2.25	1.77	34.880	27.91	
				5104	39	2.20	1.71	34.873	27.91	
At	6177	20° 50'	66° 09'	5014	129	2.25	1.77	34.881	27.91	
				5113	30	2.22	1.72	34.880	27.92	
At	6168	20° 09'	66° 09'	6228	234	2.04	1.39	34.835	27.91	
				6462	0	2.07	1.39	34.833	27.91	
At	6170	20° 58'	66° 08'	5220	244	2.18	1.67	34.874	27.92	
				5418	46	2.06	1.53	34.857	27.92	
At	6184	20° 47'	66° 07'	5323	100	2.22	1.70	34.872	27.91	
				5423	--	2.01	1.48	34.848	27.91	
At	6169	20° 31'	66° 06'	5233	438	2.16	1.65	34.868	27.91	
				5330	341	2.08	1.56	34.855	27.91	
V 15 Core 188		20° 23'	66° 06'	5786	0	1.97	1.39	(35.026)	(28.06)	5)
At	5167	20° 25'	64° 53'	5094	602	2.12	1.63	34.88	27.92	
At	5067	20° 46'	59° 10'	4613	487	2.23	1.80	34.88	27.91	
At	5218	20° 01'	55° 02'	4878	72	1.98	1.53	34.855	27.91	
Da II	1243	21° 04'	73° 48'	2000	220	3.44	3.28	34.96	27.85	
Cf	369	21° 54'	73° 15'	2535	220	3.18	2.97	34.974	27.88	
				2740	15	3.00	2.77	34.954	27.89	
Alb III	133	21° 00'	70° 12'	3758	612	2.43	2.10	34.95	27.94	
Cf	45	21° 17'	70° 04'	3906	45	2.30	1.96	34.86	27.89	
Gu	10	21° 23'	68° 01'	5422	0	3.00	2.4(3)	--	--	3)
Cf	323	21° 33'	67° 36'	5145	5	2.27	1.77	34.880	27.91	
V 15 16		21° 34'	67° 06'	5115	--	2.08	1.59	--	--	6)
V 15 Core 187		21° 34'	67° 05'	5295	--	2.08	1.57	--	--	
V 15 Th 2		21° 34'	67° 05'	5194	57	2.08	1.58	34.894	27.94	4)
				5213	38	2.09	1.59	34.885	27.94	4)
				5231	20	2.10	1.59	34.867	27.92	4)
				5251	0	2.08	1.57	--	--	5)
V 15 Core 183		21° 13'	66° 36'	5812	0	2.08	1.49	(34.907)	--	3), 8)
V 15 Th 3		21° 32'	66° 27'	5403	54	2.09	1.56	34.902	27.95	4)
				5421	36	2.09	1.56	34.874	27.93	4)
				5436	21	2.11	1.58	34.867	27.92	4)
At	6164	21° 25'	66° 09'	5329	141	2.10	1.58	34.860	27.91	
				5428	42	2.08	1.55	34.856	27.92	
At	6173	21° 31'	66° 08'	5223	223	2.11	1.60	34.865	27.92	
				5422	24	2.08	1.55	34.860	27.92	
At	6176	21° 03'	66° 08'	5395	137	2.02	1.49	34.850	27.91	
				5494	38	2.00	1.46	--	--	
At	6183	21° 16'	66° 07'	5885	101	2.02	1.42	34.836	27.91	
				5986	0	2.00	1.39	--	--	
At	6186	21° 47'	66° 06'	5490	112	2.07	1.53	34.849	27.91	
				5589	13	2.06	1.51	34.848	27.91	
At	6185	21° 17'	66° 05'	5414	149	2.09	1.56	34.853	27.91	
				5513	50	2.06	1.52	34.851	27.91	
At	6174	21° 39'	66° 04'	5359	116	2.06	1.54	34.852	27.91	
				5459	16	2.05	1.52	34.850	27.91	
At	6163	21° 52'	66° 04'	5522	98	2.06	1.52	34.849	27.91	
				5620	00	2.07	1.51	34.847	27.91	

[190]

North America Basin (continued)

SHIP AND STATION NUMBER	LAT. N	LONG. W	DEPTH OF OBS. m	DIST. FROM BOTTOM	TEMP °C	POT. TEMP °C	SAL. o/oo	σtp	NOTE
At 4754	21° 46'	66° 00'	4830	500	2.32	1.86	34.86	27.89	
At 6175	21° 31'	65° 57'	5297	120	2.09	1.58	34.859	27.92	
			5396	21	2.05	1.52	34.853	27.92	
Ch I 26	21° 26'	65° 16'	5121	0?	2.3	(1.8)	--	--	3)
Cf 46	22° 12'	69° 37'	5265	48	2.29	1.77	(34.93)	(27.95)	3)
Cf 322	22° 34'	67° 18'	5310	380	2.03	1.52	34.852	27.91	
V 15 Core 182	22° 00'	66° 22'	5680	0	2.03	1.46	(34.897)	27.95	3)
At 6188	22° 47'	66° 09'	5428	389	2.13	1.60	34.861	27.91	
			5623	194	2.10	1.54	34.849	27.91	
			5720	97	2.07	1.50	34.845	27.91	
At 6162	22° 14'	66° 06'	5543	203	2.10	1.55	34.856	27.91	
			5641	105	2.09	1.53	34.855	27.91	
At 6187	22° 17'	66° 06'	5426	291	2.07	1.54	34.851	27.91	
			5624	93	2.08	1.52	34.850	27.91	
			5717	0	2.07	1.51	--	--	
At 6161	22° 41'	66° 04'	5524	292	2.07	1.53	34.854	27.91	
			5719	97	2.08	1.52	34.848	27.91	
			5816	0	2.09	1.50	34.850	27.91	
Alb I 2638	23° 18'	82° 18'	1874	0	4.22	4.06	--	--	
Alb I 907	23° 37'	76° 06'	2556	0	3.56	3.34	--	--	
Alb I 916	23° 55'	75° 45'	1931	0	3.67	3.51	--	--	
Alb I 911	23° 56'	75° 26'	2215	0	3.50	3.32	--	--	
Alb I 910	23° 50'	75° 23'	1915	0	3.61	3.45	--	--	
Alb I 908	23° 46'	75° 14'	2447	0	3.44	3.23	--	--	
Alb I 2629	23° 49'	75° 11'	2136	0	3.56	3.38	--	--	
Alb I 893	23° 43'	74° 39'	2310	0	3.44	3.24	--	--	
Alb I 892	23° 50'	74° 38'	2312	0	3.44	3.24	--	--	
At 5164	23° 55'	73° 46'	5001	74	2.29	1.81	34.89	27.92	
Ra	23° 55'	70° 57'	5530	0	2.39	(1.83)	(34.90)	(27.92)	2)
Gu 9	23° 09'	69° 12'	5536	0	3.00	2.41	--	--	
Cf 321	23° 30'	67° 05'	5650	170	2.09	1.53	34.850	27.91	
V 15 14	23° 14'	66° 36'	5605		2.07	1.52	--	--	
V 15 27	23° 11'	66° 35'	5206		2.07	1.58	34.898	27.94	
			5243		2.07	1.56	(34.930)	(27.97)	
			5263		2.09	1.58	34.883	27.93	
			5310		2.07	1.55	34.880	27.93	
			5328		2.07	1.55	(34.950)	(27.99)	
Go 203	23° 46'	56° 12'	6309	0	2.28	(1.61)	--	--	3)
V 15 Th 9	24° 55'	77° 49'	1641	12	3.87	3.74	35.005	27.83	4)
V 15 Core 192	24° 59'	77° 46'	1968	0	3.25	3.09	--	--	
V 15 Th 10	24° 48'	77° 36'	1791	54	3.60	3.46	34.982	27.85	4)
			1809	36	3.60	3.45	34.975	27.85	4)
			1824	21	3.53	3.38	34.978	27.85	4)
S. Pa."Moor"	24° 35'	77° 34'	1750	6	3.74	3.59	34.98	27.83	
Alb I 949	24° 47'	77° 20'	2128	0	3.67	3.49	--	--	
Alb I 936	24° 47'	75° 56'	3594	0	2.61	2.29	--	--	
Alb I 937	24° 54'	75° 49'	4448	0	2.61	(2.19)	--	--	3)
Alb I 915	24° 01'	75° 39'	1922	0	3.67	3.51	--	--	
Alb I 902	24° 09'	75° 06'	4012	0	2.89	(2.52)	--	--	3)
Di II 3623	24° 32'	74° 56'	4877	33	2.19	1.73	34.88	27.92	
Alb I 903	24° 08'	74° 56'	4539	0	2.61	(2.18)	--	--	3)
Alb I 904	24° 08'	74° 45'	4124	0	2.50	(2.12)	--	--	3)
Alb I 905	24° 07'	74° 38'	3770	0	2.61	2.27	--	--	
Alb I 888	24° 50'	74° 37'	4954	0	2.61	(2.12)	--	--	3)

North America Basin (continued)

SHIP AND STATION NUMBER	LAT. N	LONG. W	DEPTH OF OBS. m	DIST. FROM BOTTOM	TEMP °C	POT. TEMP °C	SAL. o/oo	σ tp	NOTE
Da II 1242	24° 05'	74° 36'	3500	100	2.57	2.27	34.92	27.91	
Alb I 889	24° 25'	74° 36'	4826	0	3.11	2.62	--	--	
Alb I 890	24° 08'	74° 35'	2076	0	3.67	3.49	--	--	
Di II 3622	24° 30'	73° 47'	5304	23	2.19	1.67	34.87	27.91	
Di II 3621	24° 33'	71° 53'	5511	16	2.10	1.56	34.86	27.92	
Gu 8	24° 46'	70° 18'	5596	0	2.50	(1.93)	--	--	3)
Di II 3620	24° 29'	70° 10'	5525	36	2.28	1.73	34.87?	27.91	
Di II 3619	24° 28'	68° 20'	5678	37	2.10	1.53	34.85	27.91	
Cf 320	24° 29'	66° 50'	5730	45	2.11	1.54	34.855	27.92	
Di II 3618	24° 32'	66° 28'	5168	152	2.06	1.56	34.87?	27.92	
Ch I 28	24° 39'	65° 25'	5212	0	2.44	(1.92)	--	--	3)
Di II 3617	24° 30'	64° 47'	5902	25	2.10	1.50	34.85	27.91	
Alb II 371	24° 26'	63° 28'	5471	144	2.07	1.53	34.85	27.91	
			5591	24	2.07	1.51	34.85	27.91	
			5606	9	2.07	1.51	34.87	27.93	
			5612	3	2.06	1.51	(34.98)	28.02	1)
Di II 3616	24° 27'	62° 57'	5751	101	2.08	1.50	34.85	27.91	
Di II 3615	24° 31'	61° 08'	5885	17	2.09	1.50	34.85	27.91	
Di II 3614	24° 29'	59° 18'	5294	530	2.03	1.52	34.85	27.91	
Di II 3613	24° 32'	57° 30'	5790	6	2.08	1.50	34.85	27.91	
Di II 3612	24° 31'	55° 41'	5716	56	2.08	1.51	34.85	27.91	
V 15 31	25° 01'	77° 47'	1500	700	(4.13)	(4.01)	--	--	3)
Alb I 991	25° 11'	77° 47'	2184	0	4.83	4.62	--	--	
Cn 250	25° 06'	77° 45'	2566	7	3.11	2.90	34.956	27.88	
V 15 Th 7	25° 15'	77° 42'	2172	528	3.45	3.27	34.980	27.87	4)
			2447	253	3.22	3.01	34.979	27.89	4)
			2667	33	3.07	2.85	34.961	27.89	4)
			2685	15	2.98	2.77	34.959	27.90	4)
			2700	0	2.96	2.75	34.959	27.90	8)
Alb I 992	25° 02'	77° 40'	1982	0	4.33	4.16	--	--	
Alb I 947	25° 25'	77° 28'	2725	0	3.94	3.69	--	--	
Alb I 946	25° 15'	77° 25'	2576	0	3.56	3.33	--	--	
At 5332	25° 20'	77° 19'	2509	50	3.20	2.99	34.958	27.87	
V 15 32	25° 28'	77° 15'	∼ 2500	∼ 1200	3.11	2.90	--	--	
V 15 Th 8	25° 28'	77° 15'	2718	1006	2.88	2.65	34.955	27.91	4)
			3321	403	2.46	2.18	34.940	27.93	4)
			3669	55	2.37	2.05	34.942	27.94	4)
At 5163	25° 28'	76° 05'	4415	215	2.32	1.91	34.91	27.93	
Alb I 938	25° 03'	75° 43'	4872	0	2.61	2.14	--	--	
At 4537	25° 00'	75° 01'	4404	131	2.22	1.82	34.91	27.94	
Hd 58-4-37	25° 10'	74° 58'	4460	110	2.07	1.67	(34.83)	(27.88)	1)
Su	25° 18'	74° 29'	4746	0	(2.0)	(1.56)	--	--	3)
Da II 1241	25° 18'	74° 00'	2500	0	3.12	2.91	34.94	27.87	
Ra	25° 19'	58° 07'	6007	0	(2.17)	(1.55)	(34.86)	27.92	2)

Hispaniola Basin

SHIP AND STATION NUMBER	LAT. N	LONG. W	DEPTH OF OBS. m	DIST. FROM BOTTOM	TEMP °C	POT. TEMP °C	SAL. o/oo	σ tp	NOTE
Alb II 132	19° 48'	69° 24'	3536	814	2.48	2.17	34.96	27.95	
Cf 368	20° 23'	73° 34'	2580	10	3.20	2.98	(34.96)	(27.87)	2)
Da II 1244	20° 23'	73° 24'	2900	90	2.95	2.70	34.94	27.89	
V 17 Core 5	20° 26'	73° 20'	3477	0	2.52	2.22	--	--	
Alb III 136	21° 33'	76° 35'	1683	857	3.88	3.74	34.97	27.81	
Alb III 135	21° 03'	74° 39'	2463	317	3.25	3.04	34.96	27.87	
Hd 58-4-34	21° 15'	74° 30'	2461	464	2.46	2.27	(34.97)	(27.95)	1)

Tobago Basin

SHIP AND STATION NUMBER		LAT. N	LONG. W	DEPTH OF OBS. m	DIST. FROM BOTTOM	TEMP °C	POT. TEMP. °C	SAL. o/oo	σtp	NOTE
Ch II	1789	12° 09'	60° 21'	2200	396	3.68	3.49	34.97	27.83	
At	5227	12° 17'	60° 21'	2382	68	3.65	3.44	34.976	27.85	
At	5226	12° 45'	60° 07'	2237	113	3.65	3.46	34.971	27.85	
At	2746	13° 11'	60° 31'	1997	435	3.62	3.45	34.96	27.83	

Virgin Islands Basin

SHIP AND STATION NUMBER		LAT. N	LONG. W	DEPTH OF OBS. m	DIST. FROM BOTTOM	TEMP °C	POT. TEMP. °C	SAL. o/oo	σtp	NOTE
Re	75-12	17° 52'	65° 56'	1800	29	3.81	3.66	34.99	27.83	
At	5285	17° 54'	65° 51'	1818	137	3.82	3.67	34.99	27.83	
At	5286	17° 53'	65° 18'	3440	380	3.80	3.47	34.98	27.85	
Alb I	46	17° 51'	65° 08'	4431	~ 0	3.94	3.48	--	--	
Da II	1189	17° 58'	64° 41'	3030	160	3.76	3.48	34.97	27.83	
Da II	1186	17° 58'	64° 41'	4000	?	3.89	3.49	34.96	27.83	
At	5287	17° 54'	64° 16'	1739	236	4.05	3.91	34.98	27.80	
At	1493	18° 01'	64° 36'	2646	337	3.71	3.47	34.97	27.84	
Cf	330	18° 20'	64° 17'	2340	0	3.70	3.50	34.981	27.84	
Cf	331	18° 07'	64° 16'	2660	245	3.97	3.73	34.982	27.82	
				2855	50	3.98	3.72	34.986	27.82	
Bl		Anegada Passage		2076	0	3.33	3.16	--	--	
				2076	0	3.61	3.44	--	--	

Venezuela Basin

SHIP AND STATION NUMBER		LAT. N	LONG. W	DEPTH OF OBS. m	DIST. FROM BOTTOM	TEMP °C	POT. TEMP. °C	SAL. o/oo	σtp	NOTE
At	2792	11° 56'	64° 43'	1573	374	4.15	4.02	34.96	27.78	
At	5235	12° 35'	68° 35'	2820	130	4.09	3.83	34.987	27.82	
At	5234	12° 10'	68° 35'	1486	4	4.13	4.01	34.975	27.79	
At	1506	12° 28'	68° 34'	2309	206	4.05	3.85	34.99	27.82	
At	1507	12° 53'	68° 32'	2000	235	4.03	3.86	34.97	27.80	
At	5694	12° 33'	68° 30'	3041	204	--	--	34.974		
				3199	46	4.14	3.83	34.979	27.81	
At	5693	12° 17'	67° 16'	2796	313	4.07	3.81	34.974	27.81	
				3041	68	4.13	3.84	34.975	27.81	
At	2797	12° 07'	67° 10'	2314	146	4.07	3.87	34.95	27.78	
S F B	0013	12° 32'	64° 50'	4142	148	4.25	3.82	34.986	27.81	
At	2791	12° 13'	64° 40'	2444	327	4.08	3.86	34.99	27.81	
At	1502	12° 38'	64° 34'	2973	535	4.11	3.83	34.96	27.79	
At	1503	12° 12'	64° 34'	3000	200	4.13	3.84	34.97	27.80	
Cf	341	12° 30'	64° 32'	3600	125	4.19	3.83	34.981	27.81	
Cf	342	12° 06'	64° 32'	1630	115	4.08	3.94	34.976	27.80	
At	5257	13° 07'	68° 37'	3402	248	4.16	3.83	34.977	27.81	
At	1509	13° 58'	68° 36'	4000	892	4.25	3.84	34.96	27.79	
At	1508	13° 30'	68° 34'	4960	51	4.35	3.80	34.97	27.80	
At	5272	13° 30'	65° 24'	3562	298	4.18	3.83	34.99	27.82	
At	1500	13° 48'	64° 35'	3224	255	4.16	3.85	34.97	27.80	
At	2788	13° 42'	64° 35'	3197	277	4.15	3.84	34.99	27.82	
At	1501	13° 13'	64° 33'	2982	429	4.12	3.84	35.01	27.83	
Cf	340	13° 05'	64° 32'	3165	200	4.15	3.85	34.981	27.81	
				3365	0	4.17	3.84	34.980	27.81	
V 18	7	13° 38'	64° 32'	3838	0	4.17	3.78	--	--	8)
					0	4.23	3.85	--	--	6)
Cf	339	13° 47'	64° 28'	3190	225	4.16	3.85	34.982	27.81	
Ch II	1792	13° 21'	64° 10'	2500	413	4.10	3.87	34.96	27.79	
Re	63-3	14° 26'	69° 21'	4500	~ 0	4.24	(3.76)	(35.17)	(27.97)	3)
At	5258	14° 04'	68° 48'	4360	290	4.27	3.81	34.970	27.80	

Venezuela Basin (continued)

SHIP AND STATION NUMBER	LAT. N	LONG. W	DEPTH OF OBS. m	DIST. FROM BOTTOM	TEMP °C	POT. TEMP °C	SAL. o/oo	σtp	NOTE
S F B 8	14° 55'	64° 53'	3660	299	4.20	3.83	34.985	27.81	
Cf 338	14° 32'	64° 41'	3720	15	4.19	3.82	34.979	27.81	
At 2786	14° 43'	64° 33'	3646	85	4.21	3.85	34.96	27.79	
At 1499	14° 38'	64° 30'	3092	438	4.13	3.83	34.97	27.80	
At 2787	14° 15'	64° 30'	3580	32	4.20	3.84	34.96	27.79	
Gu 19	15° 15'	71° 16'	4278	0	4.11	(3.66)	--	--	3)
At 5259	15° 11'	68° 44'	4400	50	4.27	3.80	34.977	27.81	
At 1511	15° 47'	68° 30'	2964	1288	4.12	3.85	34.99	27.82	
V 15 Core 177	15° 28'	64° 56'	4242	--	4.21	3.77	--		
At 2784	15° 48'	64° 42'	3613	492	4.18	3.82	34.98	27.81	
Cf 337	15° 08'	64° 34'	3860	0	4.23	3.84	34.982	27.81	
At 1498	15° 24'	64° 29'	3383	390	4.15	3.82	34.97	27.80	
Cf 336	15° 48'	64° 26'	3875	10	4.24	3.84	34.980	27.81	
Ch II 1803	15° 33'	64° 11'	2800	93	4.08	3.82	34.99	27.82	
At 5260	16° 14'	68° 38'	4125	25	4.24	3.81	34.977	27.81	
Gu 18	16° 57'	68° 15'	5177	0	4.50	3.92	--	--	
At 5284	16° 03'	66° 02'	4179	122	4.25	3.81	34.99	27.83	
S F B 0006	16° 05'	64° 51'	3927	350	4.23	3.83	35.040	27.86	
At 1497	16° 17'	64° 33'	3223	736	4.16	3.85	34.97	27.80	
Cf 335	16° 25'	64° 28'	3800	25	4.22	3.84	34.979	27.81	
At 1514	17° 43'	68° 36'	1952	361	4.05	3.88	34.99	27.82	
At 5261	17° 05'	68° 35'	5445	0	4.42	3.80	34.981	27.81	
At 1513	17° 27'	68° 33'	3500	231	4.16	3.81	34.99	27.83	
Da II 1251	17° 48'	67° 22'	2450	100	4.08	3.86	34.97	27.80	
At 2807	17° 28'	67° 15'	3103	802	4.15	3.85	34.97	27.80	
Pu 32	17° 26'	65° 26'	2822	470	(4.12)	(3.85)	(35.03)	27.85	3)
V 15 12	17° 21'	65° 11'	4169	--	4.19	3.76	--	--	6)
V 15 Core 178	17° 21'	65° 11'	4283	--	4.28	3.73	--	--	
V 18 6	17° 07'	65° 02'	4411	0	(4.32)	3.85	--	--	6)
Da II 1269	17° 13'	64° 58'	4000	250	4.22	3.81	34.96	27.80	
S F B 0004	17° 17'	64° 50'	3976	64	4.22	3.81	35.126	27.92	
Cf 334	17° 05'	64° 32'	3670	75	4.20	3.83	34.980	27.81	
At 1496	17° 06'	64° 29'	3548	344	4.18	3.83	34.97	27.80	
Cf 333	17° 30'	64° 25'	3265	95	4.16	3.84	34.977	27.80	

Grenada Basin

SHIP AND STATION NUMBER	LAT. N	LONG. W	DEPTH OF OBS. m	DIST. FROM BOTTOM	TEMP °C	POT. TEMP °C	SAL. o/oo	σtp	NOTE
Ch II 1784	11° 55'	62° 44'	2000	195	4.13	3.96	34.99	27.81	
At 5663	12° 29'	62° 49'	2665	261	4.12	3.87	34.970	27.80	
At 2755	12° 00'	62° 23'	1874	339	4.10	3.94	34.97	27.79	
Ch II 1788	12° 39'	62° 02'	2900	63	4.23	3.96	34.97	27.79	
Ch II 1791	13° 25'	62° 37'	2900	117	4.17	3.90	34.95	27.78	
At 5282	13° 09'	62° 15'	2643	242	4.15	3.91	34.98	27.80	
Da II 1183	13° 47'	61° 26'	2800	225	4.16	3.90	34.93	27.76	
At 2760	13° 44'	61° 09'	1956	54	4.12	3.95	34.97	27.79	
At 2759	13° 35'	61° 09'	2014	71	4.11	3.94	34.97	27.79	
Ch II 1801	14° 56'	62° 05'	2500	350	4.09	3.86	34.97	27.80	
At 2765	14° 58'	61° 20'	1849	401	4.11	3.95	34.99	27.81	
Ch II 1795	14° 01'	61° 20'	2500	378	4.16	3.93	34.99	27.81	
At 2763	14° 22'	61° 04'	1809	93	4.10	3.94	34.97	27.79	
Ch II 1804	15° 42'	63° 04'	1900	132	4.09	3.93	34.95	27.77	
At 2767	15° 10'	61° 24'	1956	119	4.10	3.93	34.97	27.79	

Bonaire Basin

SHIP AND STATION NUMBER		LAT. N	LONG. W	DEPTH OF OBS. m	DIST. FROM BOTTOM	TEMP °C	POT. TEMP °C	SAL. o/oo	σtp	NOTE
At	5696	11° 47'	68° 30'	1760	2	4.08	3.93	34.978	27.79	
At	2795	11° 21'	67° 08'	1726	277	4.06	3.91	34.96	27.79	

Colombia Basin

SHIP AND STATION NUMBER		LAT. N	LONG. W	DEPTH OF OBS. m	DIST. FROM BOTTOM	TEMP °C	POT. TEMP °C	SAL. o/oo	σtp	NOTE
Ha	233	9° 30'	81° 49'	1910	237	4.00	3.84	34.92	27.76	
Ha	234	9° 40'	81° 44'	1948	538	4.00	3.83	34.96	27.79	
Ha	235	9° 57'	81° 36'	2273	651	4.04	3.84	--	--	
Ha	240	9° 29'	81° 20'	1898	432	3.97	3.81	(34.90)	(27.75)	5)
Ha	224	10° 38'	82° 05'	1880	405	4.05	3.89	34.96	27.79	
Ha	236	10° 14'	81° 26'	2432	492	4.05	3.83	(34.92)	(27.76)	5)
At	1951	10° 44'	81° 15'	2826	438	4.09	3.83	34.98	27.80	
Ha	201	10° 01'	80° 38'	2478	0	4.03	3.81	34.96	27.80	
At	1950	10° 15'	80° 28'	2911	222	4.10	3.82	34.97	27.80	
Ha	205	10° 32'	80° 24'	3360	222	4.16	3.83	34.94	27.78	
Cf	398	10° 22'	79° 18'	2735	0	4.10	3.85	34.979	27.81	
At	1946	10° 19'	79° 17'	2418	325	4.06	3.84	35.00	27.82	
Gu	22	10° 02'	79° 08'	1982	0	3.89	(3.71)	--	--	3)
At	1945	10° 55'	79° 04'	3077	535	4.12	3.83	34.98	27.81	
V 15 Core 8		10° 22'	78° 31'	1798	0	4.05	3.90	(34.92)	(27.76)	5)
At	1952	11° 15'	81° 50'	2470	374	4.05	3.83	(34.90)	(27.74)	5)
Cf	396	11° 52'	79° 22'	2640	215	4.09	3.85	34.979	27.81	
Cf	397	11° 03'	79° 18'	3245	285	4.16	3.84	34.980	27.81	
At	1944	11° 38'	78° 30'	2946	712	4.12	3.84	34.98	27.81	3)
Gu	21	11° 35'	77° 05'	3510	0	4.00	(3.66)	--	--	
V 15 Core 7		11° 36'	75° 47'	2800	0	4.04	(3.78)	(34.99)	(27.83)	3),12)
At	1531	11° 55'	74° 52'	2971	385	4.11	3.83	34.97	27.80	
At	1529	11° 52'	74° 19'	1800	175	4.05	3.90	34.99	27.80	
Cf	355	11° 51'	73° 46'	1720	45	4.09	3.94	34.978	27.80	
Cf	395	12° 26'	79° 18'	3425	60	4.17	3.83	34.981	27.81	
At	1943	12° 39'	77° 41'	2674	1258	4.09	3.84	34.99	27.82	
At	1533	12° 53'	76° 18'	2998	852	4.21	3.92	34.98	27.80	
At	1532	12° 21'	75° 29'	2971	677	4.13	3.85	34.97	27.80	
Cf	356	12° 26'	73° 45'	2665	70	4.10	3.86	34.979	27.81	
Cf	394	13° 00'	79° 15'	3405	0	4.18	3.85	--	--	
Cf	393	13° 45'	79° 12'	3000	105	4.12	3.84	34.978	27.81	
				3100	5	4.14	3.84	34.982	27.81	
At	1535	13° 47'	77° 48'	2952	1071	4.10	3.82	34.99	27.82	
At	1534	13° 20'	77° 03'	3488	462	4.23	3.88	34.97	27.79	3)
Gu	20	13° 22'	74° 02'	4034	0	4.00	(3.59)	--	--	
Cf	358	13° 44'	73° 56'	4005	0	4.25	3.84	34.986	27.81	
Cf	357	13° 06'	73° 55'	3770	180	4.22	3.84	34.987	27.81	
At	1965	14° 09'	79° 40'	1930	146	4.05	3.88	34.99	27.81	
At	1966	14° 42'	79° 18'	1855	439	4.02	3.86	(34.83)	(27.69)	5)
At	1537	14° 36'	79° 14'	2382	105	4.06	3.85	34.97	27.80	
Cf	392	14° 38'	79° 06'	2205	115	4.06	3.87	34.968	27.80	
At	1941	14° 46'	76° 47'	2897	898	4.11	3.84	34.97	27.80	
V 15 Core 6		14° 05'	75° 27'	4074	0	4.26	3.84	(34.92)	(27.76)	5)
At	1526	14° 15'	74° 01'	2814	1261	4.10	3.84	34.97	27.80	
Cf	360	14° 59'	73° 58'	4155	30	4.27	3.84	34.979	27.80	
Cf	359	14° 20'	73° 58'	3675	250	4.21	3.84	--	--	
At	1538	15° 12'	79° 54'	1773	211	4.08	3.93	34.99	27.81	
At	1967	15° 08'	79° 16'	1979	371	4.07	3.90	35.00	27.82	
Cf	391	15° 11'	79° 13'	2205	60	4.06	3.87	34.977	27.80	

Colombia Basin (continued)

SHIP AND STATION NUMBER		LAT. N	LONG. W	DEPTH OF OBS. m	DIST. FROM BOTTOM	TEMP °C	POT. TEMP. °C	SAL. o/oo	σtp	NOTE
Re	63-6	15° 14'	78° 54'	2240	?	4.04	3.84	(35.06)	(27.87)	1)
V 15 Core 5		15° 51'	75° 12'	3110	0	4.12	3.82	(34.90)	(27.75)	
At	1525	15° 11'	74° 01'	2954	1234	4.11	3.83	34.97	27.80	
Cf	361	15° 38'	73° 56'	3940	290	4.24	3.84	34.983	27.80	
At	1938	16° 56'	76° 29'	1792	403	4.09	3.94	34.965	27.78	
At	1939	16° 10'	76° 28'	1642	690	4.07	3.93	34.97	27.79	
Cf	362	16° 26'	73° 57'	3570	45	4.19	3.83	34.982	27.81	
At	1524	16° 09'	73° 55'	4000	225	4.24	3.83	34.96	27.79	
At	1937	17° 12'	76° 33'	1789	256	4.08	3.93	34.98	27.80	
At	1522	17° 34'	73° 55'	2944	576	4.11	3.83	34.97	27.80	
At	1523	17° 04'	73° 55'	3491	313	4.17	3.82	34.97	27.81	
Cf	363	17° 04'	73° 55'	3635	0	4.20	3.84	34.977	27.81	
At	1521	17° 56'	73° 54'	1600	229	4.12	3.98	34.99	27.80	
Cf	364	17° 45'	73° 49'	3840	0	4.23	3.84	34.982	27.81	
Alb I	179	17° 37'	72° 56'	4431	0	4.28	3.81	--	--	
Da II	1247	17° 57'	72° 51'	2000	500	4.07	3.90	34.97	27.79	
At	1558	18° 05'	75° 31'	2371	89	4.11	3.90	34.97	27.79	

Cayman Basin

SHIP AND STATION NUMBER		LAT. N	LONG. W	DEPTH OF OBS. m	DIST. FROM BOTTOM	TEMP °C	POT. TEMP. °C	SAL. o/oo	σtp	NOTE
V 17	13	17° 01'	84° 44'	2448	11	4.05	3.83	34.982	27.81	
Cf	373	17° 46'	84° 29'	5140	0	4.40	3.83	34.987	27.81	
Cf	372	17° 07'	84° 28'	2160	5	4.06	3.87	34.976	27.81	
At	1594	17° 54'	83° 58'	4890	514	4.33	3.79	34.97	27.80	
V 17 Core	35	17° 49'	82° 55'	5217	0	4.39	3.81	--	--	
V 17 Core	34	17° 13'	82° 50'	1975	0	4.11	3.94	--	--	
V 17	17	17° 13'	82° 50'	2003	17	4.05	3.88	34.983	27.80	
V 17	32	18° 02'	84° 12'	5099	0	4.39	3.83	--	--	
V 17	16	18° 22'	84° 00'	3474	439	4.17	3.83	--	--	
At	1581	18° 58'	81° 21'	5472	563	4.40	3.78	34.99	27.83	
Da II	1217	18° 50'	79° 07'	3500	0	4.15	3.80	34.99	27.83	
At	1569	18° 58'	77° 29'	3754	814	4.18	3.80	34.97	27.80	
At	5070	18° 31'	76° 51'	1932	718	4.15	3.98	34.99	27.81	
S Pa	74-11	18° 50'	75° 09'	2200	86	4.10	3.91	(35.07)?	(27.88)	1)
At	1987	19° 30'	81° 23'	1924	572	4.12	3.95	34.89	27.73	
At	1578	19° 30'	80° 31'	1768	61	4.09	3.94	34.97	27.79	
At	2809	19° 06'	80° 06'	6478	545	4.56	3.78	(34.99)	(27.83)	2)
Cf	385	19° 16'	79° 11'	7060	0	4.70	3.83	34.977	27.81	
At	1572	19° 38'	77° 42'	4975	182	4.34	3.79	34.99	27.83	
V 15 Core 4		19° 25'	75° 13'	4024	0	4.22	3.81	34.96	27.80	
Ha	5	19° 12'	75° 12'	2500	~ 500	4.10	3.87	(35.03)	(28.00)	1)
V 12	61	19° 55'	75° 08'	2500	124	4.09	3.86	35.00	27.82	
At	1564	19° 55'	73° 52'	2274	1201	4.05	3.85	34.99	27.82	
At	1563	19° 52'	73° 41'	2012	375	4.07	3.90	34.97	27.79	
Da II	1245	19° 35'	73° 27'	1950	52	4.10	3.93	35.01	27.82	
Hd	58-4-32	20° 05'	73° 54'	1987	338	4.07	3.90	34.95	27.78	
Cf	367	20° 04'	73° 39'	2610	195	4.13	3.89	(35.006)	27.82	
				2805	0	4.11	3.85	--	--	
Bl		Windward Passage		1705	0	3.89	3.85	--	--	

Yucatan Basin

SHIP AND STATION NUMBER		LAT. N	LONG. W	DEPTH OF OBS. m	DIST. FROM BOTTOM	TEMP °C	POT. TEMP °C	SAL. o/oo	σtp	NOTE
V 17	10	18° 22'	86° 21'	4084	257	4.24	3.82	34.976	27.81	
				4288	53	4.36	3.91	--	--	
V 17 Core	30	18° 14'	85° 47'	4501	0	4.21	3.73	--	--	
At	1597	18° 56'	84° 08'	2483	480	4.06	3.83	34.98	27.81	
V 17	9	19° 06'	85° 41'	4003	561	4.27	(3.86)	(34.998)	(27.87)	7)
At	1598	19° 07'	84° 47'	4455	117	4.29	3.81	35.01	27.84	
Cf	376	19° 47'	84° 31'	4425	149	4.28	3.81	34.988	27.82	
Cf	375	19° 06'	84° 30'	3895	25	4.23	3.83	34.989	27.82	
At	1992	19° 32'	83° 50'	2212	1455	4.05	3.86	34.99	27.82	
Re	63-8	19° 30'	83° 10'	1718	661	4.05	(3.90)	(35.05)	(27.86)	1),3)
S Pa	74-18	19° 58'	79° 34'	2100	95	4.12	3.94	(34.92)	(27.75)	
Cf	377	20° 28'	84° 30'	4530	24	4.32	3.83	34.988	27.82	
V 17	6	20° 01'	84° 21'	4500	57	4.32	3.84	34.993	27.82	
V 17 Core	25	20° 00'	84° 22'	4575	0	4.31	3.82	--	--	
V 17	5	20° 31'	84° 03'	4421	123	4.30	3.83	--	--	
V 17 Core	23	20° 47'	83° 27'	4508	0	4.29	3.81	--	--	
At	1981	20° 53'	79° 11'	2175	108	4.08	3.89	(35.17)	(27.85)	9)
Cf	382	20° 35'	79° 10'	2865	215	4.11	3.84	34.992	27.82	
Cf	383	20° 06'	79° 10'	1895	205	4.11	3.95	34.988	27.80	
Cf	378	21° 06'	84° 29'	4260	220	4.28	3.83	34.992	27.82	
				4480	0	4.31	3.83	34.982	27.81	
Cf	379	21° 36'	84° 28'	3230	270	4.14	3.84	34.986	27.82	
At	1995	21° 27'	84° 22'	2796	916	4.10	3.85	34.96	27.79	
Hd	58-4-16	21° 47'	83° 28'	1868	142	4.18	(4.02)	(34.95)	(27.77)	3)
V 17	3	21° 13'	83° 00'	4293	79	4.28	3.83	34.988	27.82	
At	1983	21° 16'	81° 33'	2807	1418	4.09	3.83	(35.02)	(27.84)	1)
Cn	238	21° 29'	80° 20'	3278	87	4.13	3.81	34.985	27.82	
Bk		Yucatan Passage		2190	0	4.17	3.98	--	--	

Gulf of Mexico Basin

SHIP AND STATION NUMBER		LAT. N	LONG. W	DEPTH OF OBS. m	DIST. FROM BOTTOM	TEMP °C	POT. TEMP °C	SAL. o/oo	σtp	NOTE
At	1606	21° 51'	85° 53'	1732	179	4.19	4.04	34.98	27.79	
Da II	1221	21° 49'	85° 41'	2000	138	4.12	3.95	35.01	27.82	
At	1999	21° 43'	85° 38'	1985	136	4.07	3.90	34.97	27.79	
Al	4-16	21° 50'	85° 35'	1918	130	4.05	3.88	(34.90)	(27.74)	
Cn	242	21° 48'	85° 35'	1948	129	4.10	3.93	34.988	27.80	
				2077	0	4.22	4.04	34.989	27.79	
S Pa	62-10	21° 38'	85° 28'	1909	121	4.10	3.94	34.92	27.75	
At	1608	21° 53'	85° 26'	1945	250	4.11	3.94	35.00	27.81	
Hd	58-4-11	21° 52'	85° 23'	1807	273	4.20	4.04	(34.88)	(27.71)	5)
Al	4-34	23° 28'	85° 17'	2389	116	4.20	3.98	(34.90)	(27.73)	5)
Ja	54-10-13	23° 29'	84° 42'	2009	624	4.18	4.00	34.92	27.74	
Al	4-32	23° 24'	83° 55'	2192	94	4.17	3.98	(34.93)	(27.75)	3)
Ja	54-10-31	23° 22'	83° 53'	1910	1016	4.20	4.03	35.02	27.82	
S Pa	62-11	23° 39'	83° 44'	1959	236	4.15	3.98	(35.14)	(27.92)	1)
Al	4-31	23° 15'	83° 09'	1998	105	4.16	3.99	(36.43)	(28.94)	1)
At	2004	23° 30'	82° 20'	1740	85	4.17	4.02	35.00	27.81	
Al	4-11	24° 53'	87° 00'	2875	51	4.21	3.93	34.99	27.81	
Al	1-32	24° 22'	86° 30'	1813	287	4.19	4.03	35.05	27.84	

Gulf of Mexico Basin (continued)

SHIP AND STATION NUMBER		LAT. N	LONG. W	DEPTH OF OBS. m	DIST. FROM BOTTOM	TEMP °C	POT. TEMP. °C	SAL. o/oo	σ tp.	NOTE
Al	4-12	24° 25'	86° 28'	1847	256	4.18	4.02	35.04	27.84	
At	2340	24° 11'	86° 25'	1782	47	4.16	4.01	34.97	27.78	
Ja	54-10-37	24° 57'	85° 52'	1944	1399	4.18	4.01	34.93	27.75	
Al	1-30	24° 23'	84° 40'	2278	1052	4.20	4.00	34.96	27.78	
At	2350	24° 26'	84° 06'	1713	171	4.16	4.01	34.97	27.78	
Al	1-35	25° 09'	88° 00'	2275	1025	4.20	4.00	34.85	27.69	
Ja	55-3-12	25° 00'	86° 00'	2851	44	4.24	3.97	34.92	27.75	
Ja	54-10-16	25° 09'	85° 44'	2314	1232	4.18	3.97	34.93	27.73	
Ja	55-3- 3	25° 14'	85° 17'	2644	648	4.21	3.96	34.99	27.81	
Ja	54-10-28	25° 13'	85° 08'	1997	1432	4.16	3.99	34.90	27.73	

SOURCES OF DATA

SHIP	ABBREVIATION	REFERENCES
Alaska 1951, 1952, 1953	Al	Data received from National Oceanographic Data Center, Washington 25, D. C. Conseil Permanent International pour l'Exploration de la Mer; Bulletin Hydrographique pour les années1951, 1952, and 1953. Physical and meteorological data, cruise 1 data report no. 1, Nov., 1952; Research reports of the Department of Oceanography A and M College, Texas . Physical and meteorological data, cruise 4, data report no. 2, June 1953; Research reports of the Department of Oceanography A and M College of Texas. Physical and meteorological data, cruise 5, data report no. 3, Oct., 1955; Research reports of the Department of Oceanography A and M College of Texas
Albatross I 1886	Alb I	U. S. Commission of Fish and Fisheries, Part XIV, Appendix D. Report of The Commissioner for 1886. Washington D.C. 1889
Albatross II 1948	Alb II	Reports of the Swedish Deep-Sea Expedition 1947-1948, Vol. III,Physics and Chemistry no. 31, appendix; Göteborg
Albatross III 1952	Alb III	Conseil Permanent International pour l'Exploration de la Mer; Bulletin Hydrographique pour l'année 1952. Reduced data cards received directly from

SHIP	ABBREVIATION	REFERENCES
		Woods Hole Oceanographic Institution, Woods Hole, Massachusetts.
Atlantis 1933, 1934, 1935, 1937, 1949, 1952, 1953, 1954, 1955, 1958, 1961	At	Data received from National Oceanographic Data Center, Washington 25, D. C. Reduced data cards received directly from Woods Hole Oceanographic Institution, Woods Hole, Massachusetts. Conseil Permanent Internation pour l'Exploration de la Mer; Bulletin Hydrographique pour l'années 1940-46, 1947, 1942, 1950, 1954, 1955.
Blake 1877, 1878, 1879	Bl	Three cruises of the U. S. Coast and Geodetic Survey Steamer, "Blake" Vol I, Boston, Massachusetts, 1888
Britannia 1897, 1898, 1899, 1900	Br	Deutsche Atlantische Expedition "Meteor" Band VI, Erster Teil, Berlin, 1936
Carnegie 1928	Ca	Data received from National Oceanographic Data Center, Washington 25, D. C. Scientific Results of Cruise VII of the Carnegie during 1928-29; 1-A, Observation and Results in Physical Oceanography, Washington, 1944.
Caryn 1956	Cn	Data received from National Oceanographic Data Center, Washington 25, D. C. Reduced data cards received directly from Woods Hole Oceanographic Institution, Woods Hole, Massachusetts
Challenger I 1873	Ch I	Report on the Scientific Results of H.M.S. Challenger. Physics and Chemistry, Vol. I London, 1889
Challenger II 1933, 1938, 1939	Ch II	Conseil Permanent International Pour l'Exploration de la Mer. Bulletin Hydrographique pour l'années 1933, 1938-39
Crawford 1956, 1958	Cf	Reduced data cards received directly from Woods Hole Oceanographic Institution, Woods Hole, Massachusetts The Woods Hole Oceanographic Institution

SHIP	ABBREVIATION	REFERENCES
		Atlas Series, Vol.I, 1960, F. C. Fuglister, The Atlantic Ocean Atlas of Temperature and Salinity Profiles and Data from International Geophysical year, 1957-58, Woods Hole Oceanographic Institution, Woods Hole, Massachusetts
Dana II 1921, 1922	Da II	The Danish "Dana" expeditions, 1920-22 Oceanographic Report No. 1-8, Copenhagen, 1929 Data received from National Oceanographic Data Center, Washington 25, D. C.
Discovery II 1957	Di II	The Woods Hole Oceanographic Institution Atlas Series, Vol.I, 1960, F. C. Fuglister, The Atlantic Ocean Atlas of Temperature and Salinity Profiles and Data from International Geophysical Year 1957-58, Woods Hole Oceanographic Institution, Woods Hole, Massachusetts
Goldfinch 1902, 1903	Go	Deutsche Atlantische Expedition "Meteor" Band VI, Erster Teil, Berlin 1936.
Guide	Gu	Deutsche Atlantische Expedition "Meteor" Band VI, Erster Teil, Berlin 1936
Hannibal 1934, 1936	Ha	Data received from National Oceanographic Data Center, Washington 25, D. C.
Hidalgo 1958	Hd	Data reports for two IGY Cruises; Ref. No. 59-15D, April, 1959. The Agricultural and Mechanical College of Texas, Dept. of Oceanography and Meteorology. Data received from National Oceanographic Data Center, Washington 25, D. C.
Jakkula 1954, 1955	Ja	The A and M College of Texas, Dept. of Oceanography and Meteorology. Oceanographic Survey of the Gulf of Mexico, Ref. No. 57-15A Data received from National Oceanographic Data Center, Washington 25, D. C.
Pursuit 1953	Pu	Data received from National Oceanographic Data Center, Washington 25, D. C.

SHIP	ABBREVIATION	REFERENCES
Rambler 1895, 1896	Ra	Deutsche Atlantische Expedition "Meteor" Band VI, Erster Teil, Berlin, 1936
Rehoboth 1950, 1953	Re	Data received from National Oceanographic Data Center, Washington 25, D. C.
San Pablo 1950, 1953, 1960	S Pa	Data received from National Oceanographic Data Center, Washington 25, D. C.
S. F. Baird 1960	S F B	Preliminary Date List (Cr-B-6001) Scripps Institution of Oceanography, University of California, La Jolla, California.
Sheldrake 1953	Sh	Data received from National Oceanographic Data Center, Washington 25, D. C.
Surveyor 1919	Su	Department of Commerce, U.S. Coast and Geodetic Survey, Spec. Publication 97, 1923, Bulletin Scripps Institute of Oceanography, Vol III 1931-35
Vema 1955, 1958, 1959, 1960 1961	V	Manuscript data, Lamont Geological Observatory, Palisades, New York

Notes

1) Salinity probably too high
2) Salinity interpolated
3) Auxiliary values
4) Trawl head temperature
5) Salinity probably too low
6) Thermistor temperature
7) Temperature probably too high
8) Core head temperature
9) Mud in bottle
10) Nansen bottle observation
11) Doubtful temperature
12) Doubtful depth